THE LIVING LOTUS

Ethel Mannin

THE LIVING
LOTUS

"I go for refuge to the Lord Buddha."
—from the Ti-sarana, The Threefold Refuge

G. P. Putnam's Sons
New York

ACKNOWLEDGMENT

IN the writing of this book I have been assisted with information by many people, outstandingly U San Win, Publicity Officer of the Burmah Oil Company, Rangoon. Mr. Francis Story, founder of the Burma Buddhist World Mission, and Mr. David Maurice, editor of *The Light of the Dhama*, Rangoon. Mr. Leigh Elsum, of the Lode Tin Mines, Mergui, Lower Burma, also supplied information and patiently answered endless questions in the checking of Burmese Buddhist life and customs.

For assistance with proofs I am indebted as always to Mr. Gilbert Turner, and also to Mrs. Evelyn Broughton-Smart, to whom I am also grateful for valuable points regarding Burmese life.

E. M.

CONTENTS

PART I. THE PAGODA

I. ANGLO-BURMAN

CHRISTOPHER FINCHING, Forest Officer of the Bokoko district of
Upper Burma, had married his Burmese wife first in the Buddhist way
to please her family and then before a Registrar in token of his sincerity.
He was 'decent'—a word to which he attached great importance. Any
children of the marriage would of course be brought up to be completely
English and C. of E. Christian.

Little Ma Hla was his second wife. When he had first come out to
Burma to join the Forest Service as a young man he had had an English
wife, but the life had bored her. When it became apparent that there
were to be no children of the union she spent longer and longer periods
in England and had finally asked for a divorce. When she had married
again it had occurred to Christopher that it might be a good thing to do
likewise, for the life of an unmarried D.F.O. was singularly dreary. He
had been resolved this time to take no chances, but marry someone unlikely to be bored by the life, and for whom the periodic change of scene
and climate at a cool hill-station would not be merely a change of boredom
but an adventure. He took the advice of a colleague who was himself
living with a Burmese village girl and married one of that girl's sisters.
In this way when he was forty-five he had acquired the fifteen-year-old
Ma Hla. She had been quite willing. Her sister was happy enough with an
English husband, and the family considered that Ma Hla would be even
better off with the *thakin* Finching, for he proposed to marry her in the
European way as well, which meant that he would not leave her when his
time in Burma was up; she was very lucky. The girl herself had been
pleased with her good fortune and grateful to the *thakin*. But for him she
would have married a village boy and gone to work with him in the paddy
fields, like all the womenfolk of poor paddy cultivators, thigh-deep in mud
and water in the heat of the day, eaten alive by insects; instead she would
have a life of ease and comfort, with servants, and chests full of *longyis*,
handwoven of the purest silk from China. That he would make her a
good husband neither she nor anyone else doubted; he was well-liked in
the district.

There was a time when Christopher Finching had shared his English
wife's view that it was deplorable that middle-aged Englishmen should
marry these very young Burmese girls—though he had never gone quite as

far as to declare it disgusting. But having taken this step he told himself that he would stand in some relation to the girl as a father; he
would look after her, educate her to Western ways, and teach her to speak
good English. Her Buddhism did not worry him; as a religion he conceded
that it had points—even points in common with Christianity; though he
no more doubted that the Christian religion had the monopoly of truth
than he doubted the racial superiority of white people as against black,
brown or yellow. There were some, he knew, who whilst acknowledging
white superiority, were physically attracted by coloured people, but he
was not of those. He thought some of the Burmese girls and the younger
women pretty and charming, with their olive complexions and their slanting eyes and their brightly coloured *longyis* wrapped tightly round their
little behinds, but though he found the little Ma Hla quite one of the
most attractive of them he did not think her more desirable than his
English wife had been in her youth in her slim English-rose manner. But
apart from the fact that there had been no English girls available for his
second marriage he had required, this time, a quality of temperament
which could only be found in a native of the country.

His family, he had realized, would not approve; they might even be a
little shocked—but they were not having to live his life, and he could not
expect them to understand. That this young Burmese village girl would
suit him very well he had felt convinced from his first meeting with her;
she was pretty, smiling, and docile. She was prepared to do what her
family wanted, and when she was married to transfer this obedience to
her husband. When he began to know her he found that his first impression had been right; she was good-natured, affectionate, placid. It was
some time before he realized that her submissiveness in all matters was
not humility but indifference; she seemed to bring to all things a smiling
acquiescence. At first he had been puzzled, wondering what really went
on inside her; then he decided that nothing very much went on, and left
it at that. Their children, of course, would not be purely white, but he had
been confident that the English strain would predominate, both in their
appearance and characters; their whole outlook would be moulded to the
English pattern—he was quite determined on that.

The first child, a girl, was born within a year of the marriage. He had
her christened Jennifer, after his favourite sister—who had been, after all,
most remarkably tolerant about the marriage; the important thing being,
she wrote him, was that any children of it should be brought up English
and Christian, which she did not doubt they would be.

The English strain did not emerge in Jennifer as strongly as her father
would have liked. She had black hair and slanting eyes; but her nose,
her father observed with relief, was definitely European—good European
at that. All the Finchings had good straight noses. Unfortunately they

also had dark hair, so that in an Anglo-Burman alliance there was no chance of producing a blonde, and with her black hair, slanting eyes and golden skin the child was much more like her mother than her father, in spite of her straight nose. Finching had been disappointed, but had told himself—and was continually telling himself—that European clothes, schooling, and general upbringing would Anglicize her.

The second child, a boy, born almost four years later, he named Peter after his father, and put his name down immediately for his own public school. The boy, too, had the Burmese strain more clearly marked than the English—if anything he looked even more like Ma Hla than Jennifer did. Both children had lighter skins than their mother, which fact, Christopher thought, in alliance with their straight noses, should see them through—by which he meant secure them acceptance in England as English. In time, too, he thought, the children would complete their mother's education. By the time he was retired, at the age of fifty-five, and ready to leave Burma for good and settle in England, Ma Hla would have become sufficiently Westernized—between him and the children—to take her place in English country life as what she in fact was: Mrs. Christopher Finching.

Ma Hla listened and smiled and said nothing when he talked of all this, as he frequently did. England, Europe in general, was as remote as Nirvana. And when he was away on forestry affairs, down in Rangoon, or up at Mandalay, or at Bhamo in the far north, where the great forests were, she and Jennifer inhabited their own private world, which had nothing whatever to do with the West, with England and Christianity and Western education, but everything to do with the *nats* and *dewas*, the spirits who haunt the forests and waters and the upper air, and the ghosts who are everywhere.

Ma Hla was devoutly Buddhist, but before she was Buddhist she was Burmese, and peasant at that, and *nat*-worship was in her blood. There were times and seasons for attendance at the pagoda, but the spirit world was omnipresent, demanding daily propitiation. But of all this, and her secret offerings, she said nothing to her husband, from an instinctive self-protectiveness. Western people, she had noticed, from those who came to the house, were tolerant of Buddhism, though they did not seem to understand it, but they ridiculed the idea of ghosts and spirits, even when strange things happened to themselves. She had more than once heard her husband refer to it as superstitious nonsense, so she did not tell him that when he went on a journey she sprinkled the house with sacred water, and kept a pot of the sacred *thabyé bin* growing in the house to keep away all harm. He was under the impression that she grew it only to have some leaves of it to put into the pots for the water-festival, the *thingyan-pwè*, when the king of the *dewas* descends to earth to open the New

Year. That was a spirit she could acknowledge openly, for, said her husband, he was no more generally believed in as a fact than was the Father Christmas, the Santa Claus, of the English Christian Festival of Christmas.

But Ma Hla believed in the reality of the *dewa* king as she believed in the reality of all *nats* and *dewas*, and all who in one form or another, for good or ill, inhabit the spirit world, in all its spheres. She could not talk about all this to her husband but Jennifer listened intently and cowered in terrified belief.

When they were alone they spoke always in Burmese, and Ma Hla never called her little girl by her English name, but Mālā, which is a Pali word meaning garland, and beginning with M was suitable for a Thursday child. The Indian servants called her by this name, though never in the presence of the master.

Jenny's special friend was Ganesh, the Hindu houseboy, who lived with his wife and children in a bamboo hut across the compound. She played with his children, but Ganesh himself she loved, though she did not speak of this to either of her parents, for already by the time she was five she was aware that she lived between two worlds. Her father began to talk to her about England, his own country—*her* country, he insisted—and how, soon now, she would go to school there, and how one day they would all live there, but she was not sure if she would like it. In England, it seemed, it rained at all times of the year, and it was cold even when the sun shone, and there was no river as wide as the Irrawaddy, nowhere near as wide, said her father, and he smiled as he said it, as though it were a good thing that this should be so, but Jenny had nothing to measure by and could not imagine a river that was not immensely wide and shining and the colour of the sky, which was no real colour, being made of the heat which danced over all the land and was itself like water.

The township of Bokoko lay three miles inland from the river. It was an oasis of toddy palms and plantains and vivid green patches of ground-nuts in a brown plain of loose sand, semi-desert. Sandhills stretched east and west behind the town, and when the monsoon broke the flat country between the sandhills became miniature lakes, and snipe and duck found their way to them, and all but these wild birds seemed dissolved into water. When the rains ceased and the floods subsided the country people went out and sowed paddy where the lakes had been, and presently there were stretches of green, and earth and sky which had been one separated, and all that had been lost and strange and unreal became familiar and real again. Then the little white egrets, the paddy birds, came back, perching on the ridges banked up from the mud and water of the paddy fields, and the leafless branches of the flame-of-the-forest trees were suddenly

covered with scarlet blossoms—red lilies that fell continually to the dust
without ever seeming to denude the tree.

It was the good time of the year when the paddy birds came back and
the flame trees dropped their lilies to the dust, for then it was sunshine
all day and every day, and the coppersmith bird knock-knock-knocking all
day long made the hot days seem long and somehow safe. There was another bird which trilled all day long, You're-ill, you're-ill, you're-ill, but no
one minded what the bird said for no one was ill, but singing and happy
because the sun shone and the paddy was growing and the mangoes ripen-
ing, and the juicy tamarinds. Then earth and sky became one again, melted
in the translucent heat.

There were low cliffs of dust above the river, with a row of ramshackle
wooden buildings at the top where the business of the waterside was done,
for Bokoko was a busy trading place; it was a collecting centre for timber,
and there was a trade in embossed silver, woven silks, wood-carvings, rice.
It was also a boat-building centre, and a port of call for the paddle-steamers from Mandalay.

The steamers called three times a week. On those days there would be
a traffic of women through the hot dust, which rose in a mist about them as
they moved; they carried on their heads baskets piled with handwoven
table-cloths and *longyis*, and some had poles across their shoulders from
which were suspended garish inflated rubber toys—elephants, owls, dolls,
crudely painted and monstrous. There was a great busyness of loading and
unloading up and down the gang-plank on to the steamer deck, where
men, women and children, soldiers and monks numerous in the company,
squatted or lay among their bundles and brass vessels, sandwiched between
the heat of the awning above them and the heat from the furnace below
the deck. There was always a barge—known as a flat—attached to every
steamer and here the heat was even more intense because of the corrugated iron roofing. The flat would be laden with wood for feeding the
steamer's furnace, and there would be a cargo of sacks of flour and rice,
and cattle stalled at the sides.

Jenny often went down with her mother and Ganesh to meet the
steamer and collect provisions from Mandalay. They drove out the three
miles in a gharry, holding handkerchiefs to their eyes and mouths and
nostrils against the dust. When they stepped out of the gharry at the quay
the dust was burning to their feet where it overflowed their slippers, which
were merely soles with a strip of leather or velvet to pass over and between
the toes. Jenny would go with Ganesh on to the flat, whilst her mother
waited in the gharry, drawn into the hot shade of a neam tree where an
Indian kept a stall of cold drinks—with ice brought out from Mandalay
bedded in crates of sawdust. Jenny enjoyed the excitement of the movement and shouting as the Indian coolies went up and down the gang-plank

with the great sacks and bales and crates on their heads. She was fascinated by the monstrous garish toys, and by the small boats that rocked
alongside the steamer at the other side, where there was no flat. Sweets
and cakes were sold from these boats, and helpings of rice and curry par-
celled up in plantain leaves. Jenny always leaned on the rail at this side of
the steamer whilst Ganesh did whatever business had to be done on the
flat; then he would come and collect her. Sometimes he lingered with her,
watching, the Indian melancholy of his dark sensitive face dissolved in a
smiling interest. He had been born in Burma, and he and the child spoke
Burmese together, and he called her by her Burmese name. His own name,
he told her, was from Ganesha, the elephant-headed god. Ganesh offered
many prayers to Ganesha that he would remove the obstacles which stood
between him and Mother India, the land of his fathers. That his prayer
would ultimately be answered he did not doubt. Then in the course of
time, with the further assistance of Ganesha, he would make a pilgrimage
to Benares, stand at last in the sacred waters of the Ganges. This Irrawaddy was alien to him. At the end of this Burmese incarnation he hoped
to be reborn in India.

Jenny liked Ganesh talking about India better than her father talking
about England. India was in some respects like Burma, Ganesh told her;
there were the hot months, when the mangoes ripened; then came the
wet monsoon and the months of rain. There were the same flowers in
India, too, the scarlet flame-of-the-forest trees, the golden golmohur, the
jasmines and oleanders with their great scents; and many temples, but not
for the Lord Buddha, though he had come from India.

Jenny knew that in a corner of his hut across the compound Ganesh had
a little image of the elephant-headed god. He kept flowers in front of it,
and bowls of rice—for Ganesha was a god who liked to eat well. And her
mother had a small room called a shrine room, where there was a large
Buddha image all of gold, and her mother, too, kept flowers and bowls of
rice in front of the image, and glasses of water. Her father never went into
this room, but her mother spent long hours there, kneeling, resting back
on her haunches, her hands clasped—not praying, for you did not pray to
the Lord Buddha, Jenny knew, for he was no longer in the world, having
entered into the blessedness of Nirvana. Before the Lord Buddha you only
repeated the precepts and blessings from the scriptures. This much Jenny
knew, from her mother, from the servants. Her father had no image of the
Lord Jesus, and no shrine, and when she asked him why, he said because
all that sort of thing was Roman Catholic, which the Reformation had
swept away, and one day, when she went to England, she would learn all
about this at school. All she had to remember now was that she was a
Protestant Christian, and that Protestants didn't bow down to images, but
worshipped God in the spirit. It was difficult for him to say this, as he was

not a religious man, and he felt self-conscious using the language of religion. It would be a good thing, he thought, when the child began to receive proper religious instruction, such as he was not equipped to impart. He taught her to say the Lord's Prayer and Gentle Jesus. She understood that God was the Father referred to in the prayer, and that he had made the earth and everything in it; this was not difficult to understand, for the gods, she knew, from Ganesh, were all-powerful, and there were the spirits of the earth and the air that her mother talked of, who were also possessed of great and terrifying powers. The Lord Jesus Christ she understood to be God's son, who had come down from heaven, which she took to be Nirvana, to live on earth and die there so that everyone might have a chance to go to heaven when they died. But you had to be good and not tell lies or be disobedient, and you had to say your prayers night and morning. 'Gentle Jesus, meek and mild, look upon a little child . . .' She always thought that Jesus looked like the Lord Buddha, and that made all of gold and precious jewels he looked down from a shrine somewhere out of sight in the blue deeps of the sky.

But she did not think about all this very much, except briefly when it impinged on her from the repetition of her prayers, or something her father sought to impress upon her. She was English and Christian, he insisted, and she was forbidden to enter the shrine room or go with her mother to the pagodas. The pagodas were real to her, nevertheless. The *chinthes*, the great monsters who kept guard at the gates, half-dragon half-lion, were part of her childhood. With their huge red open mouths they did not seem fierce to her, but to be laughing—friendly fairy-tale monsters such as were shown in the English story-books. They would not turn into princes and princesses, though there were Burmese fairy-tales, which her mother told her, in which such things happened. There was no escaping the pagodas, for they were everywhere, floating like white sails over the distant hills, emerging from groups of palm trees along the river; and the pagoda at Bokoko she saw every day, white and fairylike, its golden top hung with golden bells that tinkled with a thin music in the wind. Sometimes there would be fairy lights strung like necklaces from the pagoda—when the moon was full more people than usual went to the pagoda, and the fairy lights burned till daylight.

Every morning, soon after daybreak, a *pongyi*, an orange-robed monk, came to the house with his lacquer bowl into which her mother put rice and curry, after which she crouched at his feet and bowed her forehead three times to the ground; but the monk always kept his eyes cast down and said no word and gave no sign, in accordance with the law. The *pongyis* were everywhere with their shaved heads and orange robes. Ganesh declared that in some of the villages there were more *pongyis* than people.

When her father was at home they had their meals sitting at table using knives and forks and spoons. When he was not there they did not use the dining-room of the red brick, half-timbered, English-style house, but had meals sitting on bamboo mats on the floor of a room that was exclusively her mother's. There was very little in this room; there was a low sleeping-platform in one corner with a furled mosquito net and some coloured rugs, and against a wall a chest-of-drawers, and stretched across the room a wire upon which to hang clothes. There was a verandah to this room, with a drum-stick tree with its strongly scented velvety white flowers reaching up to it, and beyond that a tall dark mango tree, and you could get a glimpse of the white and gold of the pagoda quite close along the dusty road beyond the compound. Jenny liked this room very much, more than any other room in the house; she felt free in it as nowhere else, and she thought that Ganesh liked it, too, the days they ate in this room, eating with their fingers from mats of plantain leaves spread on the floor.

When Ganesh waited on just the two of them in this room he chatted and smiled, as though he also felt free. When he waited on them all in the dining-room, with its big pictures of the English king and queen, and the heavy silver along the sideboard, and the cutlery set out on the table, then he served silently and unsmiling, and they ate different food. They had many more dishes when her father was away; there was always a huge bowl of rice, and sweet dishes and sour dishes to be taken together, and curries of different kinds, and always prawns, and for each of them a little bowl of soup with leaves and buds floating in it, and sometimes a dish of leaves and strips of small green mango and a white flower like an orchid for salad, and always the strong-smelling paste of salted fish called *ngapi*, which her father detested and would never have on the table, though a huge earthenware pot, big enough to hide in, stood in the kitchen full of it. When they had eaten all they wanted from the various dishes, and the plantain leaves were rolled up and taken away, Ganesh would spread mats on the verandah and bring the betel box to her mother. Jenny liked to watch her mother remove the sectioned tray from the round lacquer box and select a leaf from the bottom, smear it with lime paste, then take betel nuts and various seeds from other sections of the tray, and roll all in the leaf so that it formed a kind of fat cigar, which she put whole into her mouth and chewed—a habit which Jenny knew her father considered disgusting, particularly in a woman. But Ma Hla had been brought up to chew *pan*, and in the privacy of her room she did it even when he was not away from home. Jenny observed, with detached interest and no revulsion whatever, that when you chewed *pan* you had to spit a lot—long purple-red spits shot into a spittoon like a po.

There was also a dish of pickled green tea-leaves, when her father was away, a great delicacy at the end of the meal. At five years old Jenny did not chew betel, but she liked the pickled tea-leaves as an English child likes sweets. Her mother also smoked big fat white cheroots, but this she did in her husband's presence; he liked Burmese cheroots himself, but not the kind Ma Hla favoured, which, he declared, were too strong for him.

Jenny would have liked to have worn a *longyi*, like her mother, the long skirt wrapped tightly round the hips and tucked in at the waist; her mother wore a different one every day, sometimes two different ones during the day, and always flowers in her hair. Jenny liked the bright colours and patterns of the *longyis*, but to allow her little girl to wear Burmese clothes behind her father's back was more than Ma Hla, who broke so many rules when her husband was away, dared to do. If such a thing were repeated back to him by a servant she felt quite sure that he would beat her; certainly he would tear the garment from the child and shout in a loud and terrifying voice. She knew in her heart that all the Burmese life she and the child lived together was so much make-believe; that little Mālā was really little Miss Jennifer Finching, in spite of her jet-black hair and her slanting eyes and her golden brown skin, and that one day her father's country would claim her; and in due time the boy as well; and that for Mālā the time would soon come; in one more year, perhaps. When that happened, she knew also in her heart, there would be an end of little Mālā; there would be then only little Jenny Finching, in the dark ugly clothes of an English school-girl.

When she felt these things sadness seemed to enclose her as in a mist from which she could not break out. For though it is true that life is *Anicca*, *Dukka* and *Anatta*, Impermanence, Suffering, Illusion, and though endlessly she repeated this before the Buddha shrine in her own home, and at the pagoda, still it was difficult to accept when you were young and joy sprang in you, eager to sing like a bird on a bough. Life, so sad, so full of pain and struggle and disillusion, was yet so beautiful, so desirable, and the craving for happiness so strong, that perhaps it was not making such very bad *karma* to loiter along the road, in each rebirth, in no hurry to achieve Nirvana and end the cycle of rebirths?

There was a *nat* shrine not far from the house, at the foot of a big old neam tree. That the *nat* inhabited the tree could not be doubted, for often when all else was still the thick dark foliage of the tree would be all astir, beyond the power of any birds to contrive. Many of the *nats* are evil and to be feared; their aid cannot be invoked, they can only be propitiated; but this *nat* was a guardian spirit, like the one at the pagoda, and being a good spirit one of his concerns was that people should not be led astray from the Buddhist truth, the Light of the *Dhamma*, into false religions. Strictly, spirit-worship has no place in Buddhism, but what springs from the soul of a people is ineradicable, as the pious King Mindon found when he sought to eliminate *nat*-worship in Burma by issuing an edict forbidding it, with the threat of dire penalties for those who persisted in it. The *nats* are still subject to the law of *karma*, and rebirth on a higher or lower plane; though they live for thousands of years, yet ultimately that cycle must come to an end, and they have great and sometimes terrible powers.

Ma Hla knew nothing of the metaphysics of her religion, but her belief in the spirit world was profound, and she invoked her favourite *nat* as Catholic Christians invoke their favourite saint, and the one who lived in the neam tree was closer to her and more personal than the one at the pagoda. To the *nat* of the neam tree she prayed that her children would be saved from being swallowed up in the West, lost to her in her husband's unimaginable country, lost to the Light. She placed flowers and fruit on the ledge which encircled the neam tree, and lit candles there, and kneeling before the shrine she prayed. Every day she slipped away from the house and across the compound and up the dusty road to the *nat*-shrine, with her handful of candles, her jasmine flowers, and sometimes an offering of fruit. And sometimes, on her birth day of the week, she would keep the ten precepts and fast after mid-day, that merit might be added to her petition—for wishes are brought about, prayers answered, by the power of merit even more than by supplication of the *nats*, though the acquisition of merit pleases the good *nats*, and they may be associated with it and share in it, which is helpful to them, since they depend a good deal on human beings in this respect on the long, long journey to Nirvana.

Ma Hla was also very civil to the pagoda *nat*, sharing with him the merit of her offerings at the Buddha shrine, because it is always a good thing to obtain the favour of a good spirit; but it was to the *nat* of the neam tree that she brought her greatest devotion—to the end, in a way she could not foresee, that her children might be spared to her and to the Light. A *Nat-Kadaw*, a spirit woman, living in Bokoko, served this *nat*; through her a *nat*-worshipping feast could be arranged in time of great need; when the time came for Mālā to be taken from her Ma Hla was resolved to consult with the *Nat*-wife and arrange for such a ceremony, with the intention of averting that tragedy.

In the meantime she made her daily offerings and petition to the *nat*, rested her faith in the Lord Buddha, and concerned herself to acquire merit as the Law required. But all this was kept hidden from her husband behind her placid, acquiescent manner and her pretty smiling mask of a face.

II. THE TREK

UNTIL the end of April, 1942, Jenny had never been further afield than the waterfront. Then suddenly there was a great busyness of packing clothes and foodstuffs into crates and boxes, and her father did not go to the office but stayed in the house looking angry and shouting a good deal at the servants, and her mother did not smile any more, but frowned and sighed and seemed as though she might burst out crying at any moment. And for the first time that Jenny could remember she did not put a flower in her hair, nor was any jasmine brought in for the Buddha shrine. Mr. Vernon, the young Englishman who was her father's assistant, kept coming to the house, and he and her father spread out maps on the table, first one great map and then another, and they frowned at them, pointing out places to each other, and, as it seemed to her arguing. Certainly at one point her father told Mr. Vernon not to be a dam' fool and Mr. Vernon looked very offended and mumbled something about there being more than one route into India. The word 'Japs' kept recurring. It was a word often in her father's conversation lately, both with Mr. Vernon and her mother, but he said it now with a new sound to it, a new expression on his face, and it had the same effect on her as when her mother spoke of evil spirits and ghosts. She felt troubled and afraid.

Only Ganesh looked happy. "We are going to India," he said.

She asked her mother, "Why are we going to India?"

Ma Hla looked from the child to her husband, inquiringly.

"Bad people have come to the country," he explained, "and it is not safe here any more."

Jenny was afraid. "Would they hurt us? What would they do to us?"

"They would burn our house down. They might even beat us."

It was Jenny's first intimation of active evil.

She asked Ganesh, "Why would the Japs do bad things to us?"

He told her, "Because there is a war. People are fighting each other everywhere in the world."

"Why?" Jenny persisted, troubled.

"Stop asking silly questions," her father interposed, "and go and mind your baby brother. Can't you hear him crying? God knows where Nanny is!"

Her mother looked up from the trunk she was packing. "Nanny's gone," she said, calmly. "She wanted to be with her family to put out flags to welcome the Japanese when they come in!"

Jenny stared at her mother. "Won't the Japanese do bad things to her?"

"Not to Nanny," her mother said, and very faintly she smiled. She added, "They won't do bad things to the Burmese people."

"Run along!" Her father's roar and a sudden push in the back sent Jenny flying. Before she parted the curtains into the next room she looked back and saw her mother bending over the trunk again, still with that small strange smile.

She saw her father stride over to her mother and she heard him say, "I've never laid a hand on you yet, Ma Hla, but by God any more of that talk and I'll break every bone in your body!"

Jenny fled into the room where her two-year-old brother stood up in his cot, like an animal in a cage, howling his resentment and loneliness and neglect.

She pulled down the side of his cot and put her face against his wet cheeks.

"Don't cry," she said, softly, "we're going to India."

He buried his face in her neck, wetting her with his tears. She lifted him from the cot and staggered across the room with him to the verandah, where she dumped him. He was a fat little lump. She squatted down beside him and began to croon a little song her mother had taught her, a Burmese version of playing Peep-Bo. They were still playing baby-moon hiding away from mummy-moon when Ganesh came for them both.

"We go now," he said, and lifted the baby into his arms.

She went out with him into the compound, where there was her father's saloon car in which her mother was already seated, and a truck in which Ganesh's wife and children squatted amongst bundles and crates and boxes and trunks. Two Indian servant girls, with marigolds stuck into their hair knotted on the napes of their necks giggled next the driver's seat. Mr. Vernon was driving the truck, and her father's chauffeur, Husain, was seated at the wheel of the car. Ganesh deposited the baby in Ma Hla's lap and instructed Jenny to get in beside her. Christopher sat in front next the driver. Jenny heard him say, "It's main road to the river, then a fair-weather road all the way to the border. We should reach Mynmyo village by sundown. There's a rest-house there."

Husain shook his turbaned head. "Not reach Mynmyo by sundown, master. Bad road after river. Take two-three hours do twenty miles maybe."

"You blasted Job! Get going and keep going!"

Jenny shivered, made fearful by the savagery of her father's voice.

But Husain was an old man, and he had been in the service of the sahib for fifteen years or more, and one roar more or less made no difference. He permitted himself to smile into his white beard.

"*Inshallah,*" he murmured.

At first Jenny was interested and excited. She had never before seen so many motor-cars, lorries, trucks, all moving in one direction; the road was much busier than the waterfront when the steamer came in. They were travelling westward towards the Chin Hills, beyond which lay India. After the first ninety miles or so they would turn north up into the Chindwin Valley and a straight run up to the border.

They left the semi-desert of the Bokoko district behind and ran through paddy fields where buffalo grazed among the stubble, and through endless stretches of dense mixed jungle which seemed to Jenny to go on forever. There was the excitement of crossing what she thought were two rivers, but her father explained that it was the same river, which made a great loop. Soon after the second ford, the water shallow in the dried-up bed, there was a village of bamboo houses standing under plantains at each side of a road where the dust was so deep that plantains, palms, houses, jungle, were all white, and as the cars and trucks and lorries moved forward so great a cloud of dust was raised that Ma Hla begged that they should draw into the side of the road and wait a little till some of the traffic had passed them, for she and the children were choking with dust. When the windows of the car were closed the heat was stifling; when they were opened even holding handkerchieves to eyes, mouth, nose, did not keep out the dust. The baby cried fretfully, and Jenny, who was beginning to feel sick, was alternately listless and fidgety. Soon after they went on again she vomited, causing further delay.

A few miles out from the village the road deteriorated into deep loose dust in which, in places, the wheels turned without gripping. Truck and car drivers got out and placed their slippers under the wheels; lorries lurched forward with a kind of tank action. Cars driven up on to the low banks of sand and thorn at each side of the track got stuck, but no one stopped for anyone else; no one dared; the important thing was to keep going. To add to the misery and confusion bullock-carts moving at the sides of the road, in the tracks normally reserved for them, ploughed up the dust into even greater clouds, curling in thick dense folds like smoke. It took them nearly four hours to do twenty miles—as Husain had foreseen.

By sundown they had not done half the journey and had lost touch with the truck, which had fared better on the bad patch of road and had got ahead; presently Husain was separated from it by the oncoming traffic. When they were finally at the next ferry there was no sign of the truck; Vernon had gone on whilst the going was good. No useful purpose could be served by waiting about—so far as anyone could see at that point.

There was a rest-house in the village, and the compound was full of parked cars and lorries. The women and children went into the house, where the Europeans and Anglo-Burmans spread their bedding-rolls on the floor, and the Burmese their mats. The men slept in the cars and trucks, their servants in the open. Fires were lit in the house and in the compound and food was prepared. Ma Hla preferred to stay with her husband and children in the car for the night, but they went into the house to eat.

In the morning, as soon as it was light, the fires were fanned to life again, and cars and trucks started up. Many people went on without waiting to eat first, but Christopher was impatient of panic. They would have *chota-hazri* and then get going. Ma Hla was in favour of lingering as long as possible so that most of the traffic got ahead of them—far enough ahead for them not to be engulfed by their dust.

They had the road to themselves when they started out, around eight o'clock, when the sun was beginning to be hot. The road was again all deep loose dust and pot-holes, bounded at either side by dense mixed jungle. Occasionally it was flanked by tall teak trees, their bases cluttered by the dry leathery leaves they shed in the heat. The white dust lay over everything. The car bumped and bounced; Christopher cursed and swore; Husain sat immobile at the wheel, impervious to the abuse and the unjust accusations. Finally in a paroxysm of rage his master commanded Husain to stop the car, to get out, he would drive himself. Husain obeyed without a word. He got out and walked round the bonnet of the car to the other side; Christopher slid into the driver's seat, gripping the wheel savagely.

After that no one really knew what happened. The car seemed to jerk forward, shudder and collapse. Finching looked at Husain, his face contorted with fury.

Husain's face was impassive. "Back axle, master," he said, calmly, as who should say, '*Inshallah*'.

They trekked back the five or six miles to the rest-house. In the deep dust which made every step an effort it took them some two hours. Husain carried the baby, Jenny stumbled along beside her mother, her father carried the bedding-rolls which had been stowed in the back of the car. Several times Jenny looked back at the car they had abandoned. It stood almost in the middle of the road, and when they were some distance from it it looked like a little house. She did not understand why Husain could not make it go on, or why her father was so angry that no one dared to speak to him.

She was wearing European shoes, as always in her father's presence, but the sand got inside them and presently her feet began to blister. She whimpered and complained and her mother removed the shoes, speaking soothingly to her in Burmese. Her father and Husain went on and they did not catch up with them again. Now the dust was so burning to her feet it made her want to hop about in pain, but then her mother took off her own footwear—the Burmese slippers which she always wore—and when she saw her mother going smoothly barefoot through the burning dust it somehow made it possible for her to do likewise. Once her father turned and beckoned them on with a great movement of his arm—an angry sort of movement—but they could not go any faster, and presently Jenny began to whimper, from the weariness of the effort to make her feet keep passing each other in the deep dust, and because there seemed no end to the road that went on and on with the tall teak trees each side, and the dense jungle beyond, and the white dust over everything.

Jenny stumbled and clung to her mother and wept.

"I want to *be* there!" she insisted. But she did not know where she wanted to be, except, negatively, to be no longer stumbling through the hot dust.

Her mother knelt down beside her in the dust and put an arm round her. Ma Hla's face was masked white with *thanaka* as protection against the sun. She would have smeared the child's face with it before they started out but that this was something she no more dared do than put Burmese slippers on her feet. Her skin was cool against the child's sweating cheek. She addressed her again in Burmese.

"We shall soon be there," she coaxed. "It's not far now. Then we will wash our feet and quench our thirst. If we cannot find another car to take us on your father and Husain will get a bullock-cart. Then when we get to the next place perhaps there will be Europeans from the oil-fields, and they will take us in their cars. Only now we must do this part of our journey bravely. Now your father is beckoning to us again. We must go on."

She wiped the child's tears away with her fingertips, leaving runnels through the dust. She kissed her forehead and smiled.

"If we sing it will make the way seem shorter. Come now!"

She straightened herself and began to sing merrily, clutching Jenny's hand, "*Yee, lé-lé, yee, lé-lé*——" and they marched on, resolutely.

But Ma Hla was deeply troubled. Last night she had been visited by Sadi Wazadat in a dream. The spirit had appeared to her as a wild figure galloping on a horse. There was only one interpretation of such a dream. It meant failure of the attempt.

At first the bullock-cart was fun; sitting up in the straw and looking out over the high wheels Jenny enjoyed seeing the dusty landscape move slowly by, and it was fun to work a way up to the front of the cart and stand up behind the driver and watch him prodding the bullocks' ribs with a thin stick and urging them on with curious cries. When he made them run for a little the dust rose under their hooves like smoke. But after a time the lumbering slowness, the complete lack of protection from the sun blazing down from immediately overhead, the choking dust, and the inability to be comfortable which ever way you sat, began to make Jenny

once again want to *be* there. She was not to know that the adults of the
party wanted this before they ever set out.

It took them over an hour to reach the stranded car. Here they halted
and suitcases and hampers were loaded on to the cart, after which the
discomfort of travelling in it was aggravated by lack of space. Ma Hla made
a place for Jenny to lie down in the straw beside the heavily sleeping
baby; she herself sat with her feet tucked under her, in the Burmese
fashion, and took the little girl's head in her lap. Husain sat at the back of
the cart, facing outward; he sat upright and motionless, hour after hour,
and still with that suggestion of smiling faintly into his beard. Ma Hla
also sat upright and still, her face expressionless. Christopher fidgeted and
fumed, or lapsed into a scowling silence. When the baggage had been collected from the car there had been an altercation with the driver of the
bullock-cart, who had declared that there was now no point in keeping to
the road, that the cart tracks across the paddy fields would save them a
great many miles. Christopher had been equally emphatic that to remain
on the road was the only chance of getting a lift in a car or truck. The
driver pointed out that there had been no traffic of any kind on the road
since they had left the rest-house, and in his opinion there was not likely
to be; with the alternative that if there was it was not going to stop for
the occupants of a bullock-cart, or, for that matter, with the Japanese
coming up thick and fast, for anyone else. His clinching argument was
that it was his bullock-cart and he was engaged to transport the *thakin*
and his family to the next ferry, and the route he took was entirely his
affair. It was a journey of some sixty miles or so and could not be done,
even across the paddy fields, under two days; by road it would take three—
or more. If the *thakin* wished they could return to the rest-house with
the baggage and he could wait there for the chance of a car or truck. He,
Maung San, would be very happy to do this, instead of absenting himself
from his family for so many days.

But the *thakin* had been for pushing on. He knew quite as well as
Maung San that the chances of getting a lift were problematic, and at
Taungpyo there was the possibility of Europeans evacuating from the oil-
fields. But he also knew that once they left the road there was not even the
remote chance of any other form of transport. His luck was dead out; he
found a philosophic acceptance of the fact difficult, and was equally irritated by the Oriental serenity of Ma Hla and Husain and the fretfulness
of his half-European child.

They travelled for four hours across the shadeless paddy fields, sometimes at a walking pace, sometimes at a jog-trot, at an average speed of
four miles an hour. By mid-day they came to a group of old dark trees on a
hillock, curiously Biblical with their huge trunks and the cattle sheltering
in their hot shade. They formed an oasis in the golden brown wilderness

of the paddy fields which stretched away in all directions and seemed to melt into the heat-drained sky.

Maung San took the bullocks from the cart and seated himself on the ground beside the cart, which stood with its shafts tilted to the sky. Tiffin-carriers and hampers were taken from the cart, and the party ate, Husain sitting with Maung San a little distance off.

Jenny complained that her back ached, and her father, whose own back ached intolerably from the four hours in the jolting cart, told her to shut-up and stop whimpering. The baby, refreshed from his long sleep, staggered about among the pots and plates grinning and drooling. Jenny lay listlessly under the trees, too hot and tired to eat. Ma Hla sat still and smiling and cool-looking. But her dream of the haggard horseman never left her.

When they went on again the baby clambered all over the cart and was obstreperous, and Jenny already tired and fretful became more so. Christopher, his nerves after years in the tropics already worn thin, finally lost his temper and slapped her face. After that she crouched in a corner, as far away from him as she could get, sullen and resentful. Ma Hla bent low over the child in her lap so that no one should see the tears which came into her eyes. She crooned softly to him about the tuck-too lizard who calls his own name, hidden in a tree-trunk or the wall of a house, how in the stillness of night he calls it, *Tuck-too! Tuck-too!* She chucked the child under his fat little chin as she said it, smiling, coaxing the child to smile back, and like a child herself wiped away the tears from her face with the tips of her fingers, smearing the *thanaka*. Her husband did not see because he lay on his back with his eyes closed trying to sleep to pass the tedious hours, and Husain did not see because he had his back to her; but Jenny crouching in her corner saw, and remembered.

The long hot afternoon wore away. Occasionally Maung San prodded his gaunt-flanked bullocks into a jog-trot, and Finching would waken with a groan and shout at the driver. Ma Hla coaxed the sulking Jenny out of her corner to play with her and the baby. Husain alternately dozed and smoked cheroots. Once they halted in the shade of a group of trees and drank green tea kept hot in a china pot buried in a padded wicker basket.

By sundown they were back on the road and close to a pagoda. The village was another three miles farther on, but Finching decided that there was no point in going on; there was no rest-house there, whereas at the pagoda there were *zayats*, shelters for pilgrims and travellers, which were open to all. He resented the 'foot wearing prohibited' edict less than the prospect of sleeping in the open with nothing but a mosquito net between himself and the heavy dew.

Maung San drove the cart up to the high wall which bounded the pagoda precincts; he unharnessed the bullocks and tied them to a tree. An

archway in the wall, flanked by a pair of huge *chinthes*, led to the compound in which stood a small white pagoda with a golden spire and a
small multiple-roofed monastery with upturned gables. They left their
shoes at the archway, Christopher retaining his socks, in the European
manner, and entered. The *zayats*, a line of open-fronted sheds, stretched
along a boundary wall. Finching went to the nearest and flung down the
bedding-rolls. Husain took his own roll to a farther corner, then busied
himself with the preparation of a meal. Maung San went off to the *pongyi-
kyaung* for water for his beasts.

An elderly monk came from the direction of the *kyaung* and addressing
himself to the Englishman bade the party welcome and inquired if there
was anything they needed. Ma Hla immediately prostrated herself at his
feet.

Christopher thanked him, curtly, and assured him that they needed
nothing but shelter for the night. Very slightly the *pongyi* inclined his
shaven head and turned away. When he had gone beyond ear-shot Christopher demanded of Ma Hla, savagely, "Need you *shikko* to every *pongyi*
you meet?"

She answered, gravely, "Not to every one, but this one is the *sayadaw*
of this *kyaung*. It would be very discourteous not to show him proper
respect."

He turned away, impatiently. Although he had married a woman who
was both Burmese and Buddhist he was never able to overcome his aversion to the social and religious customs of the country, and any expression
of them from his wife he found repugnant, and, in some curious way, an
affront both to the British Raj and Christianity.

They left the *zayat* as soon as it was light, and the second day followed
the pattern of the first, following tracks across harvested paddy fields and
coming at sundown to the riverine village of Taungpyo, the bamboo
houses half hidden among a smother of plantains topped by tall palms.
The rest-house was a flimsy wooden chalet-like structure on stilts. Inside
it was like a great barn, and as bare. There were none of the facilities of the
previous rest-house, no bathrooms or cooking arrangements, no commodes,
no sweeper. A caretaker lived in a house across the compound; he came
and opened the place up, but was not prepared to do more than that.

Maung San asked to be paid off; he had friends in the village with whom
he would pass the night; in the morning he would return home.

Christopher questioned the Burman in charge of the rest-house as to
the possibilities of transport to Mynmyo. The people from the oil-fields,
it seemed, had come and gone, two days ago; there had also been an Englishman from the Forestry Department, with an Indian family. Since then
there had been no one. There was no local taxi; there were a few trishaws

—but it was another thirty miles or so on to Mynmyo, and no trishaw boy would wish to go so far, particularly at this time; a bullock-cart would be better because it could cut across the paddy fields, keep off the roads, and it would make the journey in a day; the *thakin* would of course have to pay the driver for the return journey. . . .

Christopher listened wearily; the prospect of another day's journeying by bullock-cart added to the ache already in every bone of his body. Ma Hla did not complain, but admitted to being a little stiff. For the first time he thought she seemed tired. When they got to Mynmyo, he told her, the worst would be over. They could be certain of transport; it was a township and subdivisional H.Q. Then once across the river a day's driving would bring them to the Indian border. Vernon would be waiting there with the truck, and if the worst came to the worst they would dump some of the stuff and make room for themselves in that. He toyed with the idea of resting up for a day, since they had the rest-house to themselves, but they had lost so much time already and Vernon would be wondering what had happened. He might even have gone on. He dismissed that idea, sharply. He would never do that. His instructions were to wait, and that meant come hell or highwater.

The trouble was, he thought, sardonically that both were in fact on the way—hell in the shape of the Japs, and highwater in the shape of the wet-monsoon. He had at that point no further news about the enemy, but the heavens were already offering intimations of the impending deluge; the last two days the humidity had been almost suffocating, and at sundown the sky had been massed with dark heavy clouds. The monsoon was not due to break for several weeks yet; it came late to the dry zone, and May was always the insufferable month. But it was unpredictable—as unpredictable as the delay which found him no further than Taungpyo three days after leaving Bokoko, when he had calculated on getting right through to Mynmyo in one day. His luck was out, and it could be part of his bad luck if on top of the delay the monsoon were to break early.

Once again the bedding rolls were spread out, this time on camp-beds, and Husain prepared a meal. Christopher went off to negotiate with a villager for a bullock-cart for tomorrow. When he got back Husain met him at the top of the wooden steps.

"Memsahib sick," he said, and now he no longer seemed to smile into his beard. He patted his belly. "Bad pains," he added.

Christopher went into the house and across the bare wooden central room and into one of the rooms opening out. He found Jenny listlessly playing with the baby on the floor, and Ma Hla lying on a bed with her face toward the wall. He lifted the mosquito net and she turned slightly. His first thought was that she had been seized with an attack of malaria,

but she was not shivering, he saw, but on the contrary her face was wet
with sweat.

"Such pain," she said, pressing both hands deep into her abdomen.
"Fierce, like knives. So much blood. And nowhere convenient here—only
that horrible little hut across the compound."

Dysentery. His heart sank. It would have been so much easier if it had
been malaria; something short and sharp, instead of this long-drawn-out
business.

"I'll arrange something," he said. "Don't worry."

"There's no sweeper——"

"Hell, can't we be our own sweeper for once? I'll get you a shot of
brandy."

He dropped the curtain and was about to move away when she said,
sharply, "Not brandy, no. Ask the butler to get me something in the
village."

"Made of cow's urine and cock's dung, I suppose!"

"There is a drug made from the bulb of a lily—the butler will know."

She turned her face to the wall again. Exasperation and despair warred
in Christopher. These devout Buddhists and their refusal to touch alcohol
even when they were ill! And now dysentery on top of all else. You could
keep a malaria patient walking—there was even a school of thought that
believed in it, walking and sweating it out, they called it—but what could
you do with anyone with dysentery? He had had it himself and knew the
pain and misery of it, and the physical weakness it entailed. He believed
that he had once cured a bout of dysentery with stiff doses of neat brandy;
how he had felt better after it and it had subsided. It was preferable to the
stiff dose of castor oil which some people recommended. But Ma Hla
should have her herbal drug; it could even be of some medicinal value,
and the fact that she had faith in it might help. He went off to find the
butler, and to order Husain to take a hot brick wrapped in something or
other, or a bottle filled with hot water, to the memsahib.

Ma Hla with her face to the wall wept silently. The herbal drug the
butler would get for her in the village might ease her pain but it could not
alter the law of *karma*; she was convinced that even if they succeeded in
crossing this river they would not cross the next, which was the last. A
Naga-daw, wife of a good spirit, might help her even now in defeating
the evil spirit who had her in his power, inhabiting her pain-wracked and
fevered body, but she did not know if there was such a woman for miles,
and even if there was she would not be allowed to come near her. But
since the Sadi Wazadat had appeared to her even a *Naga-daw* would be
unable to exorcize evil working in the life of Christopher Finching through
his wife Ma Hla. But perhaps the evil need not extend to the children.

Perhaps even now it might not be too late to petition the guardian *nat* of the pagoda, when she was able to reach there. . . .

She called Jenny to her.

"Try to put some rice outside the door, at the top of the steps, when you go to bed. Don't let your father know."

Jenny nodded. "It is for house *nat?*" she asked, gravely.

"No. For the bad one who has made me ill. If you can find a *nat* shrine tomorrow take something to it—take some flowers if you can find nothing else. But your father must not know. If there's no shrine, go to the pagoda. Don't get lost."

Jenny regarded her mother anxiously.

"Will you be better tomorrow?"

"Perhaps."

The child gazed fearfully round at the dark wooden walls of the room, and up at the rafters high in the spidery darkness of the roof.

"I don't like it here," she said.

"No harm will come to you," her mother said, and then, almost inaudibly, her face buried in the pillow, "not to you, Mālā."

In the morning after *chota-hazri*, prepared by Husain, Jenny was missing. When last seen she had been at the far side of the compound picking up the fallen scarlet lilies of a flame-of-the-forest tree which overhung from the road. Christopher was baffled and exasperated by his wife's unconcern.

"She won't have gone far," was all Ma Hla would say.

It was not difficult for Jenny to find her way to the pagoda; it stood on rising ground just outside the village, its slender white spire, crowned by the golden *hti*, emerging from a tangle of palms and plantains. She slipped out of the compound and padded along through the deep dust of the village street, feeling both bold and frightened. She carried the flame-of-the-forest blossoms and some soft white velvety blossoms of frangipani in the skirt of her cotton frock, the hem of which she gathered up into both hands. She walked as fast as the deep dust into which she sank with every step permitted. Bullock-cart drivers and women on the verandahs of the bamboo houses regarded her with interest, the little European child hurrying through the dust with her upturned dress. That she was from the rest-house they all knew, but it was impossible to conjecture what she was doing hurrying alone through the hot dust.

At the end of the village street she came to the pagoda *chinthes*, flanking a steep flight of white steps at the side of the road. Beyond the guardian lions the steps went on less steeply, twisting and turning across a low hill, to the pagoda at the top. Jenny removed her shoes and left them on the bottom step, then began laboriously to mount. Some of the steps,

hacked out of the face of the hill, were high and difficult for her to negotiate. But she came at last to the platform and saw the great image, all
of shining gold, under a high pointed roof. The great image looked down
on a row of lighted candles and brass vases in which flowers, their stalks
bound to pieces of wood, died slowly, symbol of life's intransigence. Some
women and children knelt before the shrine, resting back on their heels,
their eyes on the image. Jenny's bare feet made no sound on the hot marble of the platform and no one looked round at her approach, or saw her
when she moved away looking for something more familiar to her than the
great golden image. She began walking round the platform which encircled
the pagoda, shrinking back when every now and then a gaunt dog ran
out from the shadow of a small shrine or satellite pagoda to sniff at what
she carried in her upturned skirt. An old nun sitting on the ground, her
emaciated body swathed in faded pink robes, held out a skinny begging
hand. From her, too, the child shrank away, repelled by the shaven head,
the old shrunken death's-head face. She came to a group of three plaster
figures, realistically painted, depicting an old man, a sick man, and a
corpse, so dreadful to her that it took all her courage to pass them. She
glanced over her shoulder fearfully at them as she passed, half afraid they
would come to life and pursue her.

Then, suddenly, she came upon what she was looking for. Close to the
ground there was a little house, like a doll's house, and inside a strange
little gnome-like figure, in front of which lay a few wilting flowers and a
small bowl of rice. She had seen *nat* shrines before, at the road-side,
though never one so small and close to the ground as this. She dropped
the hem of her dress and the scarlet and white blossoms fell to her feet.
She knelt down and arranged them neatly on the ground in front of the
shrine; she did not know what else she should do, but she had seen her
mother bow three times to the ground before the Buddha image in the
shrine room at home, and it occurred to her that this might be the proper
way to show respect to the *nat*. She knelt down, leaning back on her heels
and bowed her forehead to the ground, slowly and gravely, once and twice
again, and whilst doing it she wished hard, hard, that her mother should be
made well, "I wish my mummy to be well, I wish my mummy to get
better, my mummy must get well—well—*well!*"

Then she could not think of anything else to do, and continued on
round the base of the pagoda, to come to the steps without having to pass
against the terrible figures of age and sickness and death.

It was quite as difficult going back down the steps as coming up them;
it was often necessary to put one leg down on to the step below and bring
the other one down to it, so that descent was slow. About half-way she
met Husain coming up. He had traced her quite easily, inquiring of this
and that person along the village street, and at the bottom of the roadside

pagoda steps he had found her European shoes. He was angry because he had had to traipse through the dust and heat after her, and then climb barefoot over the rough burning stones to a Buddhist temple, he, a good Moslem. She descended to him fearfully, seeing the anger written on his face.

He spoke harshly to her, in English.

"Your father sent me to find you. He is very angry. He will beat you."

She was silent. He demanded of her, as she clambered down behind him, unable to keep up, "Why did you come here?"

She did not reply. He seized her small shoulders and shook her. "Answer me!" he commanded, and terrible as the figure at the pagoda he seemed to her, the bearded old man. She wrenched herself away from him.

"No," she said. "I won't tell you. It's nothing to do with you."

He said again, "Your father will beat you."

She continued to clamber down, reaching down a bare brown leg, bringing the other one down to it.

"I don't care," she said.

Her father would beat her. She could not imagine it. He would shout at her, and that would be frightening; but whatever he did she didn't care, because she had done what Mummy had asked and now surely she would get better.

Husain strode along through the dust: she did not try to keep up with him but scuffled along behind wishing him ill, wishing him the utmost ill, even unto death. Ganesh would not have shouted at her and shaken her; Ganesh would not have told her father where she had been; Ganesh was on her side. When they had crossed the river they would see Ganesh again. With that thought it mattered even less about the punishment ahead, though she felt afraid when they turned into the compound.

Her father came out of the house as they mounted the steps. Now she was ahead of Husain. She saw that her father had on his face what she thought of as the dark look. Husain said over the top of her head, "I found her at the pagoda, sahib."

"What were you doing there?" her father demanded, angrily.

"I wanted to go," she said.

"What do you mean you wanted to go? Haven't I forbidden you to go to pagodas?"

He seized her by the shoulders as she came up with him at the top of the steps and shook her, violently.

"Haven't I?" he repeated.

Her head wobbled to and fro with the shaking; she felt dizzy and could not speak.

"Haven't I?" he shouted, even more loudly.

"Yes," she said.

"So you thought you would disobey me, eh? You thought you would just run off and disobey me whilst your mother lay ill? You wouldn't stay and look after your mother and your little brother, would you? Would you?"

With each question he shook her and she began to feel sick. Then suddenly he released her and beat her on the back with the flat of his hand.

"Get into the house!" he shouted. "Get out of my sight!"

She fled from him, rushing across the centre room and into the room, where her mother lay and the baby staggered about. The mosquito net was furled back from her mother's bed and she went across to the bed.

"I did it!" she cried, eagerly, "I did it!"

Ma Hla turned her head and looked at her. She raised herself on an elbow and put an arm round the child and drew her close to her.

"Your father shouted at you," she said, anxiously. "I heard him. Did he beat you?"

"No," Jenny said. "Just shouted."

Ma Hla sank back, weakly.

"Are you feeling better?" Jenny asked, eagerly.

"A little," her mother lied, "yes, a little."

"Will we cross the river today?"

"Not today. Tomorrow perhaps. But now I want you to help me——"

She was running a high temperature and it took an almost superhuman effort of will to concentrate on what had to be done. The butler had a wife who would have looked after her, but Ma Hla had a dread of strangers when she was ill; nor would she have her husband do for her what was necessary. Jenny went down into the yard and brought water from the well, lugging it up the steps, one step at a time; she brought soap and towels and a bowl; she brought clean clothes, putting the discarded garments into soak as instructed. When her mother was made comfortable she washed the baby and tended him generally, then sat on the floor with him, keeping him amused, whilst her mother alternately dozed and groaned on the bed.

Her father came in and out continually demanding to know how Ma Hla was, whether she thought she could make the effort for the journey tomorrow; there would be no walking; trishaws would take them down to the ferry, and at the other side she would be lifted straight into the bullock-cart. They had to get on; they couldn't wait about; they had to get on to Mynmyo. . . . A good deal of the time Ma Hla made no reply, because her pain was too great; and sometimes she hardly knew what he said, because she was light-headed with fever. He insisted that they must push on next day, but he knew that it would be monstrous to force her; yet if only they could get as far as Mynmyo, where there was a decent rest-house, where there would be transport, where there might even be a doctor.

He was worried by the fact that his wife evidently had a high temperature, which suggested that she had a more complicated and dangerous form of dysentery than any he had known; amoebic dysentery he understood, and malaria, and other fevers, but not this terrifying thing which had Ma Hla in its grip. Somewhere at the back of his mind he seemed to remember that there was a form of dysentery which could set up peritonitis, and that it was contagious. If he himself went down with it. . . . But it was no use thinking along that line, only the children must be kept away from her, for safety's sake. He could order another bullock-cart and the children could travel in it with Husain whilst he travelled with her. Somehow they must get to Mynmyo. Whatever wretchedness poor little Ma Hla suffered this was her only chance, to get her away from here where not even the simplest antiseptic measures were available to help her.

He went back into the sick room and ordered Jenny out, and to take Peter with her.

"Mummy needs me," the child protested.

At any other time he would have explained and reasoned with her; now his frayed nerves made even a child's opposition intolerable.

"Do as I say!" he shouted. "Get out!"

He bundled them both into the next room and drew the bolt on them. Henceforth he would look after Ma Hla himself, and in the morning they would go.

In the adjoining room Jenny sobbed until even with trying and screwing up her face she could not make any more tears come.

She had fantasies in which when they crossed the river her father fell in and was drowned, and Husain jumped in to rescue him and he also was drowned; then she and her mother and little Peter continued alone to the next river, where Ganesh waited for them, after which they all went on together to India and lived happily ever after, and no one went to the horrible cold hateful land her father came from.

Later, her father came and explained to her that her mother's illness could be passed on to anyone who touched her, and so they must keep away from her room until she was better. He himself would not get it because he was big and strong; he smiled, to show that he was not angry any more, and that there was nothing to worry about. Jenny listened sullenly and hiccuped occasionally, in token of her recent sufferings, and made it clear that she was not prepared to be friendly.

When she was in bed that night, with Peter beside her, she cried again, but this time softly, the tears flowing easily, and presently when the weeping fit was over she prayed to the Lord Jesus—since it was no use praying to the Lord Buddha—to make her mother well again soon, quickly, at once, and to keep her, Jenny, and Peter, and Mummy, safe from the bad men, the Japs, and get them all safely into India with Ganesh, to live happily ever after, forever and ever, Amen. Mr. Vernon could look after himself.

In the morning Christopher gave his children into the care of Husain and sent them off to the river by trishaw, then wrapped his wife in a blanket and carried her to the ferry. She was small and light, but it was a mile or more to the ferry, and in the heat and the deep dust he became aware of her weight long before he reached the river, yet his terrible urgency and despair gave him strength and he staggered on with her, along a lane made entirely of dust, and finally down a burning cliff of dust to the tawny river.

He lifted her into the waiting ferry, a heavy clumsy boat propelled by a man who stood in the stern with a huge unwieldy single oar. At the other side two bullock-carts waited. He lifted Ma Hla into one and climbed in beside her; Husain and the children climbed into the other. Most of the way Ma Hla was only half conscious, from sheer pain and wretchedness.

They kept to the road now, but no cars or trucks passed them; everyone who was getting out from that district had gone days ago; the Japanese had already moved in. Christopher began to be anxious. With no one on the roads why should there be anyone, except the Burmans, who were staying-put, at Mynmyo? Vernon would be there, of course, and by jettisoning a good deal of stuff room could be found for them all in the truck. Ganesh would somehow have to pile up his wife and kids in front; some could stand on the step and hold on as best they could; Ma Hla could be segregated in the truck; he would stay in her corner with her and Husain could look after the children; there would be motor transport, even though only the old truck. Then once across the river, which should present no difficulties, it was a straight run up to the Indian border, which they should be able to do in a day, and they could take Ma Hla straight to hospital. The important thing was to lose no more time, to keep moving, to *get* there. It was no longer a race against the Japs and the monsoon, but against the toxins working in his wife's body.

They reached the township of Mynmyo when the churned-up dust of the day hung over it in a sunset-reddened haze. There was a small traffic of bullock-carts and bicycles in the main street; women went to and from a roofed well with kerosene cans suspended from poles across their shoulders; people leaned on the verandahs of two-storey houses; pariah dogs prowled in the gutters. There were no lorry-loads of troops; no signs of refugees. Over all hung an air of normality which Christopher found sinister. The entry of his own two bullock-carts was, clearly, the only unusual event.

The rest-house was at the far side of the town, on rising ground and facing out across the river. The compound was empty of everything except a bicycle leaning up against the wall of the timbered house. A stout middle-aged Burman in a check *longyi* came out of the house. Finching greeted him by name.

"Well, Maung Maung, where is everyone? Is my assistant, Mr. Vernon, here?"

The butler told him, "Everyone went days ago, *thakin*. Mr. Vernon waited until the day before yesterday, then he said he thought you would not wish him to wait longer, for you must surely have changed your plans. He waited till the last ferry."

"The last ferry?"

"We heard that Japanese fighter 'planes had flown over the Myitkyina airfield and shot up two passenger 'planes leaving for India, and the steam-ferry crew were afraid they would be shooting up the ferries next, so they decided to quit. The row-boat ferry is still on this side, and it should be possible to find someone to row it across. But no one will go in daylight now. You must cross this evening or tomorrow."

"And what do I do on the other side—with no transport?" Christopher asked, bitterly.

"It may be possible to arrange transport, *thakin*."

"And get it across on an oar-propelled ferry?"

The Burman answered equably, "Two country boats with a platform bolted on top will take a car. It could be arranged."

"Anyhow we can't go this evening," Christopher told him. "My wife is ill. Is there a doctor left in the town?"

Maung Maung shook his head. "There were two doctors, an Indian and an Anglo-Burman; both have gone. But there is a midwife who understands something about herbal drugs."

"My wife has dysentery," Christopher said, shortly. "It may be contagious. I need two rooms and accommodation for my driver."

When Ma Hla had been made as comfortable as it was possible to make her Christopher went again to consult with Maung Maung.

"Those two doctors you spoke of—didn't they have assistants, either of them?"

"Mr. Bardon had a Burmese dispenser."

"Is he still here?"

"Yes, *thakin*. You wish that I should send for him?"

"At once. Tell whoever goes for him that my wife has dysentery with a temperature and ask him to come and at least give her a shot of morphia."

"I will send immediately, *thakin*."

Maung Maung sent a young servant off on the bicycle Christopher had observed. Half an hour later Mr. Bardon's dispenser arrived. He was a pleasant young Burman with an unassuming manner. He was anxious that it should be understood that he was in no sense qualified as a doctor; he had not even been a medical student. But he had learned a certain amount by working for Dr. Bardon and as his assistant as well as his dispenser he had had a good deal to do with dysentery, both amoebic and bacillary. He enquired what Mrs. Finching's temperature had been. Christopher said shortly that he hadn't taken it. "But it's been pretty high," he added. "There's been a good deal of fever."

The young man took Ma Hla's temperature and held the thermometer up to the light.

"Not high," he said, smiling, pleasantly.

"What d'you mean, not high? She's sweating!"

The young man offered him the thermometer, but Christopher made a gesture of impatience.

"Perhaps she sweats from the pain," the young man suggested.

"Then give her a shot of morphia."

"Better I give emetine hydrochloride. Dr. Bardon got always very good results with this, in amoebic cases."

"How d'you know it's amoebic?"

"Temperature not high enough for bacillary. Also I think if bacillary you all have it by now." He smiled reassuringly. "With your permission I give emetine injection and dose of bismuth subnitrate. We strike the enemy from within and without."

"Can you fix her up so that she's fit to travel by tomorrow evening?"

The young man looked dismayed.

"That is not possible, sir. In one or two weeks perhaps. The patient is very weak. She must regain strength. Great strain on her heart to move her now."

Christopher said grimly, "What do you suppose would happen to her if she was carried down to the ferry tomorrow evening and put on a car at the other side and motored to the Indian frontier?"

"I think possibly her heart becomes affected. Emetine can affect the heart. Therefore a patient receiving such injections must rest." He turned his grave pleasant face from the Englishman's to Ma Hla's and permitted himself to smile. "That is what I learn from Dr. Bardon," he added, conclusively.

"Then why give her emetine?" Christopher demanded, irritably. "Why not just give her a shot of morphia and a dose of the other stuff—the bismuth stuff?"

"Morphia makes dead the pain but it does not kill the amoebae. Better we destroy the enemy. I request your permission?"

"Get her well, that's all I ask!"

"Then if I could have some boiling water——"

When her husband was out of the room Ma Hla turned to the young man.

"It doesn't matter when we cross the river, this journey cannot succeed. I have seen the Sadi Wazadat."

"Nowadays I do not think people believe much in such things. The Lord Buddha did not teach them."

"The Lord Buddha did not deny the existence of the spirit world."

He smiled his pleasant smile. "I think it is necessary to become Buddha to be omniscient. Now I think I give you the bismuth medicine—the attack from within . . ."

The pleasant young man came every day; he took Ma Hla's temperature, felt her pulse, gave the injection, urged the importance of rest and of taking the medicine regularly. He was gentle, unassuming, platitudinous. And by the end of a week the patient was undoubtedly a great deal better. She was weak, but she no longer had great pain, and no fever. She could leave her bed for a rush chair on the verandah. A dozen times a day her husband asked her how she felt, and always patiently she replied, "I am better." Several times she assured him that she could travel whenever he wished.

On the third day of her convalescence he went off himself to negotiate for Mynmyo's one car. Only to discover that it was laid up. The owner was daily expecting delivery of new bearings from Mandalay, but in these days everything was uncertain; roads that were open one day were blocked by troop movements the next; there was fighting here, fighting there; no one knew what was happening. Only—with a sly look at the *thakin*—that the British were withdrawing in all directions; now it was only Chinese troops who were offering any resistance. . . . Finching let it pass. He could not afford to quarrel with the owner of the only car in the place, even if that car was out of action.

Every morning he went to find out what was happening about the car; and every evening thunderous clouds rolled up in ominous masses and there were rainless electric storms. Then suddenly the monsoon broke and the rain descended on the long-parched earth with the violence of opened sluice-gates. Christopher lay on the hard narrow bed beside the one in which Ma Hla lay and listened to the downpour.

"My luck is out," he thought, "right out." It had been out from the beginning, as though some malign force were determined that he should not reach India. He put the thought from him. He was not superstitious. He had had a series of obstacles, but he had overcome them; when the car broke down he had secured bullock-carts; with no doctor in the place he had nevertheless secured medical attention for his wife; with no vehicle ferry he had arranged with Maung Maung that one should be contrived. Only he had yet to contrive the vehicle. If only that young bastard Vernon had waited as he had been instructed. Yet even if he had they could not have gone on with Ma Hla in the condition she had been in. But now . . . He wondered how much the river would have risen by the morning.

Ma Hla also lay awake listening to the rain. Everything had been against them, and now the monsoon had beaten them. She felt no emotion; since her vision of the haggard horseman she had been convinced that they would not succeed in their journey, so that the rains overtaking them could not deepen her despair. Even if they succeeded in crossing the river they would not reach India.

But in the morning, during *chota-hazri* a message came from the car-owner that the mechanic he had sent to Mandalay had got back with the new bearings. The car would be ready by evening.

"You see!" Christopher exclaimed triumphantly. "Faith shall remove mountains! Now we've only to get the ferry organized. Husain will pack for you. You must conserve your strength."

He swallowed his coffee and rushed out. The village street was ankle deep in mud; the sky was massed with dark heavy cloud, but it was not raining. If only the rain would hold off now till they had crossed they should have no difficulties. He went first to the river. It had risen appreciably. A great volume of water had poured down from the watershed of the hills in the night. The river was now the colour of churned-up sand; always a fast-flowing river, now it raced and swirled like rapids. Would a couple of oarsmen be able to hold an improvised vehicle-ferry against it? Now his dread was that the car-owner would not risk his car on such a crossing.

That he was so prepared heartened Christopher. He was prepared to attempt the crossing, and two oarsmen were found to risk their boats— and, he thought wryly, their lives. But if they were risking their lives he was risking his own, and his family's and his servant's. He was becoming a proper old woman, he told himself. The river couldn't be said to be in spate. Not yet. It had risen a little since yesterday, and it was flowing a little faster. That was all. They might drift a bit downstream; that might be a nuisance, according to where it landed them; but the important thing was to get across. Cross your bridges when you come to them had always been his policy in difficulties. Only now, of course, if only there was a bridge to cross there wouldn't be any problem.

When the rain held off all day he felt heartened. By evening the first great rush of water down from the hills would have abated; the river would have dropped a little. Without saying anything to anyone he slipped out during the afternoon and went to have another look at the river. He was certain it had gone down a little. And the ferry had been fixed up, a platform bolted across two parallel country boats, flat-bottomed, low in the water. Ma Hla and the children, he reflected, would be best sitting in the back of the car, with Husain in front; he himself would stand beside one of the oarsmen, give a hand if need be. It was not a wide river; not like crossing the Irrawaddy. What was he worrying about? He wasn't worrying; he just wanted to get going, wanted it over with, and the last lap of the journey speeding under the wheels of the car—whilst the going was still reasonably good on a road the rains would soon turn into an impassable quagmire. But by keeping going through the night they should reach the border by dawn . . . then all that had gone before would seem like the night's bad dream. Nothing more.

Jenny was excited. They were going to cross the river in the dark and drive all night to India—where Ganesh waited. Where they were all going to live happily ever after. She had forgotten her anger against her father. He was great and splendid again, making all things possible. He had got a doctor man who had made Mummy well. He had arranged their great journey. He would take care of them all and get them safely into India, away from the bad people. There would be no more dark creepy resthouses, where the rats ran along the rafters high up in the darkness of the ceiling and evil spirits lurked in the black shadows. They would have a house of their own again, with rugs on the floors and proper furniture, and Ganesh and his family living in a little house across the compound. Ganesh had asked the elephant-god to remove the obstacles that kept him from India, and the god had granted his great wish, just as the pagoda *nat* had granted hers, that her mother should get well. Now there was only one more great wish, and that was to make the safe journey to India. Neither she nor her mother could go to the pagoda to make another offering to the *nat*, and it was no use praying to the Lord Buddha, but perhaps the Lord Jesus would help. She consulted her father.

"Shall we ask Lord Jesus to help us get safely across the river and reach India safely?"

He gave her a curious look.

"Yes," he said, "do that. Say a prayer."

"You too," she urged.

"I can't stop now. I'll say a prayer when we get to the ferry."

He went out. It was already sundown and the car would be round in an hour. He was keyed-up, his nerves taut; he did not need to pray, he felt, for his whole being was tensed to the prayer for their safe deliverance from danger.

When she was alone Jenny knelt down beside her bed, folded her hands and closed her eyes and made the familiar invocation—*Gentle Jesus, meek and mild, look upon a little child. Pity my simplicity, suffer me to come to thee.* But that wasn't quite what was wanted. *Suffer me to get safely across the river and come to India by morning. Mummy and Daddy and baby brother and me. Amen.* There was no need to mention Husain, she felt. He had his own god, called Allah, to whom he prayed five times a day. He could make his own arrangements.

III. THE RIVER

EASING the car cautiously down the planks on to the platform bolted across the boats was a tricky business which Jenny found exciting. Husain sat at the wheel with his usual impassive expression and her father shouted and swore a good deal. Her mother sat in the back of the car looking worried and a little frightened, the baby in her lap. Jenny had pleaded to be allowed to sit in front with Husain so that she might see all that went on. When her father was not shouting his instructions the noise the river made as it hurried through the darkness could be heard, and that, too, was exciting, part of the urgency.

The two boatmen stood up straight beside the great oars; the older one, whom her father addressed as Po Than, looked serious; the other was a boy rather than a man and he looked sometimes at Jenny and smiled, as though he too thought it exciting, like an adventurous game. His name was Maung Shwe, which she thought a very nice name, because Shwe is golden and there was something shining about him she thought, with his golden skin and his gleaming smile.

When the car was finally manoeuvred on to the platform, the engine no longer running and her father no longer shouting, the noise of the river rushing past seemed very loud, and as they moved out from the low bank the water seemed to come close, a little frighteningly, except, of course, that with Daddy in charge all was quite safe, really. She leaned out of the car window. Her father had instructed her that she was not to get out, which was frustrating. He stood up in front with Po Than. She watched Maung Shwe in the other boat bending heavily over the oar—bending and straightening himself, bending and straightening.

There was no moon, only a few stars, very far away and dim, and no sound now but the hurry of the water and the creak of the two boats as the man and boy bent and straightened, bent and straightened. She longed to be standing up in front with Maung Shwe, and when the baby who had been fidgety for some time began to cry and her mother busied herself trying to soothe him Jenny opened the door of the car and slipped out. Husain was staring straight in front of him and did not see her. In a moment she heard her mother call out to her, sharply, followed by a command from Husain, but she was out and not going back for anyone. She crept along the side of the car to the edge of the platform, then dropped down into the boat at Maung Shwe's feet.

She looked up at him, but though he looked down at her he did not smile or speak; with every bend he gave a kind of groan, as though what he did was very hard and took all his strength, and once he looked across to the other boat and said something in Burmese. She could not hear properly what he said because the river was making such a noise and there was the heavy creak of the great oars, but she knew it was something about the current, and now her father did not speak any more, and Po Than groaned each time he bent over the oar.

She looked back at the car and saw it rocking to and fro where it stood on its platform across the two boats. She was glad not to be inside it; it made her feel a little sick even to look at it. She crouched low so that her father would not see her, and peered over the edge of the gunwale, but all was darkness except for the white froth of the water rushing past them.

Then suddenly Maung Shwe gave a great shout and heaved wildly on the oar, and it seemed to Jenny that her father and Po Than shouted back to him, and she saw that now they strained together on the oar, but she did not know what they said because now they were going very fast, rushing with the river, and the rush and roar of the water seemed all about them. She saw that Maung Shwe stood clutching the oar with both hands, but he no longer seemed to be rowing. She had the feeling that the ferry was running away with them and that no one could stop it, that the white-frothed water was sweeping them away into a roaring darkness. The car was rocking violently now on its platform.

She heard Husain shout and her mother scream, but in the moment in which she was aware of it there was a tremendous roar and the water rushed up at them and closed over. She screamed for her mother, for her father, and there was screaming and shouting all about her, and a roar of waters and blackness and drowning and confusion.

She was swept away screaming and struggling and drowning in the darkness; and then she was not drowning any more but seized by two hands, and above the commotion of the water she heard Maung Shwe's voice telling her not to be frightened, not to struggle, that she was safe . . . Then she was on her back and her head was above water and she could see the far-away stars; she seemed to be being drawn through the water; she had the feeling of floating, and several times through the rushing tumult of the water she heard Maung Shwe telling her not to be afraid. It seemed to go on for a long time.

Gradually she began to be aware of another sound, louder than the noise of the water. A chugging like the sound the Irrawaddy paddle-steamers made. Then suddenly it was as though the moon appeared in full; as though the full moon bore down upon the river. The darkness was swallowed up in a blinding silver glare, more confusing even than the darkness. There was shouting and a ringing of bells. She heard Maung Shwe shouting, but she did not know what, or even whether it was in English or Burmese. Then hands were tugging at her; pulling her up out of the water, clutching her, and without realizing how it had happened she was standing firm on a wooden floor, and there were men in uniforms, soldiers, and they were talking, but she was dazed and did not know what they said. Then she became aware that Maung Shwe was beside her, and it came to her that they stood side by side on the deck of a small boat. One of the soldiers wrapped something round her, then picked her up and carried her down some steps into a small lighted room. She began to struggle again, frightened, then heard Maung Shwe's voice behind her, speaking softly, in Burmese.

"There is no need to be afraid. They will not hurt us. The Japanese are friends of Burmese people."

The chief officer of the Japanese patrol boat spoke Burmese and Maung Shwe answered all the questions. He and his friend Po Than had been ferrying an English *thakin* and his Burmese wife and children across from Mynmyo, but when they were out in mid-stream they had been unable to hold the boats against the current; they had been swept helplessly away and the whole ferry had turned over. The *thakin's* wife and baby and driver were inside the car at the time. He did not know what had happened to anyone in the darkness and with the water rushing so fast. He had heard the *thakin* shouting and the little girl screaming and he struck out in her direction.

He smiled down at her as he said it, where she sat on a bench huddled in a Japanese soldier's tunic. She looked fearfully from him, standing beside her in his dripping *longyi* and shirt, to the small neat man who was questioning him. She shivered in spite of the heat in the small cabin. The officer continued to question Maung Shwe, who, answering, told his name and his father's name, that he had been working in Mynmyo, but was from the village of Tatkon, where his family was.

"We are only a mile or so above Tatkon," the officer told him. "We will take you there," he added, "then you can take this child to your family."

Jenny heard and understood and began to cry, wildly.

"I want my mummy and daddy. I don't want to go to another place."

Maung Shwe said, soothingly, "We will go to my mother's house and she will give you dry clothes and a place to sleep with my sisters, then tomorrow we will see what we can do."

She sobbed despairingly, and said again, "I want my own mummy and my daddy."

The Japanese officer looked at her compassionately, and sighed.

"Poor child," he said. "Poor little child." Then to Maung Shwe, "Remain here. We will take you downstream to Tatkon."

He turned abruptly and went up the companion-way. There was a ringing of bells and shouted commands as the boat turned.

Maung Shwe sat down on the bench beside the sobbing child and put his arms round her, drawing her close to him.

"Don't cry," he besought her, "I will take care of you. Everything will be all right."

IV. THE VILLAGE

TATKON was a straggle of small bamboo houses on stilts at a loop of the Mynmyo river where it freed itself from the shadow of the Chin Hills away to the west and twisted a serpentine way northward to join the Chindwin. Behind the riverside houses was a road which was either deep dust or deep mud according to the time of the year. At the other side of the road were more houses, each similarly set in a small compound with palms and plantains and mango trees. The road ran out at one end to a small white pagoda, and a wooden multiple-roofed *pongyi-kyaung* almost hidden among tall palms and surrounded by blossoming trees of all kinds. Here the village boys received religious instruction and learned to read and write; they received further instruction later on when they went there to serve their time wearing the yellow robe.

At the opposite end of the street was the bazaar, with small open-fronted shops and stalls. The names of Indian traders and tailors appeared over some of the shops, but there was not now an Indian in the place. A sizable store which had been owned by a Sikh was now the local H.Q. of the *Kempeitai*, the Japanese military police.

The house to which Maung Shwe took Jenny was on the river side of the road. His parents were poor paddy farmers, like most of the villagers. His father, Maung Ba Tu, was a little brown gnome of a man with a furrowed face and kindly humorous eyes. His wife, Ma Chit, was a thin, worn little woman with a lined face and tightly drawn back hair which made her look severe, which she was not. Jenny thought her old and ugly. There was a boy of twelve, Maung Aung, a girl of thirteen, Mi Nu, and one of ten, Mya Mya. There was also Maung Ba Tu's mother, Daw Khin, but she was always called *Pwa-pwa*, meaning grandmother.

They all slept in one room, the girls on a low dais in one corner, the boy on a mat at the far end, the parents in a partitioned-off sleeping place jutting from a wall, the grandmother on a bed in the corner opposite the boy. The room was reached by a flight of wooden steps up to the verandah. At the far side of the room, a few steps down, was a kitchen, and adjoining that a washing-room with a slatted floor that let the water through to the pit below.

The living-room contained a teak chest, a chest-of-drawers surmounted by a small mirror, a number of bamboo mats rolled up and stood on end in a corner, a small Buddha shrine, an oil-lamp hanging from a rafter, a wire line stretched across the room diagonally. At nights wooden shutters were closed across the window apertures and securely fastened, and a high gate at the top of the steps padlocked. In the evening the cattle were brought in under the house, where also the pariah dogs sheltered.

The house did not seem strange to Jenny. The living-room was not more bare than her mother's room in the house at Bokoko, and the cooking and washing arrangements were not more primitive than in Ganesh's house across the compound. In just such a village house, she knew, her own mother had grown up. Nor were the people strange to her, since her mother was one of them. What terrified her in the first days and weeks was the thought that she would never find her way back to her parents, nor they to her. Day after day she asked Maung Shwe, "When will my daddy come for me?" or "When will you take me to my daddy?"

In the first days she cried wildly and endlessly and would not eat. Even had he thought it worth making the effort to do so Maung Shwe could not have returned to Mynmyo to attempt to find out what had happened to her father. The river was now in spate from the first torrential downpours, and even had there been any form of ferry available, which there was not, the crossing would have been impossible. And not merely was Tatkon on the opposite side of the river from Mynmyo but some miles from it, and on both sides of the river were only flooded paddy fields. Maung Shwe was moreover convinced that if the *thakin* had managed to get ashore and back to Mynmyo he would have been taken prisoner by the Japanese who entered that area the following day.

He tried to reason with the child, explaining the impossibility of either returning to Mynmyo or of her parents coming to her. "You must stay patiently with us till the rains are over," he insisted. She demanded, "Then will my daddy come for me?" He told her, resolutely, "If the Japanese have reached there by that time then we must wait for the war to end."

She cried, then, frightened, "Perhaps it will never end!"

He assured her, "Everything has an end." He thought, "Even life. Even the cycle of rebirth through life after life . . ."

Inevitably, then, being a child, she demanded, "When will the war end?"

He gave her the only possible answer, "Perhaps this year, perhaps next. No one knows. But sometime."

He came upon her once in those early days sitting on the bottom step of the house pulling apart the petals of a marigold, one at a time, and saying something in English with each petal she plucked out and flung away. He had no English and did not know the superstition. He asked her what game it was she played. She went on plucking the petals and flung the last one away with a loud cry of despair.

"The war is never going to end!" she told him, beginning to cry again. "Not this year or next year or sometime or ever. Not ever, ever, ever!"

"The war must end," he insisted. "Everything ends—the rains, the hot weather, life itself. Perhaps you will live here with us for years, but one day the war will end."

"Then my daddy will come for me?"

It seemed simplest to agree. Years were beyond her reckoning; she needed only the reassurance that one day she would be restored to her parents.

At first she cried every night as she lay on the sleeping platform with the two girls. Then the elder, who lay next to her, would reach out a hand and grope for hers.

"You mustn't cry, Mālā," she would say. "You are safe with us and one day everything will be all right again."

When on arrival they had asked her what her name was she had said, involuntarily, Mālā, because they were Burmese, and was indignant because they said it was not a Burmese name. It was Mi Nu who, later on, explained that it was a Pali word, and what it meant, and that Pali was the language of the ancient Buddhist scriptures. This Mi Nu knew from her brothers, educated by the monks.

Mi Nu was a gentle, pretty, affectionate girl, tender as her name. The little sister, Mya Mya, was all high spirits and childish heartlessness. Mi Nu was grown-up—or almost so; at the end of Lent that year she would have her *na-twin mingala*, the ear-boring ceremony which would mark the end of her childhood. She talked eagerly of this to the new little sister, and of the happy time they would have, with music and feasting, and all the neighbours coming in. Jenny thought she would be scared of having holes made in her ears, but Mi Nu laughed and said it was something that happened to every girl, and it was soon over, only a little pain, not much more than a pin prick, and then a whole day of celebration in which you were the most important person. There was no other such day in a girl's life until the day she married.

Little by little, as the rainy days passed each other like feet along a road, Jenny began to be interested in the life all about her, and the first wild homesickness for her parents began to fade, gradually diminishing in intensity, and becoming in a few weeks so dim as barely to exist. Only sometimes at night, lying listening to the rushing of the swollen river, it would overcome her again and she would cry helplessly, remembering her mother, from whom the river had swept her away, recalling the house in Bokoko that had been home, and Ganesh and the baby brother who had been part of all that lost world. Then all the people in this bamboo house would seem alien to her, for all they were so kind, and Mi Nu's groping hand and soothing words could not help the agony of longing and despair that seized her.

By day again the new life would wrap her round, as smoothly as the brightly flowered *longyi* enfolded her small body, and she would feel herself part of the family again, any other kind of life forgotten. She would

sit patiently whilst Ma Chit smeared her face with *thanaka*, combed out
and oiled her hair and secured it in a topknot with a small sharp comb.
Then she would be indistinguishable from any other Burmese little girl;
a little lighter of skin, than some, perhaps, but hardly lighter than Nu and
Mya. And never using English she began to think in Burmese. She thought
of her father now not as Daddy but as *Pé-Pé*, in the Burmese way;
she still thought of her mother, when she thought of her at all, as Mummy,
though she now called Ma Chit by the Burmese equivalent, *Mé-Mé*,
which in the Bokoko life, when they had been talking Burmese together,
she had sometimes called her mother. She continued to think her foster-
mother old and ugly, but she overcame her aversion to her, even to hugging
and kissing her on occasion. Maung Ba Tu never became *Pé-Pé* to her
because she never came close to him; she thought of him always simply
as the old man—as it might be an old grandfather. Maung Shwe quickly
became Shwe-Shwe, which his family affectionately called him. The old
grandmother impinged very little on her consciousness; she liked to eat
alone in the kitchen and she spent a good deal of her time lying on her
bed with her face to the wall and the mosquito net enclosing her. She
was silent and solitary and withdrawn; she half-smiled at the newcomer
occasionally, but that was all. To them all Jenny was always Mālā, and in
time she began to forget that she had ever answered to her English name.

They all, except Mya, who a little resented her, surrounded her with
affection. Nu liked to mother her; Maung Aung liked to make her laugh
with his tricks, hunched on the floor imitating a cock, or playing *chinlon*,
dexterously bouncing the bamboo ball from his shoulder to his knee, from
the calf of a leg to the sole of a foot, or initiating her into games played
with different kinds of seeds; he had all the loving gentleness of Nu, but
more gaiety. When he went off to the monastery every morning for his
schooling the girls went into the kitchen with Ma Chit and helped to
clean and prepare vegetables for the various curries—slicing chillis and
onions, cutting up cauliflowers and tomatoes, preparing leaves for soups
and salads. There were, Jenny found, all manner of interesting things to
do in a kitchen, which was a new world to her. Going to the market with
Ma Chit was nothing new, for she had gone often in Bokoko with her
mother and Ganesh, but it was always exciting.

The Tatkon market was very much smaller than the one she had known
at Bokoko, and since the Japanese had moved in there was very much
less in the markets everywhere, and there were no Indian traders with
their rolls of silk and cloth, and no Indian tailors sitting on the floors of
open fronted shops working their sewing-machines; instead there were the
small neat figures of the Japanese police. At first Jenny had shrunk close
to Ma Chit at the sight of the mud-coloured uniforms, but "They will
not harm us," she was assured, and she noticed that when she looked at
them and caught their eye as often as not they smiled at her. In those

early days the Japanese were the liberators from the British yoke, and the face-slappings had not begun.

At first Maung Shwe and Maung Ba Tu were away during the day ploughing and planting in the water-logged fields, returning in the evening wet and muddy with their lumbering bullocks. But when the few acres were ploughed and planted there was nothing left to do in the continuing rain, and between the downpours the two men mooched about in the village drinking plain tea, smoking cheroots, chewing betel, and gossiping in neighbours' houses, or in their own house.

In this way time passed pleasantly enough, in an idleness completely devoid of boredom. For the rest, there were the duty days at the pagoda, and the mild diversion of a change of Japanese sergeants. Japanese fighters went over, hidden in the heavy clouds, and small chugging motor-boats patrolled the river. There was the illusion of the war being remote and the occupation making very little difference. But at every monthly meeting of the village head man and elders with the Japanese the demands made on the village were increased—and it was not as though the requisitioned bullocks would be restored, for they were taken for food. One after another the villagers lost their cattle and their carts; and as time went on the rice ration dwindled, and there were fewer and fewer consumer goods. The war began to draw closer and the Japanese to be less popular. That Maung Ba Tu was possessed of only two bullocks did not prevent the Japanese confiscating one. And presently they took his elder son. They were building a new airstrip and they needed labour—and the village was full of able-bodied young men idling, or at the most weaving baskets—now that the ploughing and planting was finished. Maung Shwe was only one of a number of young men conscripted to form a labour squad.

Jenny was terrified when he was taken away. He was her beloved Shwe-Shwe. Everyone was kind to her but he was her protector. He had come to represent for her everyone she had lost; he was the authority of her father, the closeness of her mother, the special-secret that was Ganesh. She clung to him, sobbing wildly. He promised her that he would come back, but she had no faith in the promise because once again he could not say when. He told her that Maung Aung would look after her, and the younger brother put an arm round her and confirmed the promise, but she was not to be comforted. Maung Shwe was her safety and her comfort, he alone; Aung was only a boy; Maung Shwe, only four years older, was a man. He was big and strong; he had saved her from the river and brought her to this house, and he had promised that one day he would take her to her parents—how could Aung do that, who had never seen her parents and who was only a boy, going daily to school at the monastery?

Maung Shwe was distressed but helpless. Little Mālā's were not the only tears shed in the village that day.

V. FULL MOON FESTIVAL

B U T no one can cry forever, or even long, a child least of all, and gradually the place filled in Jenny's life by Maung Shwe was filled by his younger brother, the readily smiling Sunday boy. Maung Aung could very easily make her laugh and he devoted a good deal of his time to doing this. He teased her because she was afraid of the rats that scuttled along the roof rafters; the rat was her birthday symbol, he liked to remind her, and yet she was afraid of it, but he never tormented her with his teasing, and always on Thursdays took her to the pagoda to buy a candle in the shape of a rat and burn it before the Buddha image. Jenny had known about all this from her mother, but her father had never allowed her the Burmese weekly birthday; she was English, he had insisted, English and Christian, with a birthday once a year. Mi Nu, as a Saturday child, had a dragon candle, and Aung had a *galon*, a strange creature half-beast, half-bird, which she thought very fine. Jenny would have liked to have been a Friday child, with the right to a nice little guinea-pig candle. It comforted her a little that Mya was also a Thursday child, and that she also peered fearfully through the mosquito net when the rats began scratching as soon as the house grew quiet. That Maung Shwe should have been a Wednesday child, his symbol the elephant, strong and noble, seemed to her most right and proper.

She always enjoyed the visits to the pagoda, with whomever she went, but best she liked it when she and Aung went alone, whether to offer his candle-creature or hers, or on a day when it was neither of their birthdays and they lit just ordinary candles, or merely placed a few flowers before the shrine. But it was not easy to take flowers at that time, for the multi-coloured asters and cosmos which Ma Chit cultivated in a corner of the compound solely for offering at the pagoda and before the shrine in the house would as often as not be so sodden with the heavy rain as to be not worth picking; then, rather than go empty-handed, they would take a little rice, in small black and red lacquer bowls, or a sprig of the sacred *thabyé-bin* leaves.

It was often impossible to go to the pagoda at that time, because of the rain and the sea of mud it created; then it was pleasant to sit on mats in the room and look out across the verandah to the rushing brown and yellow river, and Jenny and Aung and Mya would play games with seeds, with Aung always inventing new ones, or make bamboo baskets—a process at which Jenny rapidly became as adept as the nimble-fingered Ma Chit herself, rapidly stitching the dry strips of leaves together with the needle-sharp vein of each. When she had first seen this done, watching Ma Chit stitching the leaves together so fast yet without a needle it had seemed to her like a conjuring trick, such as her father sometimes performed for her amusement; then she was shown how it was done, the sharp point always in the hollow of the hand, and though it no longer seemed a 'magic' nevertheless it was fun to do, and when he came back Shwe-Shwe would be surprised to see how quickly she could do it—just like *Mé-Mé* herself.

Sometimes Aung played an instrument like a dulcimer and Nu sang. Aung struck the notes with little wooden hammers and the sounds that came from them were thin and sweet, as from the toy dulcimer Jenny had had given her on her fifth birthday; only this dulcimer was curved like a boat and stood on a stand and Aung had to stand up to play it, which he did with quick deft movements. Everything that Aung did was somehow quick and light, and he had a ready deftness and a singularly engaging smile. His face was too droll and amusing to be handsome, but because of his immense charm people thought him as good-looking as his brother and prophesied that in a year or two the girls would be sighing over him quite as much as they did over the golden one.

Jenny knew from her mother some of the songs Aung played and Nu sang, the popular 'Sound of the Trumpet', and some little light sentimental love-songs. Her mother had explained to her about the rosebud fairies born from roses, and Baranee, the *nat* daughter, and the Princess Waythandaya, and other characters from the traditional songs, and at first hearing these songs again would start up the lonely bedtime weeping and homesickness. But always Nu's loving tenderness would console her, and slowly the old images faded and the present was the only reality.

In one fashion or another the days and nights flowed uneventfully by as though the world were at peace. The clouds rolled back, the rains lessened and the hills, so long hidden, emerged again. The south wind finally withdrew and the rains were over. The roads began to dry and the floods to subside in the paddy fields. The air was light and clear again, the days became golden, and, as the moon climbed the sky, the nights increasingly silver. Then, finally, it was full moon, and the long Lent was over.

Now was the time when the little white pagoda should be strung with coloured lights, and the house of Maung Than, the village head man festooned with lights, and paper lanterns swinging from balconies everywhere. This year there could be no lights—the Japanese police were very strict about the blackout—but Maung Than collected a little money from everyone as usual so that on the Full Moon Day a company of dancers and singers could be engaged and the pagoda festival be celebrated in the traditional manner, with music and dancing and singing and play-acting

—not as hitherto, from sundown to sunrise, but at least all day until dusk.
The company came and set up their theatre in the middle of the street,
the great Po Sein himself came in person, and people came in as always
from all parts and set up booths, selling things to eat and drink, selling
combs and slippers and garishly painted toys, selling Buddha images and
holy pictures and gilded shrines for the home, things frivolous and useful,
sacred and profane. Only this year, because of the Occupation, there was
not such a variety of things, and the displays were scanty that once were
so profuse.

But whatever material things were missing nothing and no one, neither
the retreating British nor the invading Japanese, could ration the joy of the
human heart released from the dual imprisonment of the rain and Lenten
solemnity. Nothing could blackout the radiant October moon, the splendid inviolate seal set upon the freedom to seek love again and respond to
it, to court and to marry, to enjoy dancing and singing and music again in
the open air, to be free as the birds. Now like the flowers human beings
lifted their heads again to the sun, and to the drying, breathable north
wind coming up the river, and by night to the releasing moon.

The head man's young sister came often to the house. She was a slender, graceful girl a year or two older than Nu, a little vain, but very ready
to be affectionate to the new little sister in Maung Ba Tu's household. But
Jenny had two strong reasons for disliking her: that she was called Ma Hla,
which she regarded as exclusively her mother's name, and because it
seemed to her that there was something special and secret between her
and Shwe-Shwe, something hidden in the way they looked at each other
and looked away and looked again. Other girls came to the house, but
Jenny did not feel this about any of the others; they did not make her feel
cut off from Shwe-Shwe as Ma Hla did. And after Ma Hla had come and
gone Jenny noticed that Shwe-Shwe would be silent and strange and unsmiling, and seem not to hear when spoken to; as though, she would think,
he was asleep with his eyes open and could not wake up.

And now Ma Hla came all dressed up for the festival, with jasmine in
her hair and Indian sandals with silver straps on her feet and her small
body wrapped in silks that seemed to Jenny the colour of warm moonlight.
She was glad Shwe-Shwe was not there to gaze at her as though he walked
in his sleep. When Ma Hla smiled at her she frowned and all but stuck
out her tongue at her. She ran down the steps and across the compound to
the street, where Aung was playing a 'cock-fighting' game with a group of
other boys. He and another boy, each with a sponsoring team behind,
squatted on their haunches and threw out their legs from side to side in
time with the chanting of the group. The game was to see who could last
out longest before collapsing or falling over as the tempo of the chanting

increased. Aung won the contest and withdrew laughing amid the applause. He was only too glad to join Jenny on the bench against the fence of the compound and rest his aching legs. He observed her dark look and inquired what was the matter.

"Maung Than's sister has come," she said.

"Naturally. She is Nu's friend, and one day," he added, "she will be Shwe-Shwe's wife."

"I don't want her to marry Shwe-Shwe!" Jenny declared, violently.

Aung laughed, "Ma Hla is pretty," he said. "Shwe-Shwe likes her. I think he will marry her when he comes back. What is wrong with that?"

Jenny slid down from the bench and scuffled in the dust. She had no words for what went on in her with the thought of Shwe-Shwe married to the pretty Ma Hla, but all the despairing sense of loss she had known when he had gone away renewed itself in her with the prospect.

The boy regarded her a moment, then jumped down beside her.

"Let's go and find out if the bicycle races have started."

She shook her head and went on stirring the dust with a bare toe, not looking at him.

He tried again. "If you like I'll go and fetch my kite."

"No," she said, without looking up.

"What would you like to play at then?"

"Let us go to the river."

"All right." He cast a wistful glance up the street where a group of boys were playing riders-and-horses mounted on each other's backs and pursuing a ball thrown from one to another; when the ball fell to the ground the riders dismounted and all scrambled for the ball; the one who secured it became a rider, if he was not one already; if he was he remained one. It was an exciting game, especially when you became a rider. He turned away and took Jenny's hand and they left the street and followed a track of sun-dried mud across a small stretch of recently flooded paddy fields, where now was the bright green of the springing crop.

"Where do you want to go?"

"A secret place. I will show you."

Beyond the paddy was a stretch of groundnut cultivation shelving down to a narrow strip of sandy foreshore. Some distance along the land rose sharply, forming a low cliff, at the top of which stood an ancient disused beehive-shaped pagoda from whose broken masonry thorn-bushes sprouted. A rough path climbed the cliff up to it.

Aung stopped when Jenny began, confidently, to ascend the track.

"This is a bad place," he said. "No one comes here any more. Only the bats."

She looked at him over her shoulder but went on up.

"I come here," she told him, firmly.

He went after her and caught at her, angrily.

"Who showed you this place?" he demanded.

She jerked herself away from him, facing him, defiantly.

"No one showed me. I dreamed it, then I found it."

"When did you dream it?"

"When we talked about—the head man's sister."

He gazed down at her, troubled.

"Mālā, it is bad not to tell the truth, and this is a special day when everything should be good. How could you dream of a place you had not seen?"

"I saw it behind my eyes. Like my mother saw the Sadi Wazadat before we started on our journey."

"Did she tell you she saw the Sadi Wazadat?"

She shook her head. "No, but when I was in the river, drowning, I knew it. It stood in my mind. Like this place."

She turned away from him and looked up the cliff face.

"There will be a *nat* shrine," she said.

"There is one at the pagoda. It is not necessary to come here."

"The pagoda *nat* is good. This one is an evil spirit, and I want to make a dark wish." She turned to him, adding, "You need not come if you are afraid."

He said, resolutely, "I am not afraid because the *nat* went away from here a long time ago." He insisted, "No one comes here any more."

She did not answer but went on up the slope. He followed her, protesting.

"All this is nonsense, Mālā. Bad nonsense—a bad game to play on a good day."

The path ended in a wilderness of coarse grass, flat thistles, dusty thornbushes. A few goats regarded them mildly. What had been the courtyard surrounding the pagoda was now scarcely distinguishable from the rest of the wilderness. The guardian lions had crumbled and little more than their pedestals remained, and into them, too, the weather had eaten. There was an entrance to the pagoda, dark, cavernous, with bat droppings under the ruined arch. A short distance away beside a group of palms the multiple roofs of a *kyaung* tilted earthwards on collapsing wooden pillars. Large black crows flew up with harsh cries as the boy and the child approached. The double desolation of wilderness and ruins entered into Aung and he shivered, though the sun was hot in that shadeless place. He had always known about the abandoned pagoda; he had even from a distance seen it, but he had never been there, nor had any of his family, nor anyone he knew. No one went there.

Jenny strolled about confidently and Aung followed her unhappily.

"There is no *nat* shrine," he insisted.

She did not answer. She found it under a scrawny frangipani tree at the back of the *kyaung*. It was close to the ground and broken, and the image inside was faded and featureless. She looked at Aung, smiling.

"I dreamed it," she said, triumphantly.

He turned abruptly and walked away to avoid seeing her do what he knew she would do.

Back at the house Jenny and Aung joined Mya who sat with the old woman on the verandah, where they were immediately joined by Ma Hla, who came out from the room complaining of the heat in there, where so many people were gathered smoking cheroots and chattering. She sat down next to Daw Khin and leaned her head back against the wooden wall of the house, fanning herself with a paper fan the shape of a lotus leaf. The old woman spoke her thoughts, which were also the girl's.

"It is sad that Maung Shwe cannot be with us today."

Ma Hla sighed and the old woman added, "But he will be thinking of us all—and of you especially, no doubt."

"Perhaps not of me. Of some other Ma Hla perhaps."

"Our Shwe-Shwe is not like that. I have watched him grow up, and when he has given his heart he does not take it back."

Jenny sprang up, suddenly, pulling at Aung.

"Let us go and shake down some drum-stick flowers and make garlands to take to the pagoda."

"Now it is too hot," he protested. "Later we can do that."

Ma Hla smiled at the child.

"I will come with you," she said, and made a move to rise.

Jenny turned away.

"No," she said. "Not you."

She looked again at Aung.

"I shall go back to the place I dreamed and make another wish."

He sprang up, then.

"No. We'll go and get the flowers."

Taking the hand he held out to her Jenny smiled at Ma Hla. It seemed to the girl that the smile was more than triumphant; that it was strangely malignant.

Aung shook the slender drumstick tree and a shower of velvety white blossoms starred the hot ground and caught in his and Jenny's hair. They gathered the scented blossoms into a shallow basket and then crossed the compound to the far side where with the assistance of irrigating runnels of water Maung Ba Tu cultivated a few vegetables, and a little tobacco, close to Ma Chit's flower bed. There were plantains here, and a big old mango tree that offered a little shade. Here they sat on the ground and strung the blossoms into garlands.

Watching the little girl's grave face as she threaded the flowers the boy felt troubled. He loved this little Mālā as he loved his sisters, but that morning at the ruins, and when she had looked at his brother's girl, she had seemed as though possessed by an evil spirit. He did not believe in charms and spells, but the spirits were real and many of them were evil. All that any sensible person asked was that they should lead their own existences in their own particular realms and leave humans alone, and to this end they were propitiated with offerings. This was reasonable enough; what was not reasonable was that Mālā should deliberately invite their interference. Only how to prevent her? Perhaps a strong good thought could defeat a strong bad one. He resolved that at the pagoda that night he would make a strong wish that only good should happen to Ma Hla, that Shwe-Shwe should come safely back and marry her and be happy. He would make an offering to the pagoda *nat*, and wish not only for happiness for Ma Hla and Shwe-Shwe but that little Mālā's heart should be cleansed of jealousy. Every day he would make this his strong wish, and every duty day at the pagoda invoke the aid of the good *nat*.

Whilst Jenny sat beside Aung in the hot shade, threading the fragrant white blossoms, she sang the little moon song she had often crooned to her baby brother; she sang it absently, without associating; it was just a little song that wandered through her mind thinking of the splendid moon that would crown the day, thinking of the pagoda garlanded with lights, of the golden Buddha smiling down at the great mass of flowers brought to him, of the walk through the moonlight with her hand in Aung's, living contentedly in the present and in the future, with no thought of the past. It was as though the rains had washed away all memory and a whole world. Only when she heard the name Ma Hla spoken something stirred in her, a prick of memory, but instantly, protectively, the image of Maung Shwe was shadowed forth. He had saved her from the river; one day he would come back and take her back to her mother; then they would all be together, and she would see Daddy again, and little Peter, and Ganesh; they would all be together, with Shwe-Shwe. It was all confused and shadowy, but in the thought of the beloved golden one there was safety and assurance. Until then there was Aung, but only through Shwe-Shwe was everything safe and sure.

The noon heat subsided, the glaring sunshine mellowed, and people began to stir again, in the house and in the street. The musicians went away; the party in the house broke up. There was a sound of distant drums now, prelude to the *pwè*. Now the dust rose in the village street like smoke as people set out towards the theatre erected at the cross-roads. People had already come in from outlying villages and their bullock-carts

were parked along the sides of the roads, the shafts tilting to the sky.
A few Japanese military police stood about, as happily anticipating the
entertainment as the village people.

Jenny had only previously seen a pagoda festival through the windows
of her father's car. She had never been allowed to stroll among the crowd
and be part of it, either at the pagoda or at the *pwè*. Now she was suddenly
caught up in the mystery of the one and the excitement of the other.
There were so many people at the pagoda that it looked different and
strange, as the people themselves did in their best clothes. There was an
endless promenading round the base of the pagoda, kneeling before the
shrine, lighting candles and joss-sticks, tucking sweet-smelling flowers into
vases—so many flowers, so many offerings, it was like a market, Jenny
thought, but a gayer and more beautiful one than any she had ever been
to with Ganesh and her mother. All that life was remote now, hidden
somewhere behind a curtain of rain.

She looked up at the golden *hti* of the pagoda, hung with golden bells,
glimmering in the hot sunshine and sending out a thin sweet sound when
a breath of wind moved in the upper air; and then away beyond the
pagoda to the wide dusty street where people were gathering for the *pwè*.
There was a beat of drums and the high reedy call of clarinets and an eager
clash of cymbals and clappers. It was exciting beyond all telling. She
smiled up at the slender boy at her side, and the look he turned on her
was one of infinite tenderness. She slipped a hand into his, tugging a
little in her excitement. There was an answering pressure of his own fingers
and together they threaded a way through the coloured tide of people in
the direction of the music.

Mats had been spread on the ground in front of the theatre, and men,
women and children sat with their feet tucked up under them, their
golden faces tilted to the stage, the smooth tightness of the skin cracking
into laughter when the ribald jokes of the clowns reached them, enthralled
during the presentation of a traditional romantic play of kings and queens,
princes and princesses, smiling with gentle pleasure as they watched the
women dancers dexterously kicking back their feet-enfolding skirts, their
arms and bodies gracefully posturing, and all the time the piano-like
tinkling of the dulcimer, the crash of brass, the clear notes of the flutes
overriding the wailing and whimpering and throbbing of the circular
drums, and the strong harsh voices of the singers triumphing over all. Hour
after hour the crash and clatter and wail and whimper, and the strident
singing like a lusty shout, and the crimson lantern of the sun moving
down the sky into the extinguishing dusk. But even in the dusk the great
Po Sein continued to flit about the stage like a huge white bird, knees
bent, body tilted forward, kicking up his heels, vigorously posturing,
supremely sure of himself and his power to enthral. The crowd loved him

and their love flowed out to him and he responded to it, posturing before them like some great white peacock in the glory of display, so long as the light lasted.

Then the people got up reluctantly, folding their mats, a little sad because this was the hour at which properly speaking it should all begin—the great feast of lights. The orange lantern of the moon replaced the crimson lantern of the sun. Soon everything was held in the tremendous silver flood of the moonlight. There were no lights anywhere, yet the whole world seemed made of light. Jenny felt so happy she wanted the night to last forever.

VI. WATER-MUSIC

Now the days were beautiful with unclouded skies and unhurried busyness. The Japanese had conscripted so many of the men for their labour gangs that there was a shortage of manpower for gathering the crops, but the women who had helped the men with the sowing went out to help with the harvesting, and households which still had sons at home came to the assistance of those who had none or who were shorthanded. Manpower was not the only shortage, yet there was a feeling of lightness and hope. The British had been pushed back into India; the end must surely be in sight, and then when it was all over the Japanese would withdraw and they would be a free and sovereign people once again.

In the meantime it was the dry season and possible to sit out on the verandah again for music and song; and now sometimes people came in, young men of the village band, with their bamboo clappers and their drums and flutes. Maung Shwe was one of them, and they came now to his parents' house to cheer the family up in his absence. When they came many of the neighbours came in too, and it was very fine, then, with all the instruments, and Nu sitting a little apart from the young men and singing in the appropriate places in a voice that was surprisingly strong, and even a little harsh and forced, but in combination with the thin sweetness of the dulcimer and the flutes as right as the sour foods that balance the sweet ones. The little girls, Mālā and Mya, would sit with Nu, and the mother usually joined them. Maung Ba Tu and Aung would sit with the band, the old man smoking a cheroot and nodding his head occasionally to the twanging, wailing rhythm.

Sometimes Maung Than came, with his pretty young sister. He always brought with him an oblong drum which he beat with his hands, and Ma Hla would sing, solo or with Nu. Ma Hla's voice was also unexpectedly strong for so small and flower-like a person. Jenny did not like it when the head man came with his sister, and on those occasions she would prefer to be in the kitchen with Ma Chit, preparing the refreshments to hand round to the guests. There was always the plain tea, two shallow bowls set on the floor before each person, and pickled tea, and the betel box would be passed round, and cheroots distributed. The men would sit on their mats on the floor with their backs to the walls, the women form themselves into a group at the far end of the room, convenient for the kitchen. It was no longer possible to make the big rich slab cakes, but there would usually be enough flour to make a few little plain cakes cut into the shape of butterflies and hearts and rings, and there were always fruits, oranges and plantains, mangoes and mangosteens.

Among the men there would always be a good deal of talk about the war on these occasions. Those who had not lost any of their cattle and carts and men to the Japanese had nothing against them, and would even find points in favour of them—point one always being that they had driven out the British. And then, after all, were they not all Buddhists, even though not of the pure Theravada faith? Then, too, soon now, thanks to them, Burma would be independent. And were they not constructing new roads, airfields, railways? Soon, now, Siam and Burma would be linked by rail. The Japanese had brought progress as well as freedom to the country. Others, and Maung Ba Tu was among them, complained bitterly of the shortages since the Japanese arrived in the country, and of the slaughtering of plough-cattle to provide meat for their troops. And what of all the agricultural land swallowed up by all this construction work? What would be the use of independence if they could no longer feed themselves? Under the British they had at least had enough to eat and had not been rationed, and they had been able to get all the flour and oil they wanted, and paraffin for the lamps, and combs for the hair, and gay buttons for the women's *eingyis*, and all the candles and joss-sticks they needed for the pagodas, and all manner of things that filled the markets and the stalls at the *pwès*, and made life pleasanter and easier.

All this grown-up talk went over the head of Jenny and Aung and Mya, as they sat in a pool of moonlight on the verandah, their heads bent close, giggling over their endless seed-flicking games. But it did not go over the heads of Ma Chit and Mi Nu and Ma Hla and others of the women, to whom the food shortages were a great deal more real than all the fine talk of liberation and independence and progress; and Ma Chit had lost a son to the Japanese, and Nu a brother, and Ma Hla, as she had reason to believe, a suitor who with this full moon might well have become something more, had he been allowed to remain in the village.

These gatherings were most popular when there was a moon, for then, with the great silver lamp of the heavens hung high above the world, there was no need to use the precious oil and candles to see each other's faces. Jenny liked these nights, when she and Mya and all the other village children were allowed to stay up half the night talking and singing and playing games and eating, with the exciting feeling of life going on in their own and everyone else's houses just as though it were daylight. On these nights the whole village would sit with its houses open to the warm silver night and you could hear the life going on in the houses, and could forget about the rats running along the rafters and the evil spirits lurking in the shadows. From one house would come the strong reassuring hum of men's voices, from another music and singing, and the sound of people laughing, and women's voices, shrill as birds; there would come the sound of a flute, high and thin, and the sound of children playing, and you could see people sitting or leaning on their verandahs, and strolling in the street in twos and threes, young men with their arms round each other's shoulders and waists, girls with their arms linked, followed by the young men, and in it all the exciting feeling that never again was anyone going to bed. The moonlight seemed to drip like silver water off the plantains and palms. The smoothly-flowing river was like melted silver, upon which hyacinths drifted, pushing up their blue flowers from heart-shaped leaves.

In that valley of Upper Burma, with the massive ranges of the Chin Hills away to the West, and the Pondaung of the Lower Chindwin behind, the war at that time seemed remote, despite the food shortages, the presence of the Japanese military police, and the drone of Japanese bombers on moonless nights heading out over the great hills to India.

Within the short space of six months the child who had been Jenny Finching had become completely Burmese, not only talking her mother's tongue all the time but thinking in it, and all that she had known before the river had closed over her dimmed like something dreamed a long time ago. It was as though all that had been English in her had been a veneer imposed upon her true self, and washed away by the flood which had swept all her old life from her—leaving only the new world to which Maung Shwe had brought her, up out of the river.

The days grew hotter. The flame-of-the-forest trees dropped their scarlet blossoms into the deep dust of the roads. The falling leaves of the teak trees were like pieces of dry leather. The hot wind moved over the forests and over the semi-deserts of scrub lands and empty savanna, drawing the sap of life, it seemed, out of every green growing thing. The thorn-bushes, white with dust, were like bleached skeletons; grass became the colour of the desert. The great hills were misty in the heat.

In February, General Wingate led his troops through the mountains of the Indian frontier and into the Upper Chindwin Valley; they crossed the Chindwin River, they crossed the railway line, destroying it as they came; they moved East of the Irrawaddy . . . but all that was some two hundred and fifty miles from Tatkon in its sheltered valley, and though rumors of a new British offensive reached the people it meant very little to them. The village girls were practising songs and dances for the water-festival, the *thingyan pwè*, when the Nat King would come to earth to inaugurate the New Year. On the first day of the festival they would parade the village on decorated floats displaying their skill in the traditional singing and dancing, and everyone would run wild throwing water over each other. Mi Nu and Ma Hla were always going to each other's houses to practise together. Aung was busy making squirts for himself and the two little girls for the occasion. The tall padauk trees began to be hung with golden blossoms, the sure sign of the approaching New Year. Jenny was intensely happy in anticipation of the coming festival. In the old life at Bokoko she had been allowed to join with Ganesh's children in the compound in water-throwing, and had watched the parade of the dancing and singing beauties from the top of her father's car, but this year she was to be allowed to run wild with all the other children, with Aung's happy assurance that they would all be drenched to the skin from sunrise to sundown, during which time they would do their full and glorious share of drenching others—men, women and children. Everyone except the *pongyis*—and, of course, the Japanese.

On New Year's Eve Ma Chit and Mi Nu went with the two little girls down to the river, taking with them buckets and towels and clean *longyis*. They stood on the low platform projecting out into the water, like a small landing-stage, and dipped their buckets into the river and poured them over Jenny and Mya, then soaped their heads and washed their hair, rinsing out the lather with another bucket of water. Then they were assisted in shuffling out of their wet *longyis* under the dry ones slipped over them; after which their mother and big sister similarly operated on each other. Other women and girls were engaged in this special *thingyan* bathing and hair-washing on the platform and at the edge of the river. There was a great deal of splashing, shrieking, laughter.

Ma Chit sat on the edge of the platform dangling her feet in the water, allowing her thin greying hair to dry in the sun and watching the little girls splashing in the water. Her heart was as full of tenderness for the adopted child as for her own. She found herself wondering about Mālā's father. Maung Shwe had been back to Mynmyo to find out whether Po Than had survived and had learned that the *thakin* had been captured by the Japanese that same night and taken off in a patrol boat. That meant that when the war ended he would come in search of the child; it would be only natural. And Po Than would be able to tell him that she was alive and where she was. Shwe-Shwe should never have gone back to find Po Than, yet that had been natural too. And they were none of them to know how much the child would come to mean to them, or they to her. As it had turned out, would this child who was now so happy with them want to go back to the West, to her father's world? Her mother, after all, had been Burmese, and Mālā herself was now as Burmese as any other child in the village. Would not the mother herself, if she could have any say in the matter, have preferred that the child be brought up by her own people rather than by her foreign husband's people? In the beginning, Ma Chit reflected, it was always her mother the child wept for; waking in the night it was always 'Mummy' she called for. But then later on, Ma Chit thought, she began to call me *Mé-Mé*; she accepted me as her mother; she has never taken to Maung Ba Tu; he is too old; but she loves Shwe-

Shwe as a big brother, and now she has Aung, and it could be that they are closer to her than her English father. Shwe-Shwe said he was a very stiff *thakin* who liked to give orders—like so many . . .

Ma Chit was a very simple woman, and she knew nothing at all of the big world, or even of her own country outside the village a few miles away in which she had been born and reared, and Tatkon to which she had come when she married. She was only thirty-three, but she looked forty or more, her face lined, her skin withered by too many seasons in the flooded paddy fields; the tropical sun dries up the blood in humans as it dries the sap in green growing things. Only it does not dry up the sap of the human heart, and Ma Chit felt that if the little Mālā should ever be taken from her it would be as though a child of her own had been taken.

Nu finished shaking out her long black hair in the sun and came and sat beside her mother, slipping an arm through hers. They sat watching Mālā and Mya and other children playing together at the water's edge. The women and girls looked like brilliant red and blue flowers in their bright *longyis*; the hair of many of them streamed in thick dark manes to their knees. The river was very low; in places sandbanks were laid bare, and small beaches of sun-bleached pebbles. The land at the far side was the colour of pale sand, and the sky the colour of pale water.

So high that they looked like a flight of tiny silver flying-fishes, almost invisible against the heat-misted sky, a squadron of 'planes went over towards India. Their faint drone drew the attention of the bathers for a minute or so, then, as it receded, the fused laughter and happy shrilling and shouting, and the splash of water, surged to and fro along the river, a water-music of gay voices, and somewhere out of sight above it, as though hidden in the heat, there was the knock-knock-knock, persistent as a drum-beat, of the coppersmith-bird.

Mi Nu rested her face against her mother's bare shoulder, cool from the water. She still watched the children playing.

"She is so sweet, our little Mālā," she said. "Whatever shall we do if after the war her father should come back for her?"

"We should have to give her up."

"It would be heart-breaking. For her as well as us. She is one of us now. Look at her now with Mya—they could be sisters!"

Ma Chit smiled but said nothing. She thought, Perhaps in a few years time she will be—if it is in her *karma* to remain with us. . . .

That the Thagyamin, the Nat King, descends to earth from the heavenly regions at midnight on New Year's Eve, around the thirteenth of April, is as certain to most Burmese children as the arrival of Santa Claus by reindeer-sledge, from some unspecified region, on Christmas Eve, is to most English children. In Burma, as in all parts of the world, traditional belief and superstition die hardest in the villages. Whether the adults do in fact believe in the advent of the spirit-king, or are merely as able for the willing suspension of disbelief as Westerners when it suits them, is debatable, but certainly the unsophisticated village children find no difficulty, encouraged by their parents, in believing. If any proof were needed is there not the gun which sounds at midnight to announce the lordly one's arrival?

Jenny and Mya, lying side by side on the sleeping-platform, were full of excitement when the long-awaited sound came. Now they wanted only that it should be light so that the fun could begin. Buckets, bowls and vessels had been filled with water and placed in readiness on the verandah and in the compound. The night seemed interminable, but at last there was the dawn commotion of crows and immediately the two children rushed from their corner to crouch on the verandah in the hope of taking Aung by surprise with the first dousing of the day. But Aung had filled his squirt overnight and taken it to bed with him and surprised them with it in their ambush. After which all three waited to drench their elders on their way to the pagoda to wash the Buddha images and throw water round the base of the sacred tree; they did not escape themselves, however, for everyone, young and old, was armed with a water-vessel or squirt that day.

There was such a traffic up and down the narrow lane to the river, an endless two-way procession of young people and children carrying buckets and tins, that the track became as muddy as though a heavy shower had fallen: but in the village main street, where the great water battles were fought by the children, and between groups of young men and girls, the water dried in the hot dust almost as quickly as it fell. There was a lull during the procession of the decorated floats—contrived on bullock-carts, no trucks being available—though some of the singing, posturing girls received dousings from young men enthusiasts in the crowd, whilst from other floats the battle was carried on by bevies of beflowered girls, armed with water vessels, tossing the water in handfuls into the crowd as they passed.

To Jenny it was not more beautiful than the full moon festival; it was different. That had been a silver festival; this was a golden one; that had been all feasting and music; this was all water and laughter. The water and the laughter seemed all one: you laughed as you flung it, and you laughed as you received it: it came into your face like a burst of laughter, and on a burst of laughter you flung it into another laughing face. Everyone ran and dodged and charged and shrieked and laughed; everyone was wet through, everyone was gay, and in spite of the hot sun everyone was cool, from the continual drenching.

By the middle of the morning, when most people went into their houses for the first meal of the day, Jenny for one was exhausted by so much excited rushing about. Her head continually nodded as she sat on the floor, her plate piled with rice and curry, and finally Mi Nu picked her up and carried her over to the sleeping platform and laid her there, where instantly she sank into a sound sleep in spite of all the laughter and chatter in the room.

She dreamed that she was in the river again. She felt it blinding her eyes and rushing into her ears, but she was borne along on it and not afraid. It closed over her but she could breathe through it, and it was somehow made of sunshine and full of people laughing. She was rushing very fast through it but strong hands held her up and she felt safe, and excited and exhilarated at the same time, as though it were some wonderful, thrilling game. Then Shwe-Shwe's face was somehow rushing through the water with her, laughing into her face, calling her and shaking her, bidding her wake up, wake up, calling her by her Burmese name, Mālā, little Mālā. . . .

Then there was no more rushing water, but only the beloved face, smiling, close to hers, his hands on her shoulders, pulling her up to him, brushing back her hair, kissing her brow, her cheeks, calling her by her name. Shwe-Shwe *real!*

The whole family was gathered round, laughing and exclaiming. Her arms went round his neck so tightly that, laughing, he loosened them protesting that she would throttle him. He was wet to the skin from all the drenchings he had received since the Japanese truck had put him down at the Kempetei H.Q. His face was so wet from the water running down from his thick black hair that it was impossible to know whether any of the tears, as Jenny called them, were real or not. With one arm he held her to his breast and the other encircled his mother's shoulders, and soon they were all clinging to him, and if there were tears as well as the water from the drenchings on some of the faces it was all part of the day's happy *thingyan* water-music.

When the first excitement of surprise and welcome had subsided they all sat round on the floor fanning themselves with paper fans the shape of lotus leaves, smoking cheroots, sipping plain tea, chewing *pan*, eating pickled tea, animatedly talking, asking Maung Shwe questions, and people kept coming in to say, welcome-back and happy New Year and inquire how it had been, working with the Japanese. Presently, tired of all the adult talk, in which they had no part, the two little girls ran off with Aung to resume water-throwing in the street. It was as though they could never have enough of the wild fun.

So the golden exuberant day passed. This year, because of the shortage of cattle brought about by the Japanese, there could be no ransoming of a beast due to be slaughtered. Usually the village subscribed to buy a bullock from the slaughterer, then it would be garlanded with flowers and its horns gilded and led in triumphal procession to the *pongyi-kyaung*, where it would be set free as a symbol of goodwill to all living things. But the goodwill was there, even without the symbolic bullock, and in that remote valley between the high hills the war seemed remote and impersonal.

Even for Maung Shwe, who had come close to it during the last six months or so, it seemed only like a long bad dream from which he had at last wakened. He put the dark thought of it away from him. He had come back to laughter and gaiety, to beauty and joy, to happiness and love. He felt unable to utter the name in the forefront of his mind, and which seemed to beat there with the rhythm of his heart, but when the sun went down and the pagoda and all the verandahs bloomed with coloured lights, he slipped away through the brief dusk to the head man's house.

VII. THE WEDDING

IT was soon understood in the village that Maung Shwe would marry the head man's sister as soon as he was in a position to do so—that is to say when he was able to bring some money to the wedding; after the harvest, perhaps. Always provided that he was not again conscripted by the Japanese for labour service. Life was too precarious at that time to make plans far ahead.

In the meantime, in the immediate present, it was well enough. The war encircled the valley on all sides, but distantly, not touching it; it was some three hundred miles away to the north, and far away beyond the great Arakan hills to the west. In Tatkon more real than the rumours of great Japanese successes on the Arakan coast was the approach of the Kason Full Moon Festival, in celebration of the Buddha's birth.

For Jenny it was not as exciting as the water festival, nor as beautiful as the great festival at the end of Lent, but nevertheless she shared the eagerness of the others in watching the May moon nearing its full, and the opening of the orchids carefully cultivated in the outer shells of coconuts clamped to posts at one side of the compound. Elsewhere they decorated the trunks of ancient trees with their trails of mauve flowers. No one would touch them, Nu explained to Jenny, until the Full Moon Day; then they would all be gathered and taken to the pagoda for the Lord Buddha. She went round the compound with Nu in the early morning of the great day, holding the basket whilst the big sister cut the delicate blooms. Then she went with Mya to gather baskets full of jasmine from the bushes at the river side of the house.

But the real excitement of the day was going with Aung to the river, to a creek where the lotus leaves completely covered the shallow water and the pink and white flowers glowed like thousands of Chinese lanterns. Jenny loved the lotus flowers; she could never think of them rooted in the black mud, but only springing from the water, which was why, she thought, their petals were so pure and beautiful, different from those of any other flower, as though made of wax. There was a creek at Bokoko where she had gone with Ganesh to gather lotus flowers for her mother to take to the pagoda. She remembered it now, walking to the river with Aung, and told him about it, and how her mother had waited in the gharry with a parasol over her whilst she and Ganesh went off together, and how afterwards they drove to the pagoda, and she and Ganesh waited in the gharry, then, whilst her mother took the flowers to the shrine, "because Ganesh is a Hindu and I am a Christian." There was no nostalgia in the memory: it all seemed far away and long ago, only dimly remembered, like the time before there had been a baby brother.

Aung smiled and said, "I think you are not a Christian any longer." She told him, firmly, "I was christened. When you are christened it makes you a Christian. Forever."

"Not forever." The boy's voice was no less firm. "Sometimes people change. When Shwe-Shwe was away working with the Japanese he met an Englishman who had been taken prisoner by them. He had been living in this country for years, he told Shwe-Shwe, and had become a Buddhist. It is only necessary to believe in the teachings of the Lord Buddha. Perhaps when you are older you also will believe."

Jenny, pattering along beside Aung over the sunbaked earth, her slippers flapping up and down, her best silk *longyi* swathing her small body, had no idea whether she believed in the Lord Buddha or the Lord Jesus, and Almighty God who was the father of the Lord Jesus, and who, also, in some complicated way, was the God in whom Ganesh also believed; she only knew that it was always exciting and beautiful to go to the pagoda and lay flowers and light candles and joss-sticks and kneel before the great golden image and look up and see the Lord Buddha looking down and ever so faintly smiling.

And it was exciting now to be going to the river with Aung to gather the beautiful pink and white water flowers. It was exciting because Aung was her special friend, as Ganesh had been, though not as special as Shwe-Shwe, who was big and tall and strong and grown up and could make everything safe in a way no one else could.

When they came to the creek Aung removed his snowy white jacket and tucked his *longyi* up between his legs and waded in among the leaves. Jenny stood at the edge of the water, against a background of tall bamboo, holding his jacket, not daring to go in with him for fear of wetting her best clothes. She watched his bare brown right arm diving in among the leaves and the growing bunch of pink and white flowers in his left hand. She looked along the lotus carpet of the creek to the river flowing like molten silver beyond—the river which had washed away her old life and from which she had been drawn up into this new one which was now more real than the old. All memory of that other river, that other creek, faded. She was content to be there with Aung gathering the lotus flowers, receiving them from him with both hands when he could hold no more, placing them in the big brass pot full of water at her feet; and to be going with him presently to offer them at the pagoda. And Shwe-Shwe was home again, and her world secure. The house was home again because he had returned to it.

When the vessel was so full it would hold no more, Aung slipped his feet into his slippers and his arms into his jacket and they walked back up the sun-dried lane hedged with dusty cacti to the main street and joined the straggling procession of gaily dressed people heading for the pagoda with their baskets of jasmine, their trails of orchids, their bunches of multi-coloured asters.

The Lord Buddha, Jenny knew, liked to have flowers all the time, but never so many as at festival times, and there were never such beautiful flowers to offer as at Kason, she thought, when the orchids and the lotus flowers—above all the lovely waxen lotus flowers—were in bloom. The fact that so far as she could see no one else had brought lotus flowers added satisfaction and pride to her general happiness.

She envied Aung when they arrived at the pagoda and he climbed up on to the golden image and laid the most beautiful of the lotus flowers— a great creamy white one and a glowing rosy pink one—on the sacred feet. Men and boys were allowed to go up on to the image like that, he explained, but not women and girls. So Jenny stood humbly at the base of the shrine whilst Aung placed the flowers, then he rejoined her and they lit some candles; he then knelt and repeated the Threefold Refuge of the Three Gems—the Buddha, the *Dhamma*, the *Sangha*—the avowal of belief in the Buddha, his doctrine and his order. Jenny sat back on her heels, gazing over her folded hands at the glimmering candles, the banked flowers, the placid golden features emerging from the shadowiness of the great niche, tranquil yet strong, 'like a flame in a windless place'. It was beautiful to celebrate the Lord Buddha's birthday.

But happiness stopped short this side perfection because Shwe-Shwe was not there. Maung Shwe was keeping the ten precepts, which included not eating after mid-day and spending a great part of the day in meditation on the Four Noble Truths of the Buddha's teaching—that life is *Dukka*, suffering; that the cause of suffering is craving—desire; that the conquest of craving is the way, and the only way, to gain release from *Samsara*, the cycle of rebirth, with all that means of suffering and delusion, that the end of all is the only true peace, the only real happiness, the only reality, which is *Nirvana*. To this end Maung Shwe had retired immediately it was light to the house of a neighbour where there was a shrine room and religious devotions could be practised in peace. There was a shrine room at the house of the head man, but Maung Shwe was serious about his duty-day devotions and wished to avoid distraction.

With the waning moon the clouds began to gather in threatening mass formation. The first showers came. There were electric storms making livid the starless night skies. By night and day the earth was an oven. With the first showers the river rose and became brown and turgid. The hot wind harried sky, earth and water. Then suddenly it was as though the sky cracked, releasing the long-pent burden of rain. The leaf-thatched roofs of the houses leaked, swelled, and were then water-tight. The ankle-deep dust became ankle-deep mud. Between the deluges the men went out and ploughed. The mud deepened, and people ceased to visit each other in the evenings. Ma Hla no longer came to the house, and Maung Shwe went less often to hers. He stayed at home and wove baskets and gave Jenny reading and writing lessons, and told her fairy-tales of ancient Burmese princes and princesses and ogres, and the Jataka stories, legends of the Buddha's previous incarnations.

Maung Shwe had learned these stories during his time at the monastery; he had amused his sisters and brother during the wet seasons with them, and now they served to entertain the new little sister. Out of his own simplicity he told them very simply, and Jenny sat entranced, her great dark eyes never leaving his face as he told her of how the shape of the hare came to be marked on the moon, how King Siva made a present of his eyes, how the Bodhisatta was once a big red ox, and all beginning 'Once upon a time', as all true fairy-stories must, the world over. 'Once upon a time, when King Brahmadatta reigned in Benares. . . .' Sometimes the Bodhisatta was a king, a prince, a beggar, a merchant; or an elephant, or a lion, or a frog, or a bird: animal stories, adventure stories, comic stories—Shwe-Shwe never told the dull purely moral ones; and Jenny wanted to know who King Brahmadatta was, and where was Benares, and so India, the promised land, came close again, unknown yet faintly nostalgic.

During the rains that year Jenny was peacefully happy. She had Shwe-Shwe with his lessons—which she enjoyed—and his stories, and Aung to amuse her when his brother was not there. Mi Nu mothered her, and Ma Chit, though she still thought her very old, became increasingly dear to her. To Maung Ba Tu she could never feel close; a Burmese mother was natural to her, but not a Burmese father. A new father, to be acceptable to her, had somehow to be like the one she had lost. Of the old grandmother she was a little afraid; she had no experience of anyone so old; she must surely be a hundred years old, Jenny thought, and shrank away from her as from a witch; she was as alien to her as Maung Ba Tu. Mya was her playmate, but she meant no more to her than any other village child, though every night they shared the sleeping-platform together.

In the middle of the rains, on the first of August, Burmese independence was proclaimed. This meant a great deal in Rangoon but it meant very little to the village of Tatkon, except that in due course it was supplied with a national flag, green, yellow and red, with the national emblem of the peacock in its pride in the middle, which was run up over the head man's house. There was a little mild celebration organized by Maung Than, but Burma was now officially at war with England and

America, and the air was full of uncertainty, and a confusion of hopes
and fears. All was conjecture; no one really knew what was happening or
likely to happen. Was this really independence? The Japanese were still
there, and not merely as troops. There was a Burma National Army, with
Japanese instructors, and there were rumours that it was not much more
than a glorified Japanese labour corps.

In this atmosphere of change and uncertainty it seemed to both Maung
Shwe's family and to Ma Hla's that their marriage should be hastened.
Both families agreed that it should take place as soon as Lent was over.
Maung Shwe was young, to be sure, but that was a defect—if it was that—
which time would soon cure. And that he was manly, despite his youth,
could not be denied. Maung Than was anxious to get his sister married.
He was married himself, with a large family, and he had his widowed
mother living with him. True that for a time, until Maung Shwe could
get a house built, he would have not only Ma Hla still living with him
but her husband as well, but once the rains were over it would not take
long to build a house. He owned enough land for the two families, and
Maung Shwe could build close by, and he could work part of the land
for his own use and superintend the cultivation of the rest, leaving him,
Maung Than, free for the village affairs for which he was responsible—
and which he preferred, as more suited to the man who had the most
land and wealth and education in the village. And since Ma Hla was
eager to marry Maung Shwe, however little in the matter of material
possessions he could bring to the marriage—perhaps not even a single gold
bangle—there was no point in delaying matters, particularly now that
Burma was a state at war, and no one knew, from day to day, what would
happen.

Therefore as soon as the rains lessened Maung Shwe began work on
the house, assisted by various young men friends, and so far as Tatkon
was concerned the marriage of the head man's sister was a vastly more
important event than all the momentous political doings in Rangoon. Dr.
Ba Maw was merely a name, whereas everyone knew the pretty Ma Hla
and the handsome, good-natured Maung Shwe.

In all this Jenny wandered round in the beautiful new days that followed the ending of the rains feeling lost and unhappy. It seemed that
all her dark prayers to the *nat* of the ruined pagoda had been in vain.
Nothing, it seemed, could alter the fact that Shwe-Shwe was going to
marry the head man's sister and go away to live in his own house at the
other end of the village. He would not be part of the family any more,
eating with them, sleeping with them, telling stories, giving her lessons,
going out with Maung Ba Tu in the mornings but always returning in the
evenings; he would belong to *her* . . .

Aung teased her, saying, "Never mind, little Mālā; hurry up and grow up and then we two can set up house together and be married!"

But Jenny merely tossed her head and stuck out her tongue at him and sulked—miserably.

When this was reported to Maung Shwe he was not amused as the others were, but troubled. It seemed to him that the little Mālā was learning very young that life was suffering—first the loss of her parents, indeed, of the whole world she had known till then, and now the loss of the person who had—he realized—replaced that lost world for her. The working out of each person's *karma* was so strange, he reflected. If he had not gone to Mynmyo just before the monsoon broke to offer at the five-day market some mats and baskets he had woven he would not have fallen in with Po Than and agreed to earn some additional money by helping him convert two boats into a car-ferry to get the *thakin* across the river. If that had not happened his life and that of this little Anglo-Burmese girl would not have crossed. Po Than would have found someone else to help him with the ferry, and this other one might or might not have saved the child's life.

But the Law of Karma worked inexorably; his life and that of this English child had reached a point—through the natural law of cause and effect working through other lives to this one—at which they had to meet, and speculation as to any other possibility was as idle and foolish as to speculate on the possibility of the sun rising in the west and the moon ceasing to wax and wane. Nothing could have happened other than it had; nothing could happen in the future that was not now being created in the present. And the next piece of pattern in the weave of his own *karma* was his marriage to Ma Hla.

Now there was no *pwè* to celebrate the end of Lent, and no feasting because this year there was even less of everything; but the liberating splendour of the full moon no one could black out, the golden seal set once again upon the end of the rains, the end of Lent; and no one could ration the natural joyous response of the liberated human spirit. And not even the Japanese could take all the fish in the river, even if they took most of the rice in the fields; there was still millet for flour, and every house had its carefully nurtured potato patch—and its plantains and its coconut palms. It was still possible to eat, and to give to the *pongyis*, but the gaunt pariah dogs who lived under the houses grew thinner and thinner.

People visited the pagoda and laid flowers—but no longer were there candles to light—and sat by moonlight on their verandahs, talking, smoking, chewing *pan*, playing or listening to music. Aung tried to persuade Jenny that going to the pagoda in the moonlight was an adventure—what did it matter that there were no lights, no singing and dancing, no booths lit by flares and casting long shadows and selling all manner of things? Was not the pagoda still beautiful in the moonlight, even without the lights? Could they not still see the Lord Buddha smiling down at the bank of flowers at his feet? But Jenny was not to be comforted. Shwe-Shwe was not with them any more than last year; he was spending his last unmarried evening with his young men friends. And tomorrow he would go away from them for good.

"But he will be only at the other end of the village," Aung pointed out.

"He will be with her," Jenny declared. "He won't want us any more! And then I shall have no one! No one! No one! No one!"

She was suddenly crying wildly, her hands pressed to her face. People strolling round the base of the pagoda turned to look at her. Aung put an arm round her shoulders and drew her out of the crowd. Behind a decaying satellite pagoda, whose faded red lacquer multiple roofs were darkly dragonish silhouetted against the pale sky, he knelt down to bring his shoulders level with hers and dried her tears.

"You have me," he insisted. "You have all of us. We all love you, Mé-Mé and Pé-Pé and Nu and all of us. Shwe-Shwe loves you too, just the same as ever, but it's right that he should marry."

Jenny stopped crying, not because she was comforted by Aung's words, but because it was impossible to put into words what she felt. From where they stood she could see the river racing in the moonlight, and she had again the feeling of being swept away, and of loneliness and loss.

The people strolled, talking and laughing, their bright clothes glimmering in the moonlight. Everyone was gay, in spite of there being no *pwè* and no lights. In the street a group of young men beat bamboo clappers and played flutes, and one hurled himself wildly round and round, face lifted to the moon, eyes rolling, in a dance. Tomorrow they would come and play outside the house of the head man whilst Maung Shwe, the golden one, was being married to Miss Pretty.

Once again, as soon as it was light, the whole household was astir. Jenny submitted whilst Nu smeared *thanaka* on her face and rouged her lips for the wedding. Jenny did not like the greasy red stuff on her lips, but Nu said that all the children, the boys as well as girls, would be made up in this way and commanded her to observe how pretty Mya looked with her bright red lips.

Again the best silk *longyis* were put on, flowers tucked into hair, and all available necklaces, bangles, rings. Nu was happy and excited. It was always beautiful to go to a wedding, and this was the wedding of her favourite brother and her dearest friend. It seemed strange to her that Mālā, who loved Shwe-Shwe, could be sulky and cross—but then, she reflected, Mālā was not really one of themselves; there was a Western part of her that did not belong with them: or so it seemed to her. How else could her strangeness be explained—her hostility to Ma Hla, her jealousy, as though she were a grown girl and in love with Shwe-Shwe? A Burmese child would not behave like that, she thought; perhaps mixed blood made people more complicated than human nature ordinarily is. The thought only made her feel more tender and protective towards the difficult unhappy child.

At Maung Than's house there were coloured paper garlands, and the village band playing vigorously under an awning. Inside the house every inch of floor space seemed occupied, but places were found for Ma Chit and Nu and Mya and Jenny, and Maung Ba Tu and Aung went into another room where the male guests were being served with the morning meal. The women's turn would come later; in the meantime they all sat on the floor and fanned themselves and gossiped, and there was a great scent from all the flowers in their hair, and from the mass of scented blossom banked up round two large vases of wrought silver containing money placed on the floor in front of two lace-covered yellow silk cushions.

An elder stood up behind the silver bowls reciting blessings from the scriptures. No one listened until the recitation came at last to an end and he called the bride's name, when the chatter immediately subsided and there was a listening hush, tensed with expectation. He called her three times at intervals of five or ten minutes. At the second calling the curtains at the doorway of an adjoining room parted to admit the bridegroom and two of his friends.

Jenny, in a corner with Mya and some other children, peered between the heads of the women. He looked like a prince, she thought, like one of the princes in the Jataka stories, like the Prince Siddartha himself, in his shining yellow silk *longyi* and fine white jacket with the special buttons, on his head a round white turban with an important-looking bow at the right side. The two young men who accompanied him wore similar turbans but were much less splendid and princely. They smiled a little, but his own expression was one of the utmost seriousness. He took his place on the nearest cushion, sitting back on his heels; places were found for his friends on the floor behind him, in front of the women.

When they were seated the bride's name was called for the third time, and in a moment more she came, tightly wrapped in golden silk, her hair dressed in the old court fashion, twisted round a high frame on top, with a long tress falling down her right cheek on to her shoulder. Strings of jasmine flowers were looped above this tress, mingling with it. She wore rings set with rubies, pearls, diamonds on all the fingers of both hands, numerous bracelets on both wrists, and round her neck and flowing down over her bosom, under a long scarf of golden gauze, a number of strings of pearls and several gold chains. There was a murmur of admiration as with downcast eyes she moved across the crowded room, seeming almost to glide, so smooth was her movement, and took her place on the vacant cushion beside her bridegroom, her eyes still lowered; nor did he raise his own.

It came to Jenny that she was a princess to match the prince. Then she did not look any more, but pulled a piece of string out of her waistband and started a game of cat's-cradle with Mya, who also by this time was bored and fidgety. Other children, their faces white with *thanaka*, their lips painted, their eyes rimmed with kohl, some of them with diamond studs in their ears, weaved in and out of the crowd, restlessly, impatient for the proceedings to be over and the feasting to begin.

Some more blessings were recited, then the presiding elder came forward with a silver bowl of water which he set down in front of the bridal pair. He took Maung Shwe's right hand and Ma Hla's right hand and united them in the water. As they withdrew them there was a shower of small coins—for which the children immediately scrambled. Normally there would have been rice as well, but rice was then more precious than money; so only the symbol of wealth was thrown and not that of fertility.

The couple rose from the cushions and threaded a way through the crowd to a small room almost entirely filled by a bed covered with yellow satin covers, even to the long bolster, and draped by a golden gauze mosquito net. The room was decorated with chains of coloured paper and garlands of leaves and flowers. Bride and groom seated themselves on a bench at the foot of their bridal bed and received their guests, the faces of both waxen in their solemnity.

Jenny and Mya escaped out of the house and into the compound where they entangled themselves with the band and made great nuisances of themselves. When the band stopped playing they tore shrieking round the verandah. Mya was merely bored and following Jenny's lead. All ceremonial occasions bored her. Jenny was in the grip of the feeling which always seized her when she felt herself abandoned—of being swept away by a rushing river, with no strong hands reaching out to grip her, so that the water washed over her, and she fought for breath and felt herself drowning—and the only way not to drown was to rush about, shriek, pretend the river wasn't there, pretend that firm ground was under her, and all was safe, as once . . . when there had been Mummy, and Daddy and Ganesh, and another river, very wide, and shining, and still; a river whose name she could no longer remember.

VIII. THE YOUNGER BROTHER

THERE was a terrifying day in November, a few weeks after the wedding, when a seemingly endless procession of gun-carriers, and lorries packed with Japanese soldiers, went roaring up the main road, leaving in its rear a fog of dust that hung on the air long after the last vehicle had passed. At first no one knew where they were making for; some said they were on their way to engage the Americans in the far north; others that they were heading for the Indian frontier to cut off a fresh contingent of Wingate's 'Chindits'; rumours bred like mosquitoes. Later the story went round that they were on their way to occupy strategic points in the Chin Hills, and that the nearest point was only about sixty miles away.

Everyone was very frightened. It could surely only be a matter of days now, of hours, even, before bombs at last fell at this end of the valley. The fear was aggravated by a story that the British were advancing in Arakan, which suddenly seemed very near, with only the barrier of the hills between. A great many 'planes went over, night and day, flying very high in mass formation, but no one knew whether they were Japanese or British. In the hot still nights people lay under the light thatch of their bamboo houses listening to the sinister throb of winged machines moving, it seemed to them, among the stars. Children clutched each other fearfully, and men and women groped for each other's hands in the dark, like children, and the bodies of men, women and children were tense with listening to this evil sound that proclaimed death, if not for themselves then for others who lay similarly crouching in the dark. Sometimes by day the sound of guns reverberated in the hills—in the Chin Hills to the north, and in the Arakan hills to the west.

The children were afraid because of what they heard their elders say, fearfully, about fighting and bombs, and killing and death, during those beautiful fine-weather days at the end of 1943 and the beginning of 1944. Once again in Jenny's mind the Japanese loomed as 'the bad people'; the English phrase came back to her, and the word her father had used, 'Japs', and it added to her fear that Shwe-Shwe was no longer there for protection. He came and went, but he was never there during the nights, when the fear was greatest.

Nu and Aung and their parents tried to convince her that there was no need to be afraid of the Japanese—that they were not enemies, but there for the protection of the Burmese people. They had driven out the British and given Burma independence and her own army; everyone could feel safe because so many Japanese soldiers were going up into the hills to drive the enemy back into India. She listened to all they had to say, gazing into their calm faces, but the old fear was not so easily eradicated: inexplicably they represented evil to her, all those uniformed figures roaring past with their tin helmets, their guns, their massed impersonality. The war had come close. She had seen its face and was afraid.

The Military Police were still in the village, and more came, and almost every day sinister-looking gun-carriers, and lorries laden with supplies, moved up into the hills, leaving behind the lingering fog of dust. But all that dropped in the valley were the scarlet blossoms of the flame-of-the-forest trees as the dry season climbed with daily growing heat to its climax. Jenny forgot her fears and played in the dust like any other village child, and the padauk trees hung out their golden tassels, and the mangoes ripened.

In March, American troops crossed the upper reaches of the Chindwin and General Stilwell's Chinese forces blocked the southern exit of the Hukawng Valley. But the people in the narrow valley hundreds of miles to the south, in the Lower Chindwin, did not hear these things. Instead, they heard in March how the Japanese had crossed the Chindwin and destroyed six British divisions; and in April it was announced that the Japanese were driving down on Imphal, across the mountains of the Indian frontier. There were rumours of the Americans marching through the Hukawng Valley, with mules, and supported by 'planes that dropped supplies; the Japanese held the little town of Myitkyina—that was certain; it was a long time before the news came through that in May the Americans had got through and held the airfield.

And before that news was released there was the New Year festival to distract attention from the thunder in the hills that could not be mistaken for that which came before the monsoon. Everyone said that soon now the war would be over, and then the Japanese would clear out and there would be plenty of things in the markets again—tinned foods from Japan, and all the odds and ends of things that in the past had loaded the stalls at the *pwès*; there would be an end of food shortages, oil for the lamps, matches; there would be lights again, and Burma would be better than it had ever been, because it would be free. This good time of peace and freedom would come soon now, so why should the new year not be celebrated as gaily as ever, even though there could be no lights and no *pwè*? So everyone threw water, from morning till eve, as always, and there were even the decorated floats with the pretty girls dancing and singing.

Mi Nu was again one of the dancing girls, with her long black hair flowing down her back and twisted with jasmine, but this time not Ma Hla, for she was now expecting a child. For Nu it proved to be a very memorable *thingyan*. When the parade was over she went home and removed her finery and put on her oldest clothes, then went out again to join the other girls in their water battles with the boys and young men. A good-looking boy called Maung Tin, whom she had often secretly admired in her evening strolls with her friends, contrived to cut her off from her companions, pursued her, flinging water after her, and finally catching up with her emptied the entire contents of the pot over her, nearly drowning her. She emerged gasping, laughing, protesting, from the cataract and found herself face to face with her heart's desire. For a few confusing exciting moments they were alone, islanded in a sea of running, laughing, darting people. She was too bewildered to continue the game by flinging the remaining contents of her own water pot into his face, but he was fully self-possessed. He said, smiling, "I shall call at your house with a friend in a few days' time. I hope I may be allowed."

"Yes," she said, breathlessly, "oh—yes," then turned and fled from him into the milling crowd.

So Mi Nu had a suitor, and Jenny, contemptuously, observed on her face, when Maung Tin came to the house, the look she had so often seen on Shwe-Shwe's face when Ma Hla had been there, and at other times she had that far-away look she had also come to know, and, because it excluded her, dread.

With the first mango showers and the approach of Lent Maung Ba Tu decided that the time had come for Aung to serve his time at the *pongyi-kyaung*. Not merely was he now ready so far as age and learning went, but a neighbour who had two sons similarly ready had suggested that they should share the cost of a *shinbyu*. The whole village entered into the happy excitement—there can never be too many festivals in Burmese life, and things must be very bad indeed before there can be no heart for them. And things had all the appearances of going well; with the Japanese in Imphal, in Arakan, in Myitkyina, could anyone doubt that the war was hurrying to a victorious conclusion? That the Japanese had lost more than half of the three divisions they had poured into Manipur they did not then know. Ma Chit and Nu put on their best silk *longyis* and with their neighbour's wife and daughters similarly resplendent in their best clothes went round the village issuing the invitations for the great occasion. Jenny and Mya gathered flowers and made garlands of coloured paper for decorating the house. Various people made presents of food and money so that there should be a good feast in spite of all the shortages. Everyone was very happy. An ear-boring ceremony was a pleasant festivity, and a wedding pleasanter still, but to neither could attach the profound importance of a *shinbyu*, which was a religious occasion, with *pongyis* present.

Amid all the excitement and rejoicing Jenny felt troubled. For her this occasion which made Aung so happy and the family so proud meant yet another loss. Once again someone close to her was being taken from her.

Nothing was safe; nothing had been safe since the day when they had all, Mummy, Daddy, Husain and herself, with Mr. Vernon and Ganesh and his family ahead in the lorry, set out for India. After that there had been Shwe-Shwe to love her and care for her, but first the Japanese had taken him away, and then soon after his return Ma Hla had taken him. Now Aung was going away.

"Only until the New Year," the boy tried to comfort her.

She could not think so far ahead. There was all of Lent to live through, long months of being shut in by the rain, with neither Shwe-Shwe nor Aung to give her lessons and tell her stories; it was impossible to think even so far as the end of the monsoon. The other boys were to stay at the monastery only until the end of Lent, but Maung Ba Tu was religiously devout, and Aung was dutiful as well as devout. Also he valued the educational opportunity the year represented.

When Jenny saw Aung on the great day, dressed like a prince—like a girl was her second thought, when her first awe was overcome—his face covered with *thanaka*, rings on all his fingers, gold chains round his neck, white stockings on his feet—she could not believe he was the boy with whom she had played in the dust of the road, whose hand she had held when they had gone off together to gather lotus flowers at the creek. This little silk-clad and jewelled princeling who was paraded through the village in a flower-decorated bullock-cart, with the band marching ahead, was already as remote from her as he would be when he put on the orange robe and went away with the other boys and the *pongyis* to the *kyaung*. Then he was carried back into the house, because that day he was too important to set foot to ground, and set upon the sleeping-platform, once again covered with yellow silk and cushions for a great occasion, and the other princelings sat with him, all looking very solemn. When they had all been sufficiently admired, as is the right of princes, they were carried off to be stripped of their finery, bathed, their heads shaved, and the yellow robes put on their young bodies, and the begging bowl into their hands.

When Aung's mother came back into the room with her son's thick black hair in her hands Jenny burst into tears. Ma Chit handed the treasure—which she intended to use to pad out her own thinning hair—to Mi Nu to put away for her, then put an arm round the weeping child.

"Aung is not going away forever," she assured her. "Only until the next new year. He will be back with us for the next *thingyan* and sometimes we shall see him, when he comes round with the others with his bowl."

Jenny turned her face into her foster-mother's shoulder and continued to weep, without answering, for there was no way of explaining that once again the river washed over, engulfing her.

It was terrible to her when Aung entered the room with the other boys, wearing the yellow robes, his head shaven, his eyes downcast, no longer acknowledging any of them. He was as strange to her as when he had looked like a lovely girl. She was even glad when the *pongyis* rose to their feet and left the house with the three young novices following them.

Everyone stood as they filed out, and on the faces of all were looks of pride and happiness, and they turned to each other with a smiling tenderness as they exclaimed upon the becoming gravity, the sweet purity, of the boys' faces, as though, they said, they were already touched with holiness. The men, remembering their own novitiate, the pride and solemnity of the *shinbyu*, the sense of coming-of-age when they walked out of their homes in their yellow robes, without farewell, without a backward look, were as moved as the women. Jenny took one look at Aung's solemn, unseeing face, then buried her head again in her foster-mother's shoulder.

Mya, happy with flowers in her hair and borrowed diamond studs in her ears, was impatient of Jenny's wild grief.

"I hope I am reborn a boy so that I can be a *Koyin* when I am old enough!" she declared. She added, in a sudden access of superiority, "But you are not Burmese, so you don't understand."

"I am Burmese!" Jenny cried. It was suddenly the most important thing in the world that she should be Burmese, for if she was not that, what was she? Where did she belong?

"Your father was English," the other child said, relentlessly.

"I don't care! I am Burmese now! I am not different! I am the same! Look!"—she pushed back the sleeve of her jacket and held out her bared arm. "My skin is the same colour as yours!"

"No," said Mya. "It is lighter. Much lighter!"

"Some Burmese people have light skins——"

Various of the women laughed and Jenny clung to Ma Chit beseeching, "I am Burmese! Say I am Burmese! Say I am the same as all of you!"

"You are Burmese," Ma Chit said gently, "and because you are Burmese, our little Mālā, you must be glad that now Aung wears the yellow robe for a little while. A Burmese girl does not cry at her brother's *shinbyu*."

"Aung is my brother?"

"Aung is your brother."

"But you aren't my mother!"

There was a note almost of defiance in the child's voice that was not lost on Ma Chit. A brooding grief that so often closed in on her when she thought about Mālā and the future stirred painfully in her as she answered, firmly, to convince herself as much as the child, "I am your mother now. You are my little Mālā."

Jenny repeated the name aloud, over and over. "Mālā, Mālā, Mālā. I am Mālā!"

She was vaguely comforted, but the sense of insecurity remained. Nothing was safe.

The enclosed days of the rainy season that year seemed endless to Jenny. She could never play for long with Mya without quarrelling breaking out between them. Mya had never accepted the new little sister. She would not have it that they were sisters, that their skins were the same colour, that this Mālā was any more than half Burmese. In this she was supported by Ma Hla, who was well aware of Jenny's hostility towards her, and who felt a curious jealousy concerning her husband's tenderness for the child.

Mya repeated to her mother what she had more than once heard Ma Hla declare—that when the war was over Mālā's father would come back and find her and take her back to England, and that it would be a good thing.

Such observations always troubled Ma Chit, because it was putting into words something always at the back of her mind, but which she tried not to brood upon. Somewhere, confusedly, deep down in her, she acknowledged that had the child's mother been alive she would have felt differently; the mother having been Burmese made it easy for her to feel sympathetic to her; whereas the idea of this child who was to all intents and purposes a Burmese child being carried off by an English father and remade into an English child, in far away England, was intolerable to her—totally unacceptable. Bound up in all this was alliance with another woman of her own race against a foreigner; maternal possessiveness was also involved in it, and racial resentment, and a dream that one day this little girl should become Aung's bride and thus become really one of the family, beyond any reclamation by any outsider.

She was always sharp with Mya when she spoke about Mālā's father one day coming for her. "Then she would have no mother at all!" she would say, and insist, "She is better with us." Usually she would add, "Shwe-Shwe thinks so too. So does Pé-Pé. It doesn't matter what Ma Hla thinks."

She made a special effort that Lent to draw the child closer to her. It was not difficult, for Jenny's need to feel safe, wrapped round by a protective love, had never been stronger. With Aung away and Nu lost to her because of Maung Tin, there was now only Mé-Mé left to her. And Mé-Mé was safe—she couldn't go off to the pongyi-kyaung, or leave home to marry someone, or have no eyes or ears for anyone but a boy who came in the evenings to sit on the verandah. Mé-Mé knew little songs, too, and could tell stories, she discovered—not such good ones as Shwe-Shwe told, beginning once upon a time, but about what she did when she was a little girl, about the village she came from, and sometimes, even, stories about the Buddha when he was a young man that were almost as good as the Jataka stories.

So the long rainy season passed, and it was sad when the lovely full-moon festival came round again and Aung was still away, and though they saw him in the procession of the *pongyis* when they all went out to offer their gifts he gave no sign of recognition—even when, excitedly, Jenny cried his name. She knew well enough that he mustn't, that it was against the rules of the order; nevertheless it was terrible to her when his eyes remained downcast and his face impassive.

The bright hot beautiful days were so long. The days and weeks and months seemed endless. She hung round Ma Chit all the time now, seldom joining Mya with the other children in the road. She was not unhappy; only endlessly, restlessly waiting. She went out into the fields with her foster-parents and Nu, helping to load the cut paddy on to the bullock-cart to be taken to the corner where it was to be threshed. Maung Tin came to help with the harvest that year, since it meant working beside Mi Nu, and he teased Jenny, calling her the paddy bird.

"I see we have our big paddy bird with us again this morning," he would say, laughing.

She always indignantly refuted the idea.

"I'm not a paddy bird. A paddy bird is white. I'm not white!" She would hold out her bare arms, which became browner every day that she worked in the hot sun, in proof that she was not white. She refused to have *thanaka* on her arms and face, because it bleached the skin, and she wanted to be dark—the darker the better; darker than any Burmese; as dark as Ganesh, even. Then no one could say that she was not Burmese. Then she would belong.

In spite of his teasing she liked Maung Tin, because he was good-looking and always laughing and knew what it was fun to do—such as sitting on top of the paddy in the bullock-cart and riding with it across to the threshing corner, or sitting astride a bullock's back when it was treading out the grain, or crossing the river in a wide shallow boat when a herd was being driven across to the fields on the other side, where there were bright green patches of ground nuts.

It was fun, too, she discovered that year, cleaning the rice with Nu or Mé-Mé. One of them would pound the grain in a big wooden bowl with a pounder that looked like the trunk of a small tree, and she would squat on a mat with a shallow bamboo tray which served as a sieve for the second part of the process. When there was no wind she would sometimes fan away the chaff. She liked it best when Mé-Mé did the pounding, because when it was Nu, sooner or later Maung Tin would turn up and then she would be left out. When it was Mé-Mé there were only the two of them and it was what she thought of as safe.

Sometimes Daw Khin came and sat in the shade of the shelter in which they did the work and watched them; but she was so still and silent that it was as though she were not there. Jenny would sometimes fleetingly return her smiles, but there was no real contact between them. The old woman wandered about the house and compound, solitary and silent, skeleton-thin, cadaverous, more like a plaster figure of old age escaped from a pagoda than a human being, Jenny would think, midway between repulsion and fear.

Somehow, between one activity and another, the eternities were lived through and it was April again, and Aung came home.

It was April 1945, and, incredibly, the Japanese were getting out. Aung was home in time for the New Year, but there was no festival that year; instead there were low-flying 'planes continually machine-gunning the retreating Japanese troops, and the shriek of falling bombs that had reached the quiet valley at last. The 'planes dived and swooped, the earth rocked with explosions; some of the bamboo houses collapsed, others caught fire and in turn set fire to others. People sheltered with each other, and at the *zayats* at the pagoda. Maung Ba Tu's house continued to stand, and the head man's house, and Maung Shwe's, and most of the others. By August most of Tatkon was still there; and in August, because the atomic era had been inaugurated, and obliteration writ large across two Japanese cities, it was all over. Peace was restored to the high hills and the deep valleys. The paddy was free to grow again in the blood-soaked earth, once the wreckage and the barbed wire was cleared away. People no longer lay under the leaf-thatch at nights listening to the drone of death among the stars.

The royal palace at Mandalay, that miracle of rare device, had gone up in flames in May. The Burmese declared that it was a deliberate act of destruction on the part of the British, to show that they were again the masters; that the Japanese had long gone from it, that there was no one in it at all. They declared that other national monuments had been similarly systematically destroyed. The British were back, and Burmese sovereignty was still a dream—but a dream with a flame at the heart of it.

They knew in Tatkon about the destruction of the palace at Mandalay, and they knew in due course about the terrible new bombs that had been dropped on Japan, and that Japan had surrendered. But as everyone knew that Japan was already beaten in April, and evacuating as fast as wheels would turn, in all directions, they wondered why it had been considered necessary to drop the bombs. Why it had been necessary to kill thousands of civilians, men, women and children, some of them in hospitals, like that. It was reported that in Hiroshima alone the number was two hundred thousand. It was all very puzzling. There was so much that simple people could not understand.

IX. THE RETURN

WITH the resumption of the British administration in October Ma Chit began to worry. Any day now, surely, the English *thakin* would come back for his little girl. Even if in his heart he believed that she had been drowned he would surely never rest now that the war was over until he had made inquiries in person at Mynmyo—it would be only natural. And Po Than knew that Maung Shwe had not been drowned and that he had saved the little girl. And Po Than was still living in Mynmyo. Ma Chit tried to imagine what it would be like to have the *thakin* come and take away the little Mālā; but she could no more imagine it than that she could imagine someone taking away Mya. She is Burmese, she would insist to herself and to her husband, she is one of us now. If her mother were alive it would be different; her mother was Burmese; it was always her mother she cried for in the beginning. Her father would not let her wear Burmese clothes, she told us, or speak Burmese, or go to the pagodas. Shwe-Shwe did not like this *thakin;* he said that he was the kind who shouts and treats all people who are not white as inferiors; even though he married one. Our little Mālā would be very unhappy living with such a father, far away in England. It would be different if her mother were alive. . . . Always she came back to that.

Maung Ba Tu had his own *leit-motiv.*

"If her father comes for her we have no right to try to keep the child from him. She is not our child. It would make very bad *karma* to attempt to keep a child from its parent."

"If he comes for her it will not be possible for us to keep her from him," Ma Chit replied, bitterly.

"There is nothing we can do. If it is in the *thakin's karma* that he should find her he will find her, and if it is in her *karma* to return to him she will do so."

Ma Chit was not so fatalistic. As are our deeds today, so are our lives tomorrow—had not the good monks explained it all many times? She went secretly to see Maung Shwe, slipping away whilst her husband dozed over his mid-day cheroot, and when the children were out somewhere playing in the dust, and Nu over at Maung Tin's house on the pretext of calling on his sister. She did not enter the house but went in search of her son on his land, where she found him with two other men scything a patch of paddy. He saw her from a distance and crossed the field to her. They moved into the scanty shade of a neam tree.

"Is anything wrong?" he inquired, anxiously.

"I had to see you alone," she told him. "When you come to the house the others are always there, and if I come to your house Ma Hla is there. I cannot sleep at nights for thinking that now the British are back our little Mālā's father will return for her. He will go to Mynmyo and find Po Than who will tell him that you and she were also saved, and where we are living."

"I also have thought of it, Amè. I had thought that I would go to Po Than and tell him if the *thakin* comes that it would be good if he were to believe that Mālā and I had both been drowned."

She looked troubled. "It is bad to lie," she pointed out. "We cannot ask Po Than to lie for us."

"I would not ask him to lie. I would tell him of our fear. If he does not wish to lie he will not do so, but perhaps because he does not like these English *thakins* he will like to."

Then because she still looked worried, "Mé-Mé, we ourselves do not take life, yet we eat the fishes that the fisherman takes for us from the sea. We do not ask him to do this for us; he chooses to do it, and when we find the fish in the market we are glad and buy it and eat it. It is a bad thing that the fishermen do, but good comes out of the evil; and so it would be if Po Than deceived the *thakin* should he come."

"When will you talk with him, Shwe-Shwe?"

"Tomorrow, when the paddy is cut. There will be a market at Mynmyo tomorrow and I had intended going to see what is to be bought."

She said, eagerly, "Come to the house afterwards. Don't speak of the matter in front of your father or the others, but if Po Than has been willing to help put something into my hand—an egg, an orange, anything from the market—for a present. If you give me nothing I shall know that we may expect no help from him. Then we shall have to try to think of something else."

"Don't worry, Amè. I think I shall not come empty-handed."

She hesitated a moment, then said, "There is one thing, Shwe-Shwe, Ma Hla mustn't know that we have this plan. She doesn't like Mālā, and would be glad if her father came for her—she has said so many times to Mya."

"She won't know," Maung Shwe promised his mother.

The following evening he came to the house and placed a hen's egg in her hand, with a smile.

Christopher Finching returned to Burma in January, 1946.

He had been released from a camp in the deep south in April 1945, but an infected foot had made it imperative he should get out of the tropics as quickly as possible. He had been, also, in common with the majority of the camp's inmates, weak from dysentery and malnutrition. As a stretcher case he had been flown to England and taken by ambulance from the airport to the Hospital for Tropical Diseases. At the end of a month he had gone to stay with his unmarried sister, Jennifer, at her London flat. He was as near to a nervous breakdown as his stubborn will permitted.

In the two and a half years of his captivity, moved from lock-up to prison, from prison to camp, from Central Burma to Lower Burma, he had kept a grip on himself, priding himself on his self-control and stoicism. In all that time the screams of his wife and children as the river engulfed them never left him. Sometimes in nightmares he was struggling again in the river, seeing their drowning faces close to him but unable to reach them, then wakened by his own hideous strangulated cries.

He had not, in fact, seen their faces at the time of the disaster; the darkness had been too dense. Jenny's screams had gone on for some time, receding into the distance; he had heard the younger of the boatmen shouting, then his cries, too, had been lost in the torrential rush of the water. The only body which had come within his reach had been that of Po Than, swimming close to him. At first they had both tried to strike out in the direction of the shouts and cries of the other two, but the sounds had gone beyond them or been engulfed, and they themselves had been swept downstream until the river made one of its numerous sharp bends and they had found themselves out of the current and unexpectedly close to the shore. They had struggled, then, for some distance along the low cliff above the river, alternately calling and listening, but the quest in that darkness had been obviously futile. They had been spotted by the searchlight of a Japanese patrol boat as they crouched in the bamboo at the edge of a creek. With a gun trained on them any attempt at escape would have been useless. On board, after the chief officer's interrogation of them both, Christopher had ventured to ask whether they had picked up any people in the river, or seen any bodies, and received only a slapped face for his impertinence. Later the second-in-command had told him that they had seen no one, in the river or along the banks. They had both been taken back to Mynmyo, where the Burman had been released and the Englishman had been locked up.

He had never doubted that his wife and baby and driver had been instantly drowned, trapped as they were in the overturned car, but the possibility of Jenny and the young boatman having survived, remote though the probability was, never left him. Throughout his captivity it had burned always there in the forefront of his mind, a small spark of hope that nothing had been able to extinguish. It had been so tiny a light by which to live; nevertheless he had lived by it. At his lowest mental and physical ebb it had become his link with life.

Most of his fellow-prisoners held on to life in all that wretchedness of hunger, disease, humiliations, filth, beatings, in the hope of one day being reunited with their wives, sweethearts, families. He had held on to life for the day when he would return to Mynmyo, hunt up Po Than, and if he could not find out anything positive concerning Jenny's fate make a search of every riverine village below Mynmyo. The idea had become an obsession with him.

He had taken the obsession with him to England, but even with the whole force of his will brought to bear he had not been able either to regain his strength or get cured of his crippling infection until the end of the year. His dread had been that he would be obliged to lose yet more time by having to make the return journey by sea; fortunately he had been able to contrive an air passage.

Derek Vernon—or was he now to be thought of as Major Vernon, Finching thought, ironically—had been demobilized in India and returned to Burma in August 1945, when the British Administration was restored, and was himself restored to his old post as Assistant D.F.O. of the Bokoko division. So far as the forestry service was concerned Christopher knew that he was merely going back to hand over, for he was within six months of retiring age. The war hadn't eaten into the lives of the young men as it had into the lives of those who had been forty or more when it started; they had so many years in hand when it was all over, like money in the bank. Well, it was their world now, and they were welcome to it. For him, Christopher Finching, the war had been the years that the locusts had eaten; it had taken his wife, his children, his health, his chances of promotion—though in the reckoning with all the rest the chances of promotion no longer mattered.

Any more than it mattered that Vernon had gone on without him in the 1942 exodus. He could even concede now that he would have been a fool not to have done so; if he hadn't gone on he would probably have been drowned—he would certainly have fallen into the hands of the Japs, instead of being part of the great allied victory. Vernon, he knew, was very anxious to justify his conduct—to himself quite as much as to his chief. Christopher's mind smiled wrily at the memory of the young man's explanations. "What difference," he had demanded, "would it have made to me if you had waited at Mynmyo—as it all turned out? Would it have stopped the ferry turning over? Or do you imagine you would have saved everyone alive-alive-o?"

Derek, embarrassed, had murmured something about personal integrity being involved.

Christopher said, shortly, "You'd have been a fool to have waited any longer and you can be glad that you didn't. Let's leave it at that."

But he knew that that wasn't where the young man wanted to leave it. He wanted to be assured that he had done the right thing, and Finching could not give him that assurance. He had done the sensible thing—the expedient thing. There were people who wouldn't have done it. He knew that. And that Christopher Finching himself was one of those people. But there were plenty of people who would say that Derek Vernon had done the right thing; that he had after all waited until the last ferry; and it could be asked—how long was he supposed to have waited? He was not to know that his Chief had not already been overtaken by the Japs. That was the basis of his case.

Christopher didn't know whether he was being fair to him or not. The world in which such fine ethical points were of moment had vanished long ago, submerged in tragedy and horror. He had long ago ceased to have any feeling about Derek Vernon and what he had done and ought to have done; the locusts had eaten all that away too; they had eaten away everything except the desire to know, finally and forever, whether his daughter was still alive. If she positively was not, then at least he would know; it would be liberation of a kind.

So that to return to Bokoko and the house which had once been his home was not the ordeal which he supposed Vernon assumed it would be. The Burmese assistant who had taken over when he had left was still there; the Japanese had come from time to time and taken what they needed—or fancied—from the house, and there was very little left of the home he and Ma Hla and the children had known. It irritated him that Vernon should be so sensitive on his behalf, so unnecessarily apologetic.

"I'm afraid this must be all rather ghastly for you, sir——"

As though anything that could ever touch him now could be ghastly after that night at the river, those years in Japanese prisons and camps— not because of what was done in those prisons and camps, though it was brutal and beastly enough, but because of the torment he had carried inside himself. Even allowing for hyperbole it was not even sad or depressing, because when there is darkness inside yourself whether it is light or dark outside can make no difference. There was only that pinpoint of light inside himself—the possibility that Jenny might, by some miracle, some freak of fate, still be alive.

He slept well enough his first night back in the old home. None of the rooms bore any resemblance to the rooms he had known. He could not imagine the little flower-like Ma Hla moving through those bleak bare rooms, or the child Jenny running in and out. Nothing present had any link with the past. Not even the house itself, since the life that inhabited it had gone.

Vernon watched his chief anxiously, but he saw only a grey gaunt man whose tight lips under the clipped grey moustache, and sunken grey eyes under permanently frowning brows, revealed nothing except determination. A cold determination, Derek thought; nothing impassioned or fevered about it, no hint of hidden torment; the determination, it came to him, that fighting men bring to the grimmer aspects of war.

He organized the jeep and driver his chief required to be sent round at dawn—and irritated him further by wishing him 'luck' when he saw him off.

"The fool," Christopher thought, savagely, "the fool!"

Luck didn't come into it; the child was either drowned or she wasn't, and the chances that she hadn't been were a thousand, a million to one against. If she hadn't been drowned it wouldn't be luck but a holy miracle —and the shock, he thought grimly, would probably kill him.

He sat in front with the driver and watched the familiar landscape hurtle past—the semi-desert with its clumps of jagged cactus like dusty palisades, its occasional groups of thin palms, its scatterings of thorn bushes white with dust; then the harvested paddy fields where the cattle grazed among the stubble; and after that the miles of dense mixed jungle; occasionally he frowned at the sight of a burnt tree—fired to extract the resin, regardless of the fact that it killed the tree. He missed an avenue of young teak trees—the Japanese had been quite ruthless in taking what they wanted. Their demands on the forestry department had been considered exorbitant and unreasonable. Perhaps we'd have done the same, he thought; war *is* ruthless—exorbitant—unreasonable; like the heart, it has its reasons that reason knows nothing of.

Crossing the river at its S bend he remembered explaining to Jenny that it was not two rivers but one. He remembered it quite dispassionately. Memory could not torment him; only uncertainty could do that. There was the bad patch of road where so many of the cars had got stuck in the deep dust. This time they would get through to Mynmyo in one day. There was the rest-house where they had spent the first night, but the village had been burnt out, and the road was fuller of potholes than ever. There was the point where they had abandoned the car. The pagoda in whose precincts they had spent the second night—reached astonishingly quickly, it seemed to him, by road and by car, in contrast to the weary trek across the paddy fields by bullock-cart. At one side of the road, not far from the pagoda, was a row of abandoned tanks—Japanese, the driver assured him. The jungle creepers were already twining over them in inimitable camouflage. At the circuit house at Taungpyo they halted for refreshment.

The same butler greeted him with the same respect, bowing deeply. He hoped the *thakin* had got through to India without difficulty, and that the *thakinma* fully recovered from her illness. Christopher told him, tersely, "My wife and children and driver were drowned when the ferry overturned at Mynmyo. I was taken prisoner by the Japs." The Burman made clicking noises with his tongue against the roof of his mouth to express his shock and sympathy, and before he could put his sympathy into words Christopher demanded, "How do I get the jeep across the river? Is the ferry running?"

The car-ferry was running, the butler assured him; everything was back to normal now that the British were back, he added, obsequiously.

Christopher grunted. "Then bring me an orange squash—with ice in it. And get something cooking."

The butler bowed low again, waddled out, and returned in a few minutes with the drink, the ice clinking in the glass. Christopher took it without a word.

"See that my driver gets something to eat and is ready to leave here in——" he looked at his wrist-watch, "forty-five minutes."

He stretched his long body out in a low rush chair on the verandah and tipped his straw hat forward to shade his face from the mid-day glare.

He faced the possibility that when he reached Mynmyo it might be difficult to find the boatman, whose name he no longer remembered. It would be no use inquiring for 'the boatman'; they all had boats, or nearly all of them, in those riverine villages, and this one had only obliged as ferryman for the occasion. The man might be dead, anyhow. Or gone to another village. And even if he succeeded in finding him why should be expect him to know what had happened to the two who were washed away, any more than he knew himself? But he would surely know what had happened to his companion, that boy he had engaged to help him. If the boy had been drowned the family would have found out, surely? Well, not surely. It was a possibility, that was all. If he drew a blank with the boatman he would investigate every village below Mynmyo, on both sides of the river—he had always been prepared to have to do that. But bodies could be washed up into creeks, become submerged in the mud; and the vultures . . . He switched his thoughts. One step at a time. The first was to find the boatman.

The butler came out on to the verandah to tell him his meal was ready and he got up and followed him into the dark barn of a room where a place for him had been laid at the end of a long table. In this room he had eaten with the children last time he had been there. He remembered that Jenny had been nervous of the big windmill fan trundling overhead because it was low and seemed dangerously close to them. She had been full of fears and superstitions, he recollected. Her mother had been responsible for that. Supposing she had been saved from the river—unlikely thought it was, but supposing—and brought up all these years by a Burmese family, her rehabilitation would certainly present a problem. It would be resolved, he supposed, by sending her away to a good school.

He pushed his emptied plate away from him and leaned back in his chair picking his teeth with the ivory toothpick he had cherished through all the Japanese prisons and camps. He found tooth-picking conducive to reflection, and he indulged a fantasy in which he found the boatman at Mynmyo without difficulty, and the man told him that yes his friend and the child had been saved and the boy had taken her to his village a few miles down the river, which, for the sake of convenience, this being a fantasy, was on this side of the river so that in a few minutes he was there in the jeep. And there he found Jenny, who had grown a little, as might be expected, all done up in Burmese clothes, and at first she hadn't recognized him, and then when he spoke to her in English she came running to him, eagerly, exclaiming "Daddy!" Then, he supposed, he paid the family some money for looking after her all these years, and probably promised to send them some more when he got back to Bokoko, and they all kissed Jenny and perhaps the old woman—they were all old after forty —cried a bit, but Jenny clung to him, her long-lost, new-found daddy, and finally they drove off in the jeep, Jenny all happy excitement. But then he would have to tell her about her mother and baby brother. The picture wavered and dimmed at this point. He would have to tell her before they reached the house, or her disappointment on arrival would be too great. Perhaps she asked him a question, "Is Mummy waiting at home?" Something like that to give him his cue. He left this part of the picture blurred. It cleared again with the picture of Jenny once more in European clothes, fitted up in Rangoon, her sorrow over her mother and baby brother swallowed up in the excitement of flying back to England. She would be his comfort and joy. It would be an end of loneliness, of that inner darkness in which he had lived ever since that night.

He got up, pushing back his chair, and shouted for the butler. It was time to get going.

He had the driver park the car in the compound of the circuit house, then, resolutely, walked down to the river. People lazing on the verandahs of their houses, and children playing in the dust of the road, regarded him with a mild interest, the tall English *thakin* with the straw hat on his head and his thin legs emerging from khaki shorts—they had seen many such odd-looking white men before the war, and now they were coming back. This one was no doubt something to do with the forestry department which had an office there.

When the river came into view it was a colourless glimmer that seemed the same texture as the sky. Staring at it he saw it as he had seen it nearly four years ago, a yellow-brown rushing torrent.

There were a number of the familiar heavy flat-bottomed boats moored along the foreshore. In the small shade of one of the boats three men sat on the ground, two of them mending a funnel-shaped net, the other merely sitting, smoking a cheroot. As he came closer to them Christopher saw that the man with the cheroot was the man he sought. So the fantasy, it seemed, was working out. . . .

Po Than recognized him in the same instant and scrambled to his feet and came towards him, exclaiming excitedly.

"So the fascist dacoits did not murder you, *thakin!* When did you get back to these parts? Did you go back to England when they released you? You are thinner than I remember you, *thakin.*"

Christopher broke in on the volubility. "I am glad to have found you so easily. What happened to the boy who was with you, and my little girl— did you ever get any news?"

"What news was there to get, *thakin?* We knew that they were drowned, unfortunately."

"We knew nothing of the kind. They were swept away in the darkness— that's all we knew. The boy could swim, I believe."

"Who could swim in such a torrent?"

"We did, apparently."

"We had the good fortune to be outside the current."

"We have no proof that they were drowned."

"If Maung Shwe was not drowned would he not have gone back to his village? He has a mother and father, brother and sisters."

"Are you sure he never went back? How can you be sure?"

Po Than permitted himself to smile.

"Is the *thakin* sure that he is talking to me? Am I sure that I am talking to him? The father of Maung Shwe is my friend."

The small spark which had been the only light in the darkness of the past three years was already extinguished in Christopher, but he persisted, "Their bodies must have been washed up somewhere."

"That also is sure, *thakin*, but if they were found by the fascist dacoits do you think they are going to search every village for the relatives of the deceased? The bamboo is thick in the creeks—"

Christopher cut in on him. "I never really had any hope. It was a chance in a million, but I wanted to be sure."

"Unfortunately you can be sure, *thakin*. I will tell the family of Maung Shwe that you came to inquire about their son."

"I came to inquire about my daughter." Christopher spoke harshly, out of the darkness in himself.

"Unfortunately it is the same thing." Po Than flung away the stub of his cheroot. "I am sorry, *thakin.*"

Mechanically Christopher raised his hand in a farewell gesture and turned away. He strode back purposefully across the sandy foreshore, though in fact not only was his purpose in returning to Burma finished, but so far as he could see any purpose in continuing to live.

PART II. KARMA

I. THE INFORMER

B Y October, 1947, it was clear that Burmese independence was not going
to be achieved by any long slow apprenticeship to Dominion status as
envisaged by the British administration in 1945, and the British tide
which had flowed back in the autumn of that year was turned homewards
again. Derek Vernon stayed rather longer than most, handing over to his
Burmese assistant in the same month that the last British Governor of
Burma handed over to the Shan prince appointed as the first President of
the Republic of Burma, January 1948.

The English January intensified his nostalgia for the tropical sun and
colour. London streets were drab and grey, and he had forgotten that pe-
culiarly English damp cold which seems to find its way into every joint in
the body. He felt alien and lost in his own country. It was because he
had hated the English climate and had a feeling for the East since he was a
boy that he had decided to follow in his father's footsteps by making
forestry his career and getting himself into the Imperial Forest Service,
first in India and later in Burma. He had been born in India and though
in the traditional manner he had been brought home to England when
he was six years old he had retained a number of impressions, so that
when he went back as a young man in the I.F.S. it was with a feeling of
home-coming.

His father on his retirement had not returned to England but gone
up into the hills above Dehra Dun, the forestry department H.Q., to spend
the rest of his days in Naini Tal, most beautiful of hill-stations. It was not
the war which had caused him to re-arrange this pleasant plan but India's
achievement of independence. He was pukka sahib of the old school, and
this handing over of the brightest jewel of the British Empire was too
much. In common with many of his breed he retreated to British Africa,
where a white skin still commands power and prestige. He took it for
granted that when Derek left Burma he would join him in Kenya.

Derek, however, had not the slightest urge to join his parents on the
dark continent. He regarded his father's pukka sahib attitude as out-dated
and absurd, and his mother's memsahibism as even more intolerable.
Love was too strong a word for his feeling for his parents; he was fond
of them, and into his affection for them came an infinite regret that he had
nothing in common with them—nothing that he was anyhow aware of. His

father had been delighted when he had joined up in 1942 but had completely misunderstood his motives; it had not been his British patriotism but his love for Burma which had made him feel that Japanese fascism should be driven out from that lovely land. He had left Burma in 1948 not because he resented the passing of the old regime but because he felt, with the handing over of his post, that he had no place in it. He had to think what to do, and in order to get everything into perspective it seemed to him he must get home and view it from there.

He used the conventional word 'home', but in fact England was not home for him. He had been happy in Burma. It had suited him. The climate had suited him, for he enjoyed heat, and he could tolerate the rainy months in the knowledge of the non-stop sunshine of the dry season. And he liked the national temperament—the easy-goingness, the ready laughter, the capacity for graceful idleness—of which the restless West seemed incapable. Also he was attracted to the national religion. Without going so far as to call himself a Buddhist, Buddhism made sense for him. Only the law of Karma could explain the astonishing series of 'coincidences' life continually presented. The moral laws, with the ultimate objective of complete detachment, he found more difficult of acceptance.

At thirty-three his ideas were singularly blurred at the edges. He envied, without admiring, people like Christopher Finching for whom two and two always unfailingly made four, and for whom what was not black was white. Life so often seemed like an enormously intricate mathematical problem—and he was no good at even the simplest arithmetic. Finching, he knew, had never liked him, and he didn't blame him. From Finching's point of view he was a poor specimen, lacking in self-assurance with women, and with servants and subordinates, hesitant in assuming responsibility, diffident, introspective, and, greatest weakness of all, with a profound distaste for blood sports; or, for that matter, for sports of any kind. He found himself quite as unsatisfactory as his chief had found him. He would like to have been all that he was not—self-confident, assertive, clear-cut in his ideas, addicted to the instinctively right thing. As it was, in any major decision—such as whether to go on waiting at Mynmyo or cross by the last ferry—he invariably did the wrong thing for the right reasons. Or they anyhow seemed valid at the time. Was it any better—or worse—than doing the right thing for the wrong reasons? He didn't know. It was all too difficult.

In London he was living at his club and pondering the problem of what to do when a friend who ran a bookshop specializing in Oriental books invited him to come into partnership with him in the extension of the business to include Oriental antiques—"with your knowledge of the East," he urged, "we could really make a go of it."

Derek was not sure of that, pointing out that his knowledge of the East gained in India and Burma was primarily a knowledge of the forests and jungles and villages, but the friend needed capital and Derek needed an occupation, and the friend was right in suspecting that he did in fact know rather more than his innate diffidence permitted him to acknowledge —one of the pleasures of his leaves from the I.F.S. had been wandering round the junk shops of Bangkok, and he had, the friend happened to know, an eye for the genuinely old and, among the modern things, for what was hand-made in the villages.

So Derek Vernon, late of the Imperial Forest Service and the Royal India Army Service Corps, took to wandering round the London sale rooms bidding for the treasures of the East collected by the white sahibs in an era already swallowed up in history. He would sit in the dark little office behind the shop holding in his hands a tarnished gilded figure of an Indian goddess, an ornate Siamese Buddha image, a piece of Chinese ivory exquisitely carved, a finely wrought silver bowl from Burma, cataloguing and pricing, and it would seem to him that only a small part of himself ticked over arbitrarily assessing the priceless. Every little gilded figurine brought back India, every Buddha image Burma, and endlessly he would ask himself why he sat there putting a price upon the symbols of wisdom and truth instead of paying homage to them in their rightful Eastern settings. In this commercialization, it seemed to him, everything they stood for was debased. There was a little tarnished figure of the Tibetan Buddhist madonna, Tara, goddess of mercy, the garlanded-with-lotuses queen of heaven, which moved him strangely. She was turquoise-jewelled, and lotus flowers, open and closed, reached to her shoulders. He did not know why she moved him so much; it was as though she stood for something hidden in him, awaiting elucidation. The day he came back to the shop and found that she had been sold he experienced a curious sense of loss.

He had a feeling of waiting, of marking time. His desire to return to the East was strong, but it was as though he awaited a sign, an indication of the context; he was possessed by a dreamlike sense of unreality. He moved from his club to a service flat; he dined out, he entertained, went to the theatre, played bridge, went for weekends to the country, to the houses of people he had known in the East. He went riding with a young woman whom for a little while he thought he loved—till he realized she expected marriage, when he fled from her with an appalling sense of his own inadequacy.

People saw a slightly built young man with a lean prematurely lined face and thinning dark hair; it was a sensitive face and when he smiled he had a kind of nervous charm. The women were inclined to say, "Poor Derek! He's rather a pet!" Then they would decide to ask him to dinner, and hunt about in their minds—or their address books—for some nice girl who might fall for him and 'draw him out', which, they were convinced, was all that was needed to make him less shy and reserved. The men had nothing against him. Poor old Vernon, they would say, he's quite a nice chap. But the qualifying 'quite' was always there, and he was acutely aware of it, somehow implicit in their attitude to him.

His parents came to England for a year and he went to live with them. The effect of the strain this put upon him was to make him withdraw yet deeper into himself. But for them he would have returned to Burma a year earlier than he did. As it was he returned in 1950, at the end of the monsoon. He had a great longing for the forests after his two years of exile in sunless cities; he had contrived for himself to join the D.F.O. at Bokoko and tour the division with him—insurgents permitting. In this way he eventually returned to Mynmyo.

"There is a wedding we must attend," the D.F.O. said. "The township officer is officiating at the marriage of one of our boys. We needn't stay long."

Derek felt that he would be quite happy to stay all day—he had felt ever since his arrival in the country that a new blessing should be added to the *Mingala Sutta*—'merely to be in Burma again—this the greatest blessing!' In England he had parodied the poet on love, asking himself bitterly, 'Was there sun once? I have forgotten it.' Then on the voyage out there was the sense of journeying deeper into the sun every day from Gibraltar onwards. Until at last, East of Suez, there was the sun in splendour. He discovered that he had forgotten it could be like that, just as he had forgotten the living scent of frangipani and the white flood of tropical moonlight.

At the circuit house, over which Maung Maung still presided, he discarded European clothes and wrapped a *longyi* of jade green Chinese silk round his narrow hips, reflecting with pleasure on how scandalized Finching would be if he could see him. His father, too. All the sahibs. He had worn *longyis* before in Burma, but only when on leave and away from Bokoko. Putting on Burmese clothes he had the feeling of assuming a new identity, a freer, more self-confident one, and of putting off an old one— old and stale and ineffectual.

It was fine to hear the lilt and whimper and clatter of Burmese music again; and to sit at a long table with the other male guests waited on by pretty creatures wrapped in brightly coloured silks and with flowers in their hair. The face of one of these seemed vaguely familiar. He asked the D.F.O. about her. "I have an idea I've seen her before," he said.

"Possibly. She's the sister of Maung Than, the head man at Tatkon. Her name is Ma Hla."

"It suits her."

"Her lips are too thin. Always beware of a woman with thin lips."

The D.F.O. got up, adding, "I think we should go upstairs now. I hear the bride being called."

There was a general movement towards the outside staircase leading up to the room where the ceremony was to take place and where most of the women guests had been seated on the floor for the last hour chattering and fanning themselves. The D.F.O. edged himself into the crowded room, but Derek suddenly overcome with self-consciousness again remained standing at the top of the stairs. Standing aside to let people enter the room he saw Ma Hla coming up the stairs hand in hand with a young girl, followed by others of the girls he had seen downstairs. When she saw him she said something to the young girl, then stood back, allowing the others to pass her. The young girl stopped in front of Derek. She addressed him in Burmese.

"Ma Hla wishes to know whether you knew the *thakin* Finching who was D.F.O. here until the Japanese came."

Derek told her, "I was his assistant."

"Then will you come and speak with Ma Hla please?"

Derek followed her back down the steps to where Ma Hla waited at the bottom. He was aware of the strong scent of the jasmine in her hair and of the brightness of her lips in contrast with the *thanaka* whiteness of her face. She was very pretty; but the D.F.O. was right, her lips were too thin—and too greasily scarlet. She did not smile as he came down to her, and he was conscious of a faint hostility in her manner, and of a curious intensity in the young girl's gaze. He turned on Ma Hla the smile which most people, women especially, found so charming, but she did not respond.

"I was Mr. Finching's assistant," he said, pleasantly, adding, "I am at your service."

"I want to ask you if Mr. Finching knows that his daughter is alive."

Derek started. "Alive? Are you sure? Po Than told him she was drowned. Mr. Finching came back specially in 1946 to find out. He saw Po Than himself. She was washed away with the other boatman—he also was never seen again——"

"Po Than did not tell all. The other boatman is my husband and this girl's brother. He is alive and living in Tatkon. Mr. Finching's girl was brought up with his family. She married his brother at the New Year and is living close by."

"Married? She can't be more than fourteen or fifteen even now!"

Ma Hla smiled faintly then.

"It is old enough to be married."

"But I don't understand. Why should Po Than lie to Mr. Finching?"

"Perhaps he didn't lie. Perhaps he only did not tell all that happened.

If you take the fish out of the water and place it on the bank it dies, but
have you killed it?"

"You have caused its death," Derek said sharply, "but what has that to
do with it?"

"Between lying and not telling what happened there can be a difference."

"But why should Po Than not tell? What had he to gain by it?"

"He had nothing to gain for himself, but perhaps there were those who
did not want the *thakin* to come and take his child away. How do I
know? But I think it right that Mr. Finching should know his daughter
is alive and living in Tatkon with her husband, my husband's brother. It
is right you should let him know—Mr.——"

"Vernon. Yes, of course I'll let him know. Thank you for telling me.
Perhaps I should go and see her—have a talk with her. She might remember me——"

"If you do that she and her husband will run away and Mr. Finching
will never find them. Also I should be in trouble with my husband. It is
very important you should not mention me in this matter, Mr.—Vernon.
This you must promise me."

"Yes—I see. I promise. What is it best to do, then? What do you suggest?"

"If Mr. Finching were to come to Tatkon and stroll round the pagoda
on a duty day he would find her there—by chance."

"She might refuse to go with him—now that she has a husband here."
It was all very confusing and upsetting.

Ma Hla smiled.

"I think he will find a way to persuade her. She is very young—almost a
child still, being half English, and he is her father. Now we must go—
come, Mya."

She put an arm round the young girl's shoulder and they went back up
the wooden stairs together.

Now there was upon Derek Vernon again the thing he dreaded—the
necessity to make an important decision. If he reported to Finching what
Ma Hla had told him he would profoundly disturb two lives—Finching's
and the girl's. Finching had accepted the fact that she was dead and had
accepted it and adjusted himself to it for four years now. He was a lonely
man; but if he had his daughter back with him, this child of fourteen
or so who was nevertheless a married woman, would he be any less lonely?
And what of the girl, torn away from her husband and the people who
had become, no doubt, near and dear to her. In eight years she had
grown from a child into a young woman—from an Anglo-Burmese child
into a fully Burmese young woman; by now she had probably even for-

gotten English. English ways would be as strange to her now as English food, English weather, English clothes. And then there was this boy she had married—presumably she loved him and he loved her. Finching would have no jurisdiction over her—in Burma, anyhow; before independence it might have been different; now, married to a Burman, she was a Burmese subject; Finching would not be able to compel her to return with him to England. It would not be like the case of that Dutch girl in Indonesia; there would be no question of fighting it out in the courts. Finching could only hope to be able to persuade her to go back with him—unless, of course, he kidnapped her, which would not be so easy, in a world bound and delivered over to forms, permits, visas, security measures.

The thought afforded him a certain satisfaction. In a sense it relieved him of responsibility. It was his duty, clearly, to let Finching know. It was something he could do for the Old Man. It might even make him think better of him. Though as to that business of not continuing to wait at the ferry—how long was he supposed to wait, for God's sake, with the Japs coming up thick and fast? Finching ceased to be his Chief when they left Bokoko together and joined in the flight into India. He had ceased to be his Chief and at no time could it be said that he was his friend. He owed Finching nothing; but if Finching thought he did, what he was about to do for him now should wipe out the debt in his mind.

But some weeks later, back in Bokoko at the end of the tour, when he came to write out the cable uncertainty seized him again. Was it right to intrude upon other people's lives like this? Finching was reconciled to the idea of his daughter being dead, and the girl was presumably happy in her Burmese life. If she refused to go back with him Finching would be miserable—and if she did go back *she* might be. I wish I knew what was best to do, he thought. But because he did not know he obeyed some obscure impulse and sent the cable.

II. THE ENCOUNTER

'Jenny at Tatkon married to Burman writing,' Vernon had cabled. He had hesitated about mentioning that she was married, then finally decided that it would be an even greater shock to Finching to discover it when he arrived. He tried to persuade himself that he had been subtle—that Finching would not come if he knew the girl was married. Yet he could not imagine him not coming. Speculating as to what might happen, which he did endlessly, he would feel curiously excited, with an admixture of anxiety and even a kind of guilt. He had at times the frightening sensation of having deliberately touched a spring and set in motion machinery which he had no power to stop.

He speculated a good deal too, concerning Finching's reaction to the news—the good news of his daughter's survival and the bad news of her marriage. He would probably rather have had her dead than married, a mere child, to a Burman—in spite of the fact that he himself had married a Burmese woman. He had always intended that his children should be brought up English and Christian. It would be a blow for him all right. A tragedy, even. Finching was a man used to giving orders, to having his own way. Now this little girl, his own child, had defeated him. It was all very interesting.

Christopher's reaction to the cable was first shock, then anger. Over and over again he shouted to his sister that he wouldn't have it, that it was a lot of dam' nonsense, that he had never heard of such a thing. Jennifer pointed out that even in England it was not unheard of for a girl of fifteen to marry—even to become a mother at that age—and Jenny was about fifteen. It was not a matter of 'not having it'. The point was what were they going to do about it? Burma was not Java. There could be no question of legal action. The girl was now a subject of the Union of Burma, an independent republic. Miss Finching's voice was bitter. The point was even if a way could be found to get the marriage dissolved and the child brought back to England—"Do you really want her, Christopher—in the circumstances? She might be pregnant."

"Of course she's not!" Christopher shouted. "It's preposterous! You know what these child marriages are in the East!"

Jennifer believed that she did know. Years ago she had read *Mother India* and become almost a nervous wreck thinking about it. But she also knew that in the East a girl of nearly fifteen is not a child. And that her brother knew it. And that Burma was not India. He merely found the idea of this little girl, their little Jenny, as anything other than a perfectly nice little English girl, quite unacceptable.

"The marriage has probably not been consummated," he went on. "Almost certainly not. As soon as we get her back here she'll forget about it—a lot of romantic nonsense. Marriage is nothing out there anyhow—just sticking their hands in the same bowl of water. The marriages are not even registered."

"All the same, if she doesn't want to leave her husband no one can make her," his sister pointed out. She added, "She probably won't remember you."

"Perhaps not at first. But blood is thicker than water."

"Half her blood is Burmese."

"The English strain is stronger. Bound to be."

Jennifer Finching found the news of her niece upsetting, as years ago she had found the news of her brother's marriage to a Burmese girl, but her devotion to her dear Christopher was such that whatever he did she could not be other than on his side. For his sake she had been prepared to be nice to his wife when he eventually brought her to England. Similarly if he brought his daughter back to England she would do her best to be a mother to her. Had she just been long-lost little Jenny it would have been easy; she was used to girls, having had years of experience with girls' clubs and hostels; only it seemed there was no young-girl Jenny to mother and educate, but only a Burmese young married woman, completely Easternized. How would she adapt to the West? It would really be very much better if she refused to return to England. What would they do with her? They obviously could not send her away to school; quite apart from the fact that she would have had—Jennifer faced the unpleasant fact resolutely—sexual experience, she would probably have forgotten how to speak English. Of course if she were going to have a child she would have to be sent back to Burma and her husband—and this really might be the best thing that could happen. Unfortunately, Christopher refused even to consider this aspect of the matter. He was—understandably—determined to bring his daughter back to England and bring her up English and Christian. He was lonely, and if everything worked out as he wanted it to Jenny would be a great comfort to him. Poor Christopher!

Christopher himself wanted action, not sympathy. He was in a fury over the delay in being granted a visa, and that a visa should be necessary. He regarded the government as a pack of upstarts, and the Burmese people generally as a mob of what he called base ingrates.

He got back by the end of the year and was met by a representative of the Burmah Oil Company and flown up to Chauk, to a cool European house and a garden fragrant with oleanders, with a lawn as green as any in England, there in the burning heart of the Dry Zone. All being well he would bring Jenny back to this house, and the following day fly in one of the company's 'planes to Rangoon. The company provided him with a jeep, and because of insurgents, the police insisted on an armed escort.

Through the barren red dust of the Dry Zone he came to the green valley, the hurrying river, and the village of Tatkon. He left the jeep and the escort outside the village and in accordance with the instructions in Vernon's letter set out for the pagoda, his heart plunging heavily, with mingled apprehension and excitement.

It irked him as of old having to remove his footwear at the pagoda precincts. This time he was wearing European sandals with his shorts, without socks, which meant that he had to walk barefoot round the pagoda. The stones were burning to the soles of his feet, which were further assaulted by the prick of dried birds' droppings and grains of rice. It was a duty day and there were a great many people promenading round the base of the pagoda, in twos and threes and whole families, and kneeling before the shrine. They regarded him with interest. Since independence no Europeans had come to the village. Christopher could not have arrived at a better time, in the cool of the morning, when everyone was there. Maung Ba Tu's whole family was there, including Maung Shwe who recognized him instantly and instinctively darted forward and clutched Jenny. But it was too late. The Englishman was bearing down on them and Jenny had stopped dead in his path, like a rabbit hypnotized in the path of a stoat. She had recognized him before he had seen her. Then as she stood rigid in front of him, a few feet from him, he saw her, looking more like the little Ma Hla he had married than was possible. He saw her and knew that this reincarnation of Ma Hla was Jenny. He spoke her name. It was the first time she had heard it in eight years.

He stood in front of her, almost touching her, looking down at her, and repeated her name.

"Jenny!"

It released something in her, and without knowing that she did so she formed a whispered answering word: "Daddy!"

She was aware then of Aung's hand tightening on her own and of the family closing in round her. She heard Shwe-Shwe saying agitatedly, above her head, "She is married now. This is her husband."

Ma Chit pressed forward from the back of the group, then, and putting an arm round the girl's shoulder looked up defiantly at the tall Englishman.

"She belongs with us now, thakin. I have been her mother all these years—longer than her own mother knew her. And she has married my son."

Christopher said, quietly, "May not a father visit his married daughter?" He recognized Maung Shwe. He told him, "Your friend Po Than deceived me in 1946. He assured me that you and my daughter were both drowned. Why?"

It was Maung Shwe's turn to answer smoothly.

"How should I know? Perhaps he did not understand you. Or perhaps you did not understand him."

"We understood each other perfectly."

The bitterness in him was like a darkness in which he drowned. He had the feeling that it was not only Po Than, but that they were all in a conspiracy to keep Jenny from him.

"I should like to talk to my daughter and her husband alone," he said.

Maung Ba Tu spoke for the first time.

"We could go to my house," he said. "It is close by."

"Lead the way."

Maung Ba Tu walked ahead with Maung Shwe and Ma Hla and Mya. Ma Chit stayed beside Jenny, who stood palely between her and Aung. Mi Nu and Maung Tin hovered, unhappily in the background.

Christopher asked Jenny in English as they turned to leave the pagoda precincts, "How long have you been married?"

She realized that he had asked her a question but she did not know what he said. She did not know anything; all was confusion. Names kept bobbing up in her mind, like fish coming to the surface of a dark pool: Daddy, Mummy, Peter, Ganesh.

When her father repeated the question in Burmese she still could not answer.

Aung replied for her. "We were married at the end of Lent."

Christopher tried again in Burmese.

"Have you forgotten all your English?"

Again she did not answer; she understood what he said but she could not produce a single answering word. In the hot bright sunlight she felt cold and shivery.

Again Aung answered for her. "She has forgotten," he said.

He spoke curtly, full of fear and defiance.

"How did you know Mālā was here?" he demanded.

Finching told him, briefly, "I had a cable from an Englishman out here."

"How did he know? We have had no Englishmen here."

"Is it necessary to be in a place to know what goes on there?" He was irritated. He felt that he was being cross-examined. He was aware that they all had their eyes on him and of the mingled mistrust and hostility in those eyes; in the eyes of all except the pretty young woman who appeared to be Maung Shwe's wife, and she for some reason gave him small half smiles from time to time. Maung Shwe himself looked worried; with the exception of the young woman they all looked worried, but with the others anger seemed uppermost. Jenny, he thought, merely appeared frightened and miserable. He was acutely aware of the need to make contact with her, but did not know how. He told himself that she was suffering from shock and that he must give her time to get used to his reappearance in her life. He regarded the boy at her side with distaste. Was that little whippersnapper, that little Jack Burman, to be taken seriously as his son-in-law? He must somehow get Jenny away from this mob, then he could talk to her; but how to get her away—short of kidnapping her? And presumably quite apart from her marriage she was now a Burmese citizen of this precious independent republic and not to be whisked off out of the country, as she would have been, he told himself, and in double-quick time at that, two years ago, so-called marriage or not. He must see her alone; impossible to try to do anything with her with all this lot hedging her in. Perhaps they could be bought off. He owed them something for her keep all these years. But for this marriage he would have felt grateful to them, and no doubt they would have been glad enough to let her go—to allow him to ransom her, anyhow, he thought sardonically.

At the edge of the pagoda precincts they all slipped their feet into their slippers, then waited, watching him, whilst he struggled back into his European sandals, fumbling with the straps. To his astonishment Jenny dropped down on to her knees beside him and her small golden-brown fingers accomplished swiftly what he had been bungling.

He said "Thank you, Jenny," in English, and smiled at her, but she looked nervously away from him, unsmiling, and when she stood up he had the impression that she crept in under the boy's shoulder like a bird seeking the shelter of its mother's wing. She had made this deferential gesture to him purely as a young person to an older one, in the Burmese way. If she addressed him at all, he thought grimly, it would probably be as U Finching—Uncle; every snotty-nosed little upstart of a peasant or small government official was U nowadays, instead of the title being kept as one of respect for the elderly and important.

When they went on Maung Shwe was at his side.

"You will not persuade our little Mālā to return to England with you?" he inquired, anxiously.

"I am hoping she will at least want to come for a visit—to see her mother."

Ma Chit gave a long cry, turning agonized eyes to her son.

"Your wife was not drowned?" Maung Shwe's voice was sharp with suspicion.

Everyone looked at Christopher. He smiled. When he answered his voice was very smooth.

"Only the baby was drowned. My wife and driver I am happy to say were washed up not far from Mynmyo. The Japanese sent them to camps."

His gaze rested on each in turn and when it touched Jenny his smile was renewed.

"You would like to see Mummy again?" He spoke in Burmese, but used the word Mummy.

She repeated it after him, wonderingly. She looked from Aung to Ma Chit.

"My real *Mé-Mé* is alive," she cried, in sudden excitement. "*Mé-Mé*– Mummy!"

Ma Chit's face contorted as though with pain; tears gathered in her eyes and brimmed over, rolling unheeded down her lined face.

She could only say, helplessly, despairingly, "You belong to us, now. You are married to Aung." Then she, too, looked from one face to another.

Mi Nu pressed forward to her mother's side.

"Our little Mālā would never go away from us forever. You have been her mother for so long now; she does not even remember her real mother, do you, Mālā?"

Jenny nodded her head, her small face grave.

"But I do remember my mummy. She was called Ma Illa, and she was much prettier than Shwe-Shwe's Ma Hla, and she had one hundred *longyis*, all of them silk. We had an Indian servant called Ganesh, like the elephant god of the Hindus, and we had a Moslem driver called Husain. I remember a lot of things."

The expression she turned on Aung now was eager.

"My daddy will take us both to England to see my Mummy, then we will come back here."

"No," Aung said. "We will not go to England. If your *Mé-Mé* wants to see you she must come here to Burma." He looked from Jenny to her father. "That is how it must be," he said firmly.

Christopher continued to smile, amiably.

"We will have a big talk about it all."

"We should discuss it with the head man, my brother," Ma Hla said, and the smile she turned on the Englishman was now openly sympathetic.

"There is nothing to discuss," Aung cried, angrily. "The head man himself married us—everyone in Tatkon knows it. A father cannot take a wife away from her husband."

"My son says truly, *thakin*," Ma Chit pleaded.

Aung rounded on her. "Why do you call him *thakin?* We are the *thakins* now! We are masters in our own country, and each man is master in his own house."

"You have no house," Ma Hla said, derisively.

Maung Ba Tu spoke up then.

"I am the master of the house and I say that my son's wife who lives with him under my roof should stay with him."

Ma Hla tossed her head.

"She cannot be compelled to remain. We are not like Indian women—we are free. Mālā must choose for herself." She looked at the Englishman for confirmation.

"Quite so," he agreed, and smiled from her to Jenny, but Jenny's face was grave again, the chaos in her intensified with this talk of her mother and of England. Words came swimming up to the surface of consciousness —more than names, now, words, phrases, a shoal of words driving up from the depths of the mind's dark pool, the re-emergence of a forgotten language. Mummy, Daddy, the place called England which she had heard so much about as a little girl and never wanted to go to. Now there was again this talk of England, and if Aung came too it would be exciting to go there and see Mummy; but not without Aung. If Daddy would not take Aung, or Aung would not agree to go, then Mummy must come to Burma. That much at least emerged clearly in all the confusion.

They all walked in silence through the loose dust and the hot sunlight, though questions crowded in on all of them, except Ma Hla, who watched the unfolding of her scheme with excited interest. She alone wondered if it were true that the other Ma Hla had not been drowned; if it were not, it was clever of the *thakin* Finching. Christopher himself was already half regretting the impulse which had made him say it; that it had tilted the scales in favour of getting Jenny back to England was obvious—but what of the shock to Jenny when she discovered that it wasn't true, and what of her reaction to the fact that he had lied to her and got her to England on false pretences? He could only hope that once she was out of Burma, away from these people with whom at present she felt emotionally involved, she would see the necessity for her liberation, and that it was a case of the end justifying the means.

When they came to the house he did not follow the example of the others and remove his sandals on the verandah, telling himself that after all Burmans themselves did not do it when they wore European clothes, and when they entered the room and a mat was brought from a corner and unrolled for him on the floor he lowered himself on to it with distaste. This custom of squatting on the floor was one which he detested, and in some thirty years in the country he had very seldom been required to conform to it. He looked round the bare bamboo room and tried to realize that it had been his daughter's home for eight years, but it seemed somehow improbable.

The men seated themselves on their mats in a circle with the visitor—men in council. Ma Hla, Mya, and Jenny perched at the edge of the sleeping-platform, where now Jenny slept with Aung, Mya having gone off to live with Shwe-Shwe and Ma Hla, and Nu, upon her marriage, having gone to live with Maung Tin in the house he had built for them both. The three girls sat facing Christopher, who sat with his back to the opposite wall, his long legs folded under him, as decorum required. Ma Chit and Nu went off to the kitchen to make plain tea in honour of the guest.

Alone with her daughter Ma Chit gave way to her fears and unhappiness. She stood by the rough stone stove and covered her face with her hands.

"The *thakin* will take her away from us!" she wept. "Now that she knows her real mother is alive she will want to go! Our poor Aung! What is to happen? He loves her so much. It will break his heart. My poor boy . . ."

"Mālā loves him as much as he loves her," Nu tried to comfort her mother. "Even if she does go to England to see her mother she will come back. She will go for a little time only—I am sure of it."

"She is not like you were at her age," Ma Chit mourned, "she is a child still, and Aung is only a boy. What chance have they, the two poor little ones, against the *thakin?*"

"He is not *thakin* any more," Nu said, firmly. "Mālā will do what she wants to do."

She bent down and began gathering charcoal together for the fire.

Ma Chit remained standing disconsolately by the stove.

"We could ask the *Naga-daw* to arrange a *nat*-worshipping ceremony for us," she said, in a low voice. "It might help us in our trouble——"

Nu said, without looking up, "Aung doesn't believe in such things. It's better we take some offerings to the pagoda *nat* and make a strong wish that everything will turn out for the happiness of Aung and Mālā. If we make a strong enough wish Mālā will feel it and know what is best to do. . . ."

Sitting facing her father in the room Jenny continued to feel confused and troubled. He was 'Daddy' as she had remembered him, but he no longer represented security, the world made safe; all that was now vested in Aung, who held her in his arms at night and made his body one with hers, so that they belonged as completely, it seemed to her, as an unborn baby belonged to its mother, and one day she would have a baby that was part of herself and Aung; once the thought would have frightened her; now it seemed the most wonderful and splendid thing that could happen.

It would be beautiful to see Mummy again if only to tell her about Aung. But how to see her without making Aung angry or sad, without being separated from him? It would have been better if Daddy had never come here, never found him, never broken in on the happiness of her life with Aung, and with dear Ma Chit as *Mé-Mé* enough . . . She felt so sad and troubled thinking of it all that the tears kept coming into her eyes as across the room, to and fro, like bats' wings as darkness closes in, went the questions and answers that one way or another would settle her fate and Aung's.

Christopher had a similar feeling, but he thought of it in terms of a game—a wrong move and he would irretrievably lose, a right one and he would win. Between the questions and answers, the suggestions and counter-suggestions, the explanations, the protests, he looked at Jenny, with her troubled childish face and figure and manner, and tried to realize that she was the wife of this village boy, and it seemed as improbable as the fact of his sitting there on the floor of a bamboo house discussing with these Burmese peasants his right to reclaim his daughter—his little girl who back in England would still be at school. Anger rose in him with the thought. She must be rescued from this world into which she had been precipitated by the hazard of war and to which, however much she might have adapted herself, she did not, fundamentally belong. She must be liberated—and liberation, as the war had demonstrated over and over again, was invariably a painful business.

Catching Jenny's eye at one point he brought out his wallet from the hip-pocket of his shorts and extracted the picture of Ma Hla which he always carried and passed it across to her, smiling as he did so, but saying nothing. Jenny gazed at it a long time, with Ma Hla and Mya bending their heads beside hers to share it with her.

"She is pretty," Ma Hla said.

Mya made no comment. She too thought Mālā's *amé* pretty, much prettier than her own, which added to her ineradicable resentment of Jenny. She was glad to be in the secret with Ma Hla, glad they had told Mr. Vernon where Mālā was, glad that Mālā's father had at last come for her. Aung would be sad for a little while, but then he would find another wife, a prettier one, and a real Burmese one, not an 'Anglo' like this one, a half-and-half. . . . Mālā would go away and very soon they would all forget about her; it would be as though she had never been there. Then she, Mya, would go and live at home again, be again the little sister, and when she married she and her husband would live there, sleeping where now Mālā and Aung slept, and all would be as happy-ever-after as the Jataka tale of the good Prince Kalinga and his lady.

Jenny passed the picture to Aung.

"My real *Mé-Mé*," she said, happily.

His father and Maung Shwe and Maung Tin leaned close to him, as the girls had leaned to Mālā, and exclaimed upon the prettiness of Mālā's mother, and of the likeness of the two. Under cover of this distraction Christopher took the opportunity to say to Jenny, "You would like to see Mummy again?"

She nodded vigorously. "But Aung must come too," she said.

He had a sudden inspiration. "He shall come with us to Rangoon."

Everyone had settled down again now, and Aung handed back the picture of Jenny's mother. He had heard what the Englishman had proposed. "No," he said. "We stay here, Mālā and I."

Christopher forced himself to smile appealingly.

"You can surely spare her for a few months?"

"Not even for a few days," Aung told him.

"Isn't that rather selfish?"

"Perhaps. But not more selfish than your wish to take her away."

"She is my daughter. But for the accident of war she would not be here. Is it not natural that I—that her parents—should wish to reclaim their child?"

"It is natural," Maung Shwe put in quickly, "but wars change people—change lives. Mālā belongs to this Burmese life now. To my parents she is a daughter, to my sisters and me a sister, to my brother a wife."

"She is still my daughter." Christopher forced himself to smile, amiably.

A thin wizened figure stepped in from the verandah and paused at the edge of the group. Christopher regarded the old woman with distaste; she was like a walking corpse, he thought.

"Who is this?" Daw Khin demanded, staring at the stranger.

"It is Mālā's father, *Pwa-pwa*," Maung Shwe told her. "He wants to take Mālā to England to see her mother."

"No," said Daw Khin. "A wife must remain with her husband. Let the *thakima* come here."

She continued on her way to her own corner of the room.

"You hear what our grandmother says," Aung observed. "The old are wise. In this country we have great respect for old people."

Ma Chit and Nu came in with the tea and set two small shallow bowls in front of everyone. Nu set out the cups and plates of biscuits and bowls of fruit, and her mother poured the thin green tea.

It seemed to Christopher that this discussion could go on all day and still remain a deadlock. It was now clear that Jenny wanted to see her mother again; she would go with him to England, but she wanted this so-called husband of hers with her. Even if he was prepared to take him, which he was not, it was equally clear that he would not go. He had therefore somehow to be persuaded to agree to Jenny going without him. Only Jenny could do that. If he could see the child alone, talk to her—

He turned to Maung Ba Tu as the head of the house.

"I should like to talk to my daughter privately."

"No," Aung said sharply.

Ma Hla protested, "That is not fair, Aung. How is Mālā to make up her mind unless she and her father talk together? You are her husband, but he is her father. Why should they not speak together as father and daughter without all of us round?"

The mind of Maung Ba Tu moved with difficulty round this bewildering new situation. What Ma Hla said seemed to be fair. Why should they not talk together?

"Let the *thakin* talk privately to Mālā," he commanded.

"*Thakin!*" Aung said, scornfully. "Go with your father," he said to Jenny. "He wants to persuade you to leave your husband—to leave all of us who have been your family all these years. Go with him and explain to him where you belong."

Christopher got to his feet.

"Come," he said, and held out his hand to Jenny.

Dismayed, she looked from Aung to him and back again.

"Go," the boy repeated.

Jenny got up and put her hand in her father's. Together they stepped out on to the verandah. He led the way to the far end, where there was an old sun-dried rush chair which Daw Khin used for her afternoon siestas sometimes. He sat down, but Jenny remained standing, looking out across the compound, bewildered, embarrassed, not knowing what was expected of her.

"Listen, Jenny." He spoke in Burmese. "You want to see Mummy again, but if you don't come to England you will never see her, for she will never come back here. Everything is changed here now, and she does not like to come back. You must explain this to Aung, you understand?"

She nodded. Her father continued, "You must also explain to him that you are not going for more than a few months, and by aeroplane you can get back in two days. Tell him that. That you will be only two days away from each other. Two days only. You must make him understand that you want to go. If he loves you he will do what you want—you must say that to him too. Will you do that?"

She regarded him gravely. "I will make a strong wish."

He smiled. "What will it be?"

"I cannot tell you. It is private. But I think it will be all right."

"Very well. I leave it to you. I'll go now, but I shall come back early tomorrow morning, and I shall expect you to be ready to come with me. We will go to Chauk and get one of the B.O.C. 'planes to Rangoon. We will have to stay a few days, to get exit permits, and European clothes for you. Let Aung come with you as far as Rangoon, if he likes; I will arrange for him to get back. He can regard it as a pilgrimage to the Shwe Dagon Paya—if he is a good Buddhist that will appeal to him. You want all this to happen, don't you, Jenny?"

"Yes. But I wish Aung could come all the way with me."

"Mummy wouldn't like that. And it would cost too much money. But you will be only two days away from each other. You must think of it like that and make him think of it like that. Can you do that?"

"I think so."

"Good, then I'll be off until tomorrow."

He got up and they walked to the end of the verandah together. At the top of the steps he bent and kissed her forehead, stiffly.

"Good-bye, Jenny—until tomorrow." He hesitated, with his hands on her shoulders. He had still the feeling of not having made contact with her, this child of his who was not a child and yet also not a woman, and who somehow eluded him. She was to have flung herself into his arms with a wild glad cry of "Daddy!" There should be something said that would bring them close. Groping for the right thing to say he brought out, "You knew I'd come back for you one day, didn't you?"

"At first I thought so. I thought you would come at the end of the rains. I used to cry a lot, especially for Mummy. Then it all began to seem far away and I got used to being here, and there was Shwe-Shwe, and I stopped being homesick. When the war was ending Shwe-Shwe told me that Po Than had told him you had been taken prisoner by the Japanese, but that Mummy had been drowned. I thought about it all again then and cried a little. But the Japanese were being driven out and there were aeroplanes and bombs and it was very frightening and I couldn't think about you or Mummy, and when it was all over other things happened."

She paused, and he sat down on the top step, bringing himself level with her as she stood leaning against the balustrade of the verandah.

"What sort of things?" he asked gently. I've made contact with her, at last, he thought. I am no longer the enemy. It's a beginning. . . .

"Pagoda festivals," she said. "Pwè. With lights. I had never seen it all with lights before. And there was Nu's marriage."

"Nu?"

"The big sister. And there was my na-twin mingala——"

"I noticed you'd had your ears pierced. I must find some nice ear-rings for you. But go on. What else?"

"Then we had more fighting. Men came here with guns and took taxes from everyone and said the government in Rangoon was bad, and we had to give them food. Then armed police came and there was fighting and people were killed. A young policeman was shot dead outside our compound. I saw him lying in the road with the blood running out of his mouth into the dust. It went black in the dust."

Again she paused.

"And then?"

"It was peaceful again and everything went on the same again, and Nu had a baby, and then at the last Kason festival when Aung and I went to the creek to get the lotus flowers as we did every year, everything was different. He put his arm round me and kissed me."

She fell silent, remembering. It had been so strange and beautiful; there were no words for it; there had been none then and there were none now. It had all been like something in a dream; a dream of sunshine and lotus flowers and the coppersmith bird knock-knock-knocking in the stillness, and their two hearts beating as persistently in this new exciting way. Then it had become a dream of moonlight and the pagoda strung from top to bottom with coloured lights, red, blue, and golden, and candles like rows of golden stars burning before the great image, and the great silver flood of moonlight making everything seem unreal, as they had known it many times before, but then it had a strange new beauty and mystery because of the beauty and mystery in themselves.

The rains had come and the river was again a yellow torrent whose sound filled the house night and day, and she had lain on the sleeping platform beside Mya, who did not love her, terribly conscious of Aung on his mat at the other end of the room, and that he too lay awake staring at the hot darkness, listening to the river, listening to his heart, as she listened to hers. All through that long Lent. It had all begun, he had told her, two years ago when she had been dressed like a princess for her *na-twin mingala*; from that day he had waited for her to grow up. At the end of that Lent, the longest either of them had ever known, at the time of the beautiful *Thadingyut*, the Festival of Lights, she had been once again dressed like a princess, but this time for her wedding to Aung. *Mé-Mé* had cried over her with happiness as she had fastened the jasmine in her hair and brushed the long tress falling at the side of her face. And Nu who had helped to dress her had cried too, because, she had said, "You look such a little girl—our little flower, as when you first came to us." But she herself had been proud and happy, because she was not a little girl any more, but old enough to marry. Nu had explained to her what it meant to be married, that there would be body pain, but that Aung would be gentle with her and she need not be afraid. Only she had not been afraid. Whatever had to be borne for Aung she had been prepared to bear it. Like Nu she had not cried out at her ear-piercing, and she had been resolved not to cry out in her bridal bed.

The *na-twin Saya* who had presided at the ear-boring ceremony for both herself and Mi Nu, and who had officiated at Shwe-Shwe's wedding and Nu's came to the house for her marriage to Aung. A golden mosquito net had been fixed up over the sleeping platform and it had been laid with a golden silk cover and decorated with garlands of flowers and leaves and coloured paper, and when the ceremony was over she and Aung had sat side by side on two chairs—lent for the occasion—and received their guests. And then at last the house emptied of people and *Mé-Mé* and *Pé-Pé* retired into their sleeping-place, and the old woman to her bed behind the chest-of-drawers, and they were free to creep in under the golden mosquito net and love each other. . . .

She came out of her reverie and looked at her father.

"So at the end of Lent we were married," she concluded simply.

If only I had been allowed to find her in 1946, he thought, bitterly.

"In England you would still be at school," he said, and as he said it it came to him that she had never been to school, could not read nor write English and knew nothing at all—except, he supposed, wrily, a lot of Buddhist nonsense with a strong admixture of animism.

He got up. "I must be going." Yet still he hesitated. There was in all this still a point to establish.

"Are you glad I came back for you?" he asked.

But that was something she could not answer. She looked at him, troubled. She could only say, helplessly, "I would like to see Mummy again," with no realization of the cruelty of her simple honesty.

She had still, he reflected, the honesty of a child; and he was up to his neck in duplicity. When the lies with which he had enticed her were exposed she would hate him. But not for long, he told himself, trampling on his dread; she was still only a child—a child with sexual experience, he thought, angrily—and once she began to be absorbed into English life all this Burmese life would recede, just as eight years ago all that other world, of Mummy and Peter and Ganesh and the house that was home at Bokoko, had receded into unreality—as she had told him.

He kissed her again with the same feeling of awkwardness, then went down the steps into the compound. When he looked up to wave to her she had already gone inside.

III. THE STRONG WISH

The discussion went on all day, and in the evening the family went in a body to the house of the head man for him to give his opinion and advice. The two brothers and their mother and grandmother were strongly opposed to Mr. Finching's proposals. Maung Ba Tu, backed up by Nu and her husband, and by Ma Hla, declared that it was right that Mālā should visit her mother, and that if her father would give his word that she should be sent back to Burma in a month or two they should trust him. Why, after all, should he wish to keep her there now that she was married? Perhaps even, he and his Burmese wife would return with her.

After a great deal of questioning and argument Maung Than gave it as his opinion that Maung Aung should allow his wife to go with her father, on the understanding that she should return within three months. Mr. Finching should be required to give a solemn promise that he would not attempt to influence her to remain longer, or hinder her return.

"You have nothing to fear," he adjudicated. "Ma Mālā is a birthright Burmese citizen, and she cannot be detained in another country against her will."

"She can be detained by the lack of money to return," Maung Shwe pointed out. "None of us can give her any money. You are the richest man in the village, but even you could not raise even the half of such a sum!"

"Now that we are independent we have our representatives in London," Maung Than said in his most important tone, to offset the slight on his financial resources. "If the young lady needs assistance to return home our Embassy in London will provide it," he added.

All this made a strong impression on everyone except Aung, who was not interested in how long Mālā might be away, or to what extent her father's word could be trusted, or the steps which could be taken to ensure her safe return; he, quite simply, was not prepared to let her go. She was his dear love, for whom he had waited a long time, to whom he had not long been married, and no one had a right to take her from him, even for an hour.

"How do we even know it is true that her mother was not drowned?" he demanded, angrily. "We never heard of any Burmese woman and her Indian servant being washed ashore in these parts."

"My father would not tell lies," Jenny said quickly. "He is a strong Christian and Christians are just as much against telling lies as the Buddhists are."

"Don't you think Buddhists tell lies?" Aung snapped. "All people tell lies when it suits them, whatever religions they profess."

Jenny insisted, stubbornly, "My father would not lie. When I was a little
girl he would beat me if I told a lie. He always said he hated a liar."

"How can you remember so far back?" Aung taunted her.

She flushed with anger. "I do remember. I remember a lot of things."

This was true. "I hate a liar" is what her father had said in her hearing
after sacking an Indian servant for lying to him.

Maung Ba Tu, Ma Chit, Aung and Jenny, walked back from the head
man's house with their separate miseries. Maung Ba Tu was miserable
because although he felt it right for Mālā to go with her father he felt for
his wife and son in their unhappiness; Ma Chit was miserable on Aung's
account, Aung because the whole idea was intolerable to him, and he felt
that everyone, even Mālā herself, was against him, and Jenny was in a
misery of conflict, torn between her desire to go with her father and her
desire not to make Aung unhappy. They were all nervously exhausted
and felt the impossibility of discussing the matter any more for the time
being.

Only Aung and Jenny went on to the house. Ma Chit felt the need to
go to the pagoda, and Maung Ba Tu to smoke a peaceable cheroot with a
neighbour. Aung and Jenny went into the dark house; Jenny lit an oil lamp
to welcome the others back, and Aung unfastened the mosquito net over
the bed and drew the screen round. The old woman snored softly at the
other end of the room. Occasionally a lizard chattered shrilly out of sight
on a wall.

Aung held out a hand to Jenny.

"Come," he said, "we can talk more privately in the little house of our
bed." She saw that he smiled, but it was a sad smile.

They climbed in under the mosquito net and tucked it in all round.
Aung put an arm under Jenny's head and drew her to him.

"Can you really think of leaving me?"

"It would be only for a short time, and only two days away."

"How do you mean only two days away? It is thousands of miles away."

"By aeroplane it takes only two days." She put up a hand and pushed
her fingers through his thick black hair. "Oh Aung, it will be lovely if we
go with my father tomorrow. It would be an adventure! We shall never
have such a chance again. We have never been anywhere—never seen anything of the world. Imagine it—to be in Rangoon, in the capital, and to be
able to go to the great Shwe Dagon Paya! We will have some days together
whilst my father makes all the arrangements, and then what a lot you will
have to tell everyone when you get back! And what a lot I shall have to tell
you when I get back from England!"

He pressed her closer still to him and did not answer. Then she became
aware of the vibration of his body and realized with dismay that he was
weeping.

"You want to go," he wept. "I didn't know how much you want it. The English in you wants it. You are English after all. You will go and you will never come back—not because your father will keep you there, but because you won't want to come back. You will speak English again, wear English clothes, and Burma will be much more than two days away! It will seem another world."

He wrenched himself away from her and lay on his face, clutching the hard pillow, wracked with a wild grief. She flung herself on him then in a frenzy of distress, but even with her arms round him she was willing him to agree to her going. He must not be unhappy, but he must do what she wanted. Now she was all child and could only see ahead as far as Rangoon, with its fabulous golden pagoda and the two of them walking hand in hand round its great base. Somewhere beyond all that wavered the shadowy figure of her mother; the English setting was unimaginable; there was only her mother, Mummy, the real *Mé-Mé*, smiling, welcoming, and a great feeling of happiness, and then somehow she was back in Tatkon with Aung and the great adventure was over. It could all be exciting and splendid—if only he would let it be.

She pleaded, coaxed, cajoled, till in the end she had him won over to her side, not converted to her faith in the idea but submitted to it. He had the feeling of no more strength to resist the pressure of her will, but his heart was heavy and he was full of fear.

"If you don't come back I shall die," he told her.

"I should die if I did not come back," she assured him.

They clung together, comforting each other with kisses. But when she slept he lay awake, brooding. His mother had returned early from the pagoda whilst they had still been talking. Later, when Mālā slept, he heard his father return; he listened to him shuttering the house, bolting doors. Then the old man extinguished the lamp and joined Ma Chit behind the partition. Aung heard the low murmur of their voices. They were so safe in their lives together, he thought; nothing but death could separate them. No one would come to take one of them away; having found each other they would never again lie alone. He wondered how many nights he would lie there with Mālā thousands of miles away, not knowing when she would return. What did it matter if they never saw the Shwe Dagon Paya? Or anything else in the world; if they lived out all of this incarnation in this riverine village—so long as they had each other. But there was no escaping the law of *karma*, and the law which had brought them together was about to part them; previous lives had made what was, and present life determined what was to be; there was this continual process of becoming. You could only live each day as it came with as much merit and as courageously as you could.

IV. THE LONG FAREWELL

CHRISTOPHER returned to Tatkon in the cool of early morning, an armed escort ahead of him. This time he had both jeeps drive into the village and pull up outside Maung Ba Tu's compound.

Jenny and Aung stood waiting for him on the verandah, bundles at their feet. As he came up the steps other members of the family emerged from the room behind. Everyone was grave-faced and silent. It might have been a funeral, he thought, wrily. Ma Chit looked utterly stricken and had obviously been weeping. Jenny regarded her father unsmilingly. Now that the time had come she was overwhelmed by the immensity of the adventure.

"All set?" her father inquired, briskly.

For a few moments no one spoke, then Maung Shwe said, sombrely, "We ask you to come with us to the head man's house—my wife is there, and my older sister and her husband, and my young sister; they also must say good-bye."

More tears, Christopher thought. He turned to Ma Chit.

"I thank you for looking after my little girl all these years. I should like to make you and your husband some payment——"

She shrank away from him as though he had threatened her in some way.

"Oh no, *thakin!*" she cried, and looked appealingly at her husband. "Explain to him that we cannot take anything, Maung," she besought him, then looked again at the Englishman. "She was like our own child," she explained.

Maung Ba Tu came to life then.

"My wife speaks truly, *thakin*. We cannot take money for what we did with love. No, no, *thakin*, that is not our way."

Christopher shrugged.

"As you wish." He looked at Maung Shwe. "Let's go then."

Instinctively Jenny turned to her foster-mother. Her own eyes filled with tears, then, and it was difficult to speak because of the tightness in her throat. Ma Chit raised a hand to her forehead to cover her weeping.

"Don't cry, *Mé-Mé*," Jenny whispered, "it isn't for long."

Ma Chit put an arm round the girl but could not speak. She sobbed helplessly.

Maung Shwe addressed his mother. "She will be back with us before the May moon, *Mé-Mé*. Mr. Finching will promise this in the solemn Christian way."

Jenny could only say again, despairingly, "Don't cry, *Mé-Mé*."

The old grandmother came from the dark interior of the house and stood by Maung Ba Tu at the edge of the verandah.

Jenny went to her and abased herself at her feet, bowing her forehead to the ground.

"Good-bye, *Pwa-pwa*," she said in a low voice, "I promise to come back soon."

Christopher regarded this piece of Burmese family ceremonial with distaste. He and Jennifer, clearly, had a considerable re-education programme ahead of them once Jenny was safely back in civilization.

The old woman kissed the girl's forehead when she straightened herself before her.

"You are making a great mistake, child," she said, sternly. "Your place is here, with your husband."

"Aung agrees to my going," Jenny pleaded.

"Aung's heart doesn't agree."

Jenny could only say again, choked with tears, "It won't be for long." She turned to Maung Ba Tu and whispered, "Good-bye, *Pé-Pé*."

It was the first time she had so addressed him, and for the first time he embraced her.

"Come back to us soon," he mumbled.

Jenny tried to smile reassuringly but her brimming eyes overflowed and she turned helplessly away. She had never been able to love him, but now that the time had come to say good-bye he seemed closer to her than her own father. Much closer. The good old man. What had she to do with this tall Englishman? She turned mutely to Aung.

He took her hand. "We'll go," he said.

Christopher raised a hand in gesture of farewell and led the way down the steps, followed by Jenny, Aung and Maung Shwe. They formed a solemn little procession across the compound, Jenny slightly ahead of Aung, but not quite level with her father, with Maung Shwe frowning in the rear. Only Maung Ba Tu and Ma Chit stood watching on the verandah; Daw Khin had gone back into the house in token of her disapproval.

A crowd had gathered round the two jeeps. The police boys sat with the barrels of their guns across their knees enjoying their importance. Girls formed in small groups ogling the young men and giggling. The older women stared, serious-eyed. Everyone knew that Mālā's English father had come to take her back to England. Only a little while ago they had crowded into Maung Ba Tu's house for the wedding, and now there was to be this separation. It was generally understood that she would return before the next Kason Full Moon; but who should say how it would be? England was very far away. What right had this Englishman to come and take his daughter away? What was a father's love compared with a husband's? Why was she going—since she could not be compelled? Her mother had not been drowned after all, it seemed; then why did she not come back to Burma to visit her daughter? She was, after all, Burmese . . .

Jenny waved to the two figures on the verandah, then climbed into the jeep after her father. Aung and Maung Shwe sat behind. The police jeep shot ahead and the other started up.

"Come back soon!" people called, and hands waved.

Jenny stared into the swirling mist of dust between the two jeeps. I will come back, she thought, wildly, I will come back long before the Kason Full Moon . . .

Maung Than and various of the village elders awaited them on the verandah of the head man's house, and a little apart from them stood Ma Hla and Mya, with Mi Nu and her husband. Everyone except Ma Hla looked very solemn. Christopher was struck again by the prettiness of Maung Shwe's wife and the cordiality of her smile. Jenny went over to Mi Nu who immediately raised a hand and wiped away the unheeded tears from Jenny's face.

"There is no need for tears," she said, gently, "you will come back soon to us all."

"Mé-Mé is so sad," Jenny said, her voice still uncertain.

"You will write to her and tell her about England," Nu said, "and Aung will read it to her. We will comfort her till you are home again."

Maung Shwe introduced Maung Than. "Our head man—my wife's brother."

Christopher nodded here and there.

"You remember me, Mr. Finching?" Maung Than inquired, airing his English.

Christopher held out his hand. "I do indeed, Maung Than."

They shook hands and Maung Than introduced the elders; then he said, "This is a sad day for us, Mr. Finching, and for all Tatkon. England is very far away. We hope you will send your daughter back very soon to rejoin her husband. You must know that she has no money of her own. She can go to our Embassy in London, of course——"

Christopher said stiffly, "That will not be necessary."

Maung Than bowed. "That is what we wished to know. Your daughter is a Burmese subject——"

"Quite so. She is also a British subject—inalienably. I would also point out that she is coming to London with me of her own free will and with the consent of her husband."

"Burmese women are very independent. They can make their husbands do what they wish—not like other Eastern women. Maung Aung is not happy that his wife goes to England. The separation comes too soon in their married life. Therefore we ask you not to keep our little Mālā with you long." He half turned to the others. "I speak for us all in this," he added.

There was a murmur of assent.

Christopher said, curtly, "I assure you that I have my daughter's happiness quite as much at heart as you have."

Then he left them and strode across the verandah to the family group. "Are you ready?" he demanded.

Jenny and Aung moved forward, followed by Maung Shwe and Mi Nu. Finching went on ahead of them, Maung Than waddling after him. At the gate of the compound the head man held out his hand. "We wish you a happy journey," he said.

"Thanks," Christopher grunted. With a quick handshake he turned and went out to the jeep.

He climbed in beside the driver and waited whilst what he thought of as the final bout of embracing took place. He noticed that Maung Shwe's wife and the younger girl remained on the verandah. Maung Shwe walked with Jenny to the jeep.

"Don't forget that we shall all be waiting for you," he said.

Jenny gave him a wan smile, but there were no more words. She had not known there could be such a sadness that choked back all words into your aching throat. She sat behind now with Aung and groped for his hand on the seat. The police jeep shot ahead and they followed it through the mist of dust, and behind them the dust threw up a screen between them and the forlornly waving figures of Shwe-Shwe, Mi Nu and Maung Tin.

After that all was confusion. They came into the semi-desert of the Dry Zone, with its burning dust, its palisades of cactus, its desolation of dry skeleton-white thorn bushes. There was a yellow-brown river deep down between yellow-brown sandy cliffs. There was what Jenny took to be a forest of tall burnt trees, bare and black and branchless. "The oil-fields," her father said, but it meant nothing. There was a place where they got out and there were 'planes—it was the first time either of them had seen aeroplanes on the ground. There were Englishmen who came and talked to her father, and some of them spoke to her, but in her general confusion she did not know what they said, though they addressed her in both English and Burmese. She clung to Aung and turned her face away; Aung stared straight ahead of him, and he also did not speak. It was very hot on the airfield and they waited a long time whilst crates and sacks and boxes were loaded into one of the aeroplanes and then taken out and stowed in a different way. Because the young couple seemed interested Finching explained, "These little Moths are so small they have to be loaded with an eye to balancing the weight." But it meant nothing to either of them;

they were not interested, merely bewildered. When it was time to enter the 'plane they felt neither fear nor excitement, because it was all completely unreal.

They were settled in seats apart from each other among the freight and strapped in. Aung came to life and was interested when the 'plane became air-borne; so often watching the 'planes going over during the war he had speculated as to what it must be like to travel high through the sky like that. He peered eagerly out of the window, but when he turned excitedly to exclaim to Jenny he saw that she was leaning over the side of her chair being sick. The air was bumpy with heat and the light 'plane bobbed and bounced on it like a bird blown in a gale. For the rest of the trip Jenny huddled in her seat crying from sheer physical wretchedness. When the 'plane bumped and bounced down into Mingaladon airfield she clapped her hands to her ears shrieking with piercing ear-ache.

Her father regarded her anxiously when they left the 'plane wondering how she would be on the long flight to England. It was only one of several things he was wondering. The more he considered it the more it seemed to him that they would present a very odd trio at any European hotel. He had not realized until they had left the village just how 'backward' a pair he was dealing with. If they were struck dumb with bewilderment, as they apparently were, by an air-strip, how would they be in the Westernized city of Rangoon?

He tried to reassure Jenny that the ear-ache would soon pass now that they had landed, and that the big 'plane which would take them to England would not do that to her, but she merely clung to Aung as though he were the one stable thing left in the world.

She continued to cling to him in the back of the car which took them into Rangoon, peeping out fearfully over his shoulder, remembering another car ride long ago when, as now, her father had sat frowning in front beside the driver. They were arriving along a road in which there were a great many other cars, and lorries, all going very fast, it seemed to her, and there were people on bicycles, and walking; it all went by like something in a dream.

Then suddenly there was an enormous golden pagoda poised above trees on a low hill.

"Shwe Dagon Paya," her father said, over his shoulder.

They gazed at it, the one comprehensible thing in the bewildering landscape of a dream, but now there was such a confusion of cars and lorries and bicycles and people, that even this had no reality. Then the confusion of vehicles and people increased and there were houses such as they had never seen before, not made of bamboo, but rising up massively like great cliffs, and the people seemed to dart in all directions at the base of the cliffs like ants.

"Yangon," Aung murmured, interest again beginning to assert itself. The sight of another pagoda heartened him. There were trees in the street leading to this other pagoda, and people squatting under them; perhaps after all a city was only a very much bigger village, with more of everything, and everything bigger.

Jenny was not heartened by the sight of the Sule Pagoda; she continued to feel that the only safe familiar thing in the world was Aung's protective arm round her shoulders.

Christopher consulted with the taxi-driver concerning the young country couple in his charge and was recommended to a Chinese hotel. Overcoming an instinctive repugnance he decided anyhow to look at it, and they drove along the water-front and into Chinatown. It would be less bewildering for the two young innocents abroad, he thought, and they would be less conspicuous there.

A young Chinese in clean white shirt and white linen trousers showed him several clean bare rooms, all with washbasins. Christopher tested the taps and found that they worked. The young man regarded him impassively. Christopher addressed him in Burmese and the young man replied in English with a slight American accent. Christopher engaged a double room and a single room for two nights—the day after tomorrow, surely, it should be possible to leave Rangoon.

He went back down the stairs to pay off the taxi-driver and fetch Jenny and Aung; but the sight of Jenny still clinging fearfully to the young Burman so exasperated him that he decided to take the taxi back into town and dine alone. He was beginning, too, to feel the need of a sundowner . . .

The young Chinese showed them to their room, which in spite of its bareness seemed to them full of furniture. He asked them where they were from. Aung told them and explained that the Englishman was his wife's father and that she was going to England on a visit to her mother. The young man said that he had not been in 'the U.K.' but he had been to the U.S.A. before the war. He had studied there. He demonstrated the washbasin taps and the electric light switches. He had disliked the Englishman quite intensely, but he felt sympathetic to the young couple. He told them they could eat downstairs in the restaurant. His parents owned the hotel and his father did the cooking. It was very good cooking; they would see. Chinese people understood food. He gave them a quick friendly smile.

When they were alone they went to the window and looked down into the crowded street. There was a cinema opposite, garish with lurid posters and neon signs. The gutter was littered with the garbage of street-stalls. There was the shriek of motor-horns and the clang of bells on the bicycle rickshaws. Suddenly there was a blare of Westernized Indian music as a loudspeaker on the roof of a motor-van covered with posters advertised the film showing at the cinema. The dust hung on the hot air in a haze. There was a smell of joss-sticks and of frying food, and the hot human-jungle smell of the street.

Jenny leaned her head against Aung's shoulder.

"It is so noisy," she sighed. In Tatkon the sun would be going down over the paddy fields and there would be the evening smell of the jasmine bushes, and the only sounds those of the coppersmith bird knocking his last before night fell, and the tauk-te lizard croaking his name somewhere out of sight, and perhaps the sound of a flute from the verandah of the house across the road, where lived one of the boys from the village band. *Mé-Mé* would be lighting the oil-lamp . . .

"Tomorrow," Aung said softly, "we will visit the beautiful pagoda—it will be quiet there . . ."

Finching, however, had quite other plans for the morning. Exit permits had to be secured and that meant photographs, and flight reservations had to be made; but the first item on the agenda was the purchase of a European outfit for Jenny. The sight of her in a *longyi* irritated him profoundly. He would not force the issue here, but he was resolved that as soon as ever they reached Europe, that is to say Amsterdam, she should change into European clothes. Over a *chota-hazri* of plain tea and fruit in the squalid hotel restaurant he explained that it would be cold in Europe and it would be impossible to go on wearing Burmese clothes. They must therefore go shopping.

They took a taxi into the centre of the city, dropping Aung at his own suggestion at the Sule Pagoda. He would pass the time there and meet them at the bottom of the steps in an hour's time. Finching proposed that then they should both be taken to the Shwe Dagon Pagoda where they could occupy themselves for the rest of the morning whilst he ran round after all the necessary documents for the journey to England.

They left Aung mounting the steps, slippers in hand, and continued on in the taxi to the leading stores in the town, patronized by the British during the regime, and now by the better-off Burmans. Left alone with his daughter Christopher tried to make conversation with her. She looked shadowy-eyed, he thought, and he wondered uneasily if she were pregnant. It would be a devil of a problem if she were. He dismissed the uncomfortable idea and asked her, kindly, if she was beginning to feel less confused by the city.

She shook her head. "I will never get used to it," she said. "It's so noisy, and so many people. I couldn't sleep last night for the noise, neither could Aung."

He found this oblique reference to the shared bed distasteful and said quickly, "You will get used to it in time." He changed the subject. "I hope

we can leave for London tomorrow. We shall be in India by the evening."
He refused to acknowledge the existence of Pakistan. Karachi had been
India in his time; it was India still. "I have made a provisional arrangement
for Aung to fly back to Chauk by one of the oil company's planes the day
we leave. They will look after him at Chauk and take him back to Tatkon."

"Poor Aung! I wish we could take him with us." Her voice was wistful.

"That is quite impossible," he said, curtly.

They came to the stores and he paid off the taxi. In the stores he explained his requirements to a slanting-eyed, black-haired young woman in
European clothes. She spoke English with an American accent and Burmese with an English one.

"First," Christopher said, firmly, "we need a good warm overcoat."

When the assistant inquired the colour he replied, "Something dark."

The assistant brought a dark blue velour coat suitable for an English
young lady at a good school—or a Burmese young lady attending a Christian school in Rangoon on a chilly day in the rainy season. It fitted well
enough, but Jenny thought it very ugly.

"Why can't I have a red coat?" she demanded.

"In England," her father told her, "well-bred people wear dark clothes."

"Red would suit the young lady," the assistant suggested.

Red did of course suit her; Christopher had to admit it when he saw the
red coat on her, so red it was. And after that a red woollen dress. Shoes
were more difficult; she declared that they all hurt her, and they compro-
mised with sandals. The nylon stockings puzzled Jenny; they were so thin
and transparent there seemed no point in putting them on, since they
wouldn't keep the legs warm and the legs would be as naked as with
nothing on them. She regarded those on the legs of the assistant, and
laughed.

"They are silly," she said.

The assistant looked inquiringly at Finching.

"The young lady could have thick stockings," she suggested, adding,
"Going to Europe for the first time she may feel cold."

Her father, however, felt that he had made concessions enough. Properly dressed females in Europe wore nylons; very well, then . . .

As he did not care to give the address of the hotel in Chinatown all the
purchases were put into a large cardboard box—which he proposed to leave
in the cloakroom of the big European hotel where he had dined the previous evening and where he intended to lunch.

Jenny was not excited by the purchase of the clothes. She thought them
ugly and silly. If it was so cold in Europe that you had to wear big heavy
overcoats why had dresses to be so short they left your legs bare except for
the transparent stocking things which there was no more point in putting
on than a spider's web? If it was cold in Europe why couldn't she wear

her Burmese clothes with something warm on top—such as was worn in Burma during the cold days, a woollen jacket, or a loose flannel coat such as *Mé-Mé* had given her to take to Europe, sparing it from among her own things? But when she got to England Mummy would help her with all this; she would know what was best to wear. It was a wonder, really, that she hadn't sent out some suitable things for her for the journey. With the thought of her mother her heart quickened with eagerness; it would be strange to see Mummy again; but beautiful, too. It had always been beautiful to be with Mummy. Only for a long time she had forgotten how it was, and had wanted to forget, since they were not to meet again.

The visit to the photographers was brief and for Jenny unimpressive; she had no idea what it was all about. Afterwards they found Aung waiting by the Sule Pagoda steps. He got into the taxi with them and they drove to the south entrance of the Shwe Dagon, along what seemed to them both an exciting royal way with palm trees leading up to the enormous *chinthes* flanking the great staircase. Christopher gave Aung twenty rupees.

"When you want to eat," he said, "there is a cheap café-restaurant across the road from here——" He pointed it out to them. "You have here more than enough money to eat all you want and take a taxi back to the hotel when you are ready. You remember the name of the hotel and the street?"

Aung repeated it.

"Good. Then you can't get lost." He added, ironically, "You speak the language! I will see you at the hotel this evening. It is probably your last day together for some time, so make the most of it."

He got back into the taxi and they watched it turn and disappear in the direction they had come. Then they slipped their feet out of their slippers and began the ascent of the south steps of the fabulous pagoda which the sixteenth century traveller Ralph Fitche declared was 'the fairest place that doe be in all the worlde'.

It took them a long time to reach the top, there was so much to look at on the way, so many things in all the open-fronted little shops at each side of the staircase. You could buy Buddha images, gilded shrines, marionette dolls decorated with tinsel, tinselled holy pictures of the Buddha or his disciples, tortoise-shell combs, oblong drums, wood-carvings, paper-backed books of the life of the Buddha, or the Jataka tales, flowers, joss-sticks, candles—a jumble of the sacred and profane. And behind the booths were dark little shelters where people sprawled on benches or cooked food over charcoal fires or slept—a whole world of narrowly concealed life lived at the edge of the steps. Gaunt pariah dogs prowled hungrily in the vicinity of this pagoda hinterland or sat scratching themselves in the sunshine beyond the stairs. Pigeons perched high up under the roof, the steps were covered with their droppings, and with grains of rice spilled from offerings, and with the butt ends of cheroots. The dried bird-droppings and the rice grains were rough to the soles of bare feet, but the crowd that flowed up and down the stairs in its brightly-coloured clothes moved as lightly as though walking on rose petals, talking and laughing, loitering as people do who live happily in the present.

At the top of the steps, where the flower-stalls were thickest, Aung bought an armful of tuberoses, waxen in their whiteness, and over-poweringly sweet, a feathery bunch of cosmos, white and pink and mauve, some yellow roses, packets of candles and joss-sticks. They were about to cross the marble tiled terrace to the great shrine opposite the stairs when one of the flower-sellers held out a bunch of pink and white lotus flowers.

Jenny gave an exclamation of surprised delight and turned eagerly to Aung. He smiled back at her.

"Our special flowers!" He bought a bunch and divided the half-opened buds between them.

"We'll offer them in memory of our creek at home," he said, "and with a deep wish that we may soon be back there together."

They went forward on to the wide platform with its innumerable gilded shrines and Buddha images, and its satellite red lacquer pagodas grouped round the base of the tremendous golden pile of the Shwe Dagon itself, bell-shaped and tapering to a slender spire above an umbrella of hundreds of small golden and silver bells which made a thin fitful music in the upper air.

They stood gazing up in wonder at this incredible glory, its gold so brilliantly burnished by the strong sunlight that it was like a golden fire against the deep cloudless blue of the sky. All about them strolled men, women and children bright as flowers in their gay *longyis;* occasionally the orange robes of a monk added a deeper note to the reds and blues and yellows, the luminous whites, the pink robes of nuns. There was a smell of tuberoses and jasmine and joss-sticks on the warm still air. Tall palms rose above gilded spires and lacquered multiple roofs.

Now neither Jenny nor Aung could think of their imminent separation, so filled with awe were they in the presence of such tremendous beauty. They gazed until their eyes ached from the burnished brilliance, then still in a dream of wonder turned away and went up the steps of the great golden-pillared shrine facing the stairs. They found a place among the many people who knelt there and sank down on their haunches before the great golden Buddha glimmering in ponderous presence among the shadows of the high canopy. They held their flowers circumspectly upright in their clasped hands and made their declaration of faith: "*I go for refuge to the Buddha . . . I go for refuge to the Dhamma . . . I go for refuge to the Sangha . . .*"

Then they went up to the flower-massed altar to present their offerings, tucking their flowers into the already full brass vases, setting out their candles among the guttering rows, planting their joss-sticks in a vase where some still burned and others had burned out, lingering for a few moments in the precious sense of coming close to the heart of beauty and blessedness. The thin blue smoke of the joss-sticks drifted across the bank of flowers, blending its scent with that of tuberoses and jasmine. Their own offerings, which had seemed so many when they had bought them, were lost in that wealth of flowers; but it did not matter, any more than the knowledge that in a few hours they would wither and die. They were not there to decorate the shrine, but in token of the transience of life.

It seemed to Jenny, raptly gazing, that all the most beautiful flowers in the world gathered at the lotus-feet of the Lord Buddha wherever his image was found, whether here at the great Shwe Dagon, or at the humble village pagoda of Tatkon. She remembered the last Kason festival when she had gone to the creek with Aung to gather lotus flowers, as every May, and this time he had put his arms round her and kissed her, sealing the end of childhood in this incarnation. This she remembered, with love and happiness, and not the imminent parting.

They went down from the altar and continued their devotions, repeating the Five Precepts and bowing their foreheads three times to the ground; then stayed awhile sitting back on their heels, reluctant to leave that blessed place. To and fro in the bright sunlight of the terrace the people moved like flowers walking, the women with flowers in their hair; at the shrine people knelt or sat on the ground, murmuring their devotions, or gazing at the golden image, or just sitting, relaxed and happy, some of them, both men and women, smoking cheroots.

It was all so beautiful, all that had to do with the Lord Buddha, Jenny thought, as she had thought many times at the Tatkon pagoda, but here at the great Shwe Dagon Paya it was more beautiful, surely, than anywhere else in the world. Beautiful the stillness of the candle flames, and the calm gentleness of the face of the Blessed One looking down on the forest of flowers at his feet; but that was beautiful at the humblest pagoda; what was so wonderful here was the hilltop feeling of being raised above the world—almost of having entered upon another plane of existence, where life was something other than the Impermanence, Suffering, Illusion, of all mortal incarnations.

Presently they left the shrine and joined the promenade round the terrace, continually stopping to gaze with wonder at the numerous shrines, great and small. Tucked away in a corner between some old stone stupas they came upon a *nat*-shrine—a doll's-house of a shrine so low it was necessary to kneel down to see inside. Aung had no more than a passing interest in it, but Jenny knelt down and peered fearfully in. What her eyes saw was a tarnished gnome-like little figure with a few dead flowers at its feet. Her spirit saw the symbol of a power inhabiting the spirit world. She made respectful obeisance, whilst Aung looked on, smiling a little, a little disapproving. She thought suddenly of her mother, wondering if there were *nat*-shrines in England.

They came to a short avenue of tall palm trees, and soon after to the wall encircling the hilltop. Here there were shady neam trees, and one old sacred tree. People sat on the wall, looking out over the city to the lakes and wood beyond. A haze of heat hung over the city, and over the plain beyond, like smoke. They sat for a while on a bench under a tree, and suddenly to them both came the sense of time passing, of every minute bringing them nearer the time of separation, so that sadness entered into the peace of being together in that beautiful place. They began to speak of the parting.

"We will write to each other," Aung said, heavily, and asked, "Aren't you glad, now, that Shwe-Shwe and I taught you to read and write Burmese?"

She nodded her head, vigorously, in the way she had, he remembered, from the time she first came to them.

"We will send our letters by 'plane," he went on, "then they will come quickly. In two days, perhaps."

"Perhaps the 'planes don't go every day."

"In a week, then. A week is a long time." He fell silent, brooding, trying to imagine life at Tatkon without Mālā, the little sister who had become his wife.

Jenny sighed. Already, before the journey had begun, she was wishing herself safely back.

"Ma Hla is glad I am going. She hopes I will never come back. I think she made a wish that my father would come back and find me." Suddenly she turned to Aung, her eyes kindled with the idea which occurred to her. "Perhaps it was who told the Englishman I was at Tatkon."

"What Englishman?"

"The Englishman who sent the message to my father—don't you remember? He told us that day we met at the pagoda."

"Where would Ma Hla have met an Englishman?"

"I don't know. When you go back you should ask her. I made a bad wish against her—don't you remember, at the ruined pagoda where the bad *nat* lives? My wish wasn't granted, but when Ma Hla made a bad wish the *nat* listened."

"No, Mālā. We don't believe such things."

She shook her head and her face assumed its old childish stubbornness.

"I did a bad thing, so a bad thing had to come to me. That is the Law. You told me."

"Yes, that is the Law. But is it a bad thing that your father should find you? You are his child; he loves you. It was natural he should want to find you."

"If he wanted to find me why did he wait so long? It is years since the war ended."

"Mālā—there is something you should know. He did try to find you immediately the war ended. He came here at the beginning of 1946. He went to Po Than, who was in charge of the ferry with Shwe-Shwe when you all tried to cross the Mynmyo river. Po Than told him you and Shwe-Shwe had both been drowned."

She stared at him.

"Shwe-Shwe told him to say that, if ever your father came for you. Perhaps it was a bad thing to do, but we didn't want you taken away from us, Shwe-Shwe and I didn't want it, and Mé-Mé and Nu."

"But Ma Hla and Mya wanted it. Whoever that Englishman was it was Ma Hla who told him I was at Tatkon—I am sure of it . . ."

"We can ask your father. But perhaps he doesn't know who told his friend."

"It will be found out one day. But it was Ma Hla. I am sure of it."

He said, heavily, "It doesn't matter now. Whether it is a good thing or a bad thing your father has found you and is taking you away. Let us hope it will prove to be a good thing."

He got up. "Let us find our way back to the south stairs and go down and eat at that restaurant your father showed us. Then we can come back here and sit in the shade till the sun goes down . . ."

And that, he thought despairingly, will be the end of the day; then perhaps there will be only the short night, and in the morning she will be gone from me, my little Mālā, my love, my bride.

It was late before they got back to the hotel, because when they finally came down from the pagoda Aung had an idea that they should drive out to the lakes and see the sunset from there. They got there just in time to see the palms in black silhouette against a crimson arras, but it seemed to them both so beautiful there, with the thin woods going down to the water, that Aung dismissed the taxi and they set out to walk round the lake.

They did not, in fact, walk very far, because there was a tree that leaned out over the water, its twisted trunk forming a seat, and it was pleasant to sit there and watch the last light fade from the sky and the lights bloom on the pagoda. It seemed strange to Jenny that though the pagoda was so far from the lake it should nevertheless be reflected in it. Without being flood-lit the pagoda was sufficiently lighted to make its gold luminous against the night sky. At that distance the blue strip-lighting was softened, so that ancient and modern were reconciled; in the dust-laden heat haze rising from the city the lighting quivered—as though seen through tears, Jenny thought. Far away across the glimmering water two clocks struck the hour, one after the other. Where will I be this time tomorrow night, she thought, forlornly. Aung would be back in Tatkon, with Mé-Mé and Pé-Pé and Pwa-pwa, lying alone on the sleeping platform. But where will I be? It was as unimaginable as Nirvana.

"Tomorrow night we shall each remember this," she said, speaking her thought aloud, "the pagoda shining against the dark sky and glimmering with blue lights in the water, and the two clocks striking."

"In a sense we shall have it always," he said. "No one can take this time away from us; it is ours." Only it doesn't help to know that, he thought, heavily. What has been is; it lives on in memory, but we are so made, he thought sadly, that the living past is not enough; we need the living present shaped to our desire: though in our endless craving is contained all sorrow.

When the two clocks struck again they walked slowly back to the avenue of palms leading into the city. Soon a taxi came level with them and Aung hailed it.

Back at the hotel Christopher awaited them.

"I was beginning to think you'd got lost," he said, a little irritably. He looked at Jenny. "We are leaving tomorrow at mid-day," he said. They were both aware of the satisfaction in his voice. He went on, telling them of the arrangements he had made for a taxi, the time they must leave the hotel, be at the airfield, the time the 'plane would take off, and the arrangements he had made for Aung.

"You will leave half an hour after we do," he said. "You will be able to see us off."

They listened to him in silence. Now they knew that their hours were indeed numbered.

Christopher, who had only come back to tell them the arrangements for the morrow, went out again. They went into the restaurant for a meal. The pleasant young man smiled at them and set a bowl down between them, in the Chinese fashion. They dipped into it listlessly, without appetite, and refused further dishes. There was so little time left. They went up the dark stairs to their room above the noisy street and crept in under the mosquito net and lay with their arms about each other dreading that sleep would overtake them and cheat them of the few remaining hours . . . which towards dawn it did.

There had been the brief interlude of reality at the pagoda and beside the lake, but unreality enclosed them again in the morning when they got into the taxi and drove back along the waterfront, turned into the city, passed the Sule Pagoda, drove out along the Sule Pagoda Road and out towards the Shwe Dagon Pagoda, back along the road they had come in what now seemed to them both another lifetime. They saw everything and nothing—the refugees' shacks, the university buildings, the rusty railway trains that had come to a standstill during the war and now had the weeds growing up round the carriage windows, creepers twining round the chimneys of the engines; the great lake of the reservoir set among wild waste land, the thin woods of the rubber plantations; on and on through the hot brown countryside and the white dust, to the barbed wire and corrugated iron and shacklike buildings of Mingaladon airfield.

In all this time they had none of them spoken. There was nothing to say. The hands of Jenny and Aung found each other on the hot leather of the taxi seat, and when they got out of the taxi instinctively their hands found their way back to each other. Jenny's bundle was checked in with her father's suitcase. Aung held on to his bundle with one hand and to Jenny with the other. They went into the café and Christopher ordered a large whisky for himself and orange drinks for them, but they did not touch them. He explained to Aung once again what he must do when he left them, and introduced him to an official who would look after him, show him where to go. Aung stared and nodded, and once or twice mechanically smiled.

Christopher went to the bar for another drink and suddenly Aung found words.

"Soon we won't see each other any more," he burst out. "We won't see or hear or touch each other. We shall both be in the sky rushing away from each other. I shall be back in the place we've come from, but you will go on rushing away for hours and hours. Thousands of miles away. Very soon now. Not hours now. Only minutes."

Jenny said, painfully because of the tightness in her throat, "We have to have courage. We shall write to each other. It won't be for long."

"Days and weeks and months," he said, bitterly. "I should never have let you go. You are my wife. What is a mother or a father when people are married? They belong to each other, then."

Finching swallowed his drink at the bar and came back to the table. Jenny sat with her head down so that he should not see the tears which Aung's outburst had brought to her eyes.

"We shall be called in a minute or two," her father said, briskly. "We might as well go outside."

He turned and they followed him outside. A loudspeaker summoned the passengers for Karachi, Baghdad, Beirut, Amsterdam. There was a general movement towards what seemed to Jenny and Aung an enormous 'plane. Beyond its monstrous wings nothing was visible. The flight of wooden steps up to the door in its long belly was as high as the steps from the compound to the verandah of their house—higher. Their fingers tightened each on the other's. They looked at each other, mutely, stricken. This was the dreaded parting. This was it. Only a few minutes to go. Less than the fingers of one hand. The time had come. This was it.

They followed the tall Englishman to within a few yards of the steps. Then an official intervened because Aung was not travelling. Only Finching knew what was said. All that the boy and the girl knew was that their fingers unlocked and each saw the other's stricken face. Neither spoke. Their hands fell apart, then Jenny was going ahead and up the steps. At the top she turned to look back but Aung was already walking away with the official. In the cabin she was shown—she had no idea by whom—where to sit; by a window. She stood up and looked out but she could see only the monstrous wings. Her father took his place beside her. The door of the 'plane slammed. Her father buckled her safety-belt and his own. Engines roared. She had a wild impulse to tear herself out of the safety-belt and rush to the door of the 'plane to escape. She half rose in her seat, then sank back covering her face with her hands. In her frenzied weeping she had no idea when the great Constellation was air-borne.

V . THE BETRAYAL

THE stewardess came round with inquiries for drinks. Christopher ordered a whisky. Jenny still sat huddled up, her head in her hands, shaken with sobs. The stewardess looked at her pityingly.

"She'll be all right," Christopher assured her quickly. He was both embarrassed and irritated.

When the stewardess came back she inquired, "Would you like me to see if I can do anything with her? Some sal volatile, perhaps?"

"No, no, leave her alone. She'll get over it." He forced himself to smile. "No one can cry forever."

The stewardess smiled, uncertainly. "I hate to see children upset."

He resisted the temptation to tell her that the sobbing child was in fact a married woman, weeping because of separation from her husband.

It was all nonsense of course, this fourteen-year-old girl as a married woman, and that bit of a boy as a married man. Putting their right hands together into a bowl of water in the presence of relatives and friends and the village head man, and afterwards sleeping together—did that make them married? Most of the marriages in Burma weren't even registered. He was worried, though; it wasn't all to be dismissed as easily as all that. If he'd caught up with her in 1946 she would still have been, as a minor, subject to her father. She was still a minor, but she was also the wife of a Burmese subject of independent Burma and here he had no jurisdiction over her. She had in any case dual nationality, and he was pretty certain that in England her British nationality would be active. It would all need going into, of course. He would get a good lawyer on to it when he got back to London.

The immediate worry was breaking the news to her that there was no Mummy waiting for her in England. Also what Jennifer was going to say about that bit of strategy—not very clever strategy, either, now he came to deal with it. He had been a fool. But how else could he have got her to come with him? If Jennifer imagined she could have managed it better he would like to know how. The only thing to hope for, of course, was that geography would make a difference. Fortunately it wasn't true that absence made the heart grow fonder—that old sentimental lie; absence demonstrated to people that they could live quite well without each other —sometimes even better. In the new world of the West mightn't the European in Jenny emerge? Just as confined to the East the Eastern in her blood had come out on top? He must somehow make her see that he had deceived her for her own good—to get her away from a half-civilized life and back into the world to which she rightly belonged; make her see herself as a victim of war who had been belatedly liberated. The whisky heartened him; he ordered another.

When the stewardess brought the second drink Jenny had stopped crying and lay back in her seat, her eyes closed, exhausted from so much weeping. The stewardess gave her a sympathetic glance.

"Would the little girl like something now?"

Christopher motioned her away. "Presently," he said.

He turned to Jenny on a sudden inspiration. "When we reach Karachi you can write Aung a letter and post it there—then it will reach him quickly, perhaps tomorrow, even."

She brightened immediately.

"Yes. I would like to do that."

It was a good move, he thought; would give her confidence in him, make her feel he was sympathetic. And of course the letter needn't be sent; much better not. Give the boy a chance to settle down and forget her. With any luck by the end of the monsoon, with Jenny not back, and no word from her, he would be looking around for a new wife . . .

When Jenny began to look about her she noticed several Burmans and the sight of them made her feel less lonely. Only grief welled continually in her; why had she and Aung parted like that without a word? Why had he walked away immediately and not looked back? I must get back quickly, she thought, in a few weeks. Mummy will understand when I explain to her.

A steward in a white jacket came round taking trays out of the pockets in the back of the seats and fixing them as tables before each passenger. Food began to be served. Only it was nothing that Jenny understood; there was no rice, no curries, and everyone ate with knives and forks—far away and long ago she had a memory of doing this herself, but she had forgotten how. She was, anyhow, not hungry; she sank back in her seat, disregarding the food.

"Try to eat something," her father urged. "You have to get used to European food again. This is fish—you like fish. Try some."

It might be fish—though she would not have known it—but it was not any kind of fish she understood. Crumbed veal cutlets followed the fish, but meat was something about which she knew nothing at all; at Tatkon there had been occasionally a duck or chicken, but meat was out of the question. The only recognizable feature of this meal, served some seventeen thousand feet over India, was the fruit. She took and ate an orange and a banana.

Coffee and liqueurs were served, then the backs of seats were lowered and passengers lay back and read or dozed the long afternoon away. Christopher, heavy with the half bottle of Burgundy he had taken with the meal, soon dozed off. Jenny seized the opportunity to climb over his long outstretched legs to go to the toilet. The mysteries of European-style plumbing had been introduced to her in the hotel in Rangoon; she was curious to know how it worked on an aeroplane. In the wash-room adjoining the W.C. she looked at herself in the mirror; she picked up a brush from the glass shelf and brushed her fringe, then seeing a bowl of powder with some cotton-wool beside it dipped the wool into the powder and heavily powdered her face, till it was as white as though covered with *thanaka*. She looked out of the window, but the earth so far down below did not look like the earth, but like one of the maps in the books the Mass Education people had brought out to the village since independence. Aung had tried to explain one of the maps to her, showing her where was Burma, where was India, where was England, where was America, but she had found it confusing, always mistaking the seas for the land, and he had teased her calling her an illiterate—which was not true, for she had let them teach her to read and write Burmese, and when she tried could even remember her English, though she could not think in it.

She went back to her seat and began thinking about the letter she would write to Aung from Karachi, and presently she fell asleep.

There were several hours to spend at Karachi and the passengers were taken to the rest-house of the air-line. This consisted of bungalows built round a compound full of flowers, with a main building in which there was a lounge, bar, and dining-room. In each bungalow there was a sitting-room, a bedroom, and an Indian-style bathroom. In the vicinity there were similar rest-houses of other air-lines, and everywhere flower-beds full of asters, marigolds, cosmos, sweet peas. The warm air smelled of dust and flowers and spiced food, and fugitively of jasmine. Jenny sniffed it gratefully, as she eyed the familiar flowers; it was still a recognizable world.

Christopher went to the bar, having settled Jenny on a settee in the lounge with note-paper and a Biro pen. They would eat later, he said. He perched on a stool at the bar and watched her covertly as she crouched uncomfortably over the low table in front of the settee writing her letter. She had grown into a pretty little thing, he thought, though nothing like as pretty as her mother. She would have to find another hair-style, too, when she changed into European clothes, and she mustn't be allowed to flour her face with powder like that. He had often admired Anglo-Burmese girls, but they looked better as Europeans than as Burmese, he thought. The sooner Jenny was groomed into being a smart little European girl— mentally and physically—the better.

Dear Aung, Jenny wrote laboriously; she had had little practice in writing, and it was the first letter she had written in her life. *We are at Karachi. I think of you all the time. I will come back soon. I wish you were here. Love from Mālā who loves you.* It covered a good deal of paper and took a long time to write. When it was written she folded it and placed it in the envelope, sealed the envelope and addressed it—to Maung Aung, Tatkon, Burma. Then she tucked her feet up under her on the settee and waited for her father. There were a number of people in the lounge, writing letters, drinking, talking. She felt very weary.

Christopher finished his second drink and came over to her.

"We'll go and eat," he said. "Give me your letter—I'll address it in English and give it in at the office to be posted."

He spoke in English. She looked at him, confused. He said then in Burmese, "You must begin to talk English now."

He took the letter from her. "Come now," he resumed in English. She understood the tone rather than the words.

He slipped the letter into his pocket and they went into the dining-room.

Soup was set before them. Jenny shook her head.

"You must eat," he said firmly.

She replied in Burmese, "I am not hungry."

"Speak English," he commanded.

She repeated it in English, laboriously, like a lesson, the way in the beginning she had tried to teach Mya English—'His hat is on his head,' which, with 'My name is Mya,' was all the English Mya ever mastered.

She sat silently while her father took his soup, followed by fried fish, then meat and vegetables.

"English food," he said. "Try some."

She shook her head and tried again in English.

"I am tired."

"You will be able to sleep on the 'plane."

To please him, and to prevent him pestering her further, when fruit was brought she took a banana.

There was more time to pass after dinner. Christopher ordered another drink but this time sat with her. He had somehow to get to know this child of his. To make it easier for her he spoke in Burmese.

"Everything will seem strange at first—different food, different clothes, everyone with pale European faces, sitting on chairs, not eating with the fingers, speaking English—but you will get used to it. It will only seem strange for a few days. You will not be a Burmese village girl any more. You will be Jenny Finching, an English girl. Miss Jenny Finching."

She shook her head in that childish way she had which he found irritating. Her eyes filled with tears.

"I am Mālā," she said. "I am Ma Mālā, and I am married to Maung Aung. I am Burmese."

He said, more sharply than he intended, "You are also still British. In Burma you are a Burmese subject, but in England you are British, and until you are twenty-one you cannot marry without my permission."

"I am married to Maung Aung."

"In Burma. But in England that means nothing. It was not a Christian marriage. That is something you must understand. In England you are not Ma Mālā, the wife of Maung Aung. You are Jenny Finching, and if it hadn't been for the war you would still be at school."

Jenny was silent. She did not understand all this about English law and not being Mālā and not married to Maung Aung, but she sensed the menace in her father's tone. She had a sudden feeling of having been trapped. Terror filled her and she sprang to her feet.

"I don't want to go to England. I want to go home. I want to go in an aeroplane back to Burma."

In her agitation she wrung her small hands together. She besought him with the tears rolling down her face. She looked like a Japanese doll, he thought; a Japanese doll that could cry, realistically.

"Please let me go back. I want to go home. I am Mālā. I don't want to be Jenny Finching."

He pulled her down to the settee.

"I am your father. Your real father. Doesn't that mean anything to you? Don't you remember our house at Bokoko—with Mummy and Ganesh and baby brother? Mummy and Daddy, not *Mé-Mé* and *Pé-Pé*—don't you remember? You used to wear English dresses and say Christian prayers—don't you remember? *Our Father*, and *Gentle Jesus*——"

"Jesus-God," she murmured. "I remember. And the shrine room with the golden Buddha image, and Ganesh's elephant-god shrine, and the moon-song we used to sing——"

He broke in on her. "We talked about going to England one day. I came back for you early in 1946 but I was told you had been drowned. Then Mr. Vernon sent me the news that you were alive——"

"Mr. Vernon?"

"You remember Mr. Vernon?"

"Yes, I remember. How did he know about me?"

"I don't know. When he comes to England you shall ask him for yourself."

The loudspeaker summoned the passengers for Baghdad, Beirut, Amsterdam.

Baghdad and Beirut were just places in morning sunshine. The air was still warm; there were still palms and plantains, and though the people were not Burmese or Indian they were also not European, nor were their clothes. It was a different world, but still an intelligible one. Jenny refused breakfast on the 'plane, but at Baghdad the passengers sat at tables on some sun-scorched grass and there were nuts and dates in little dishes—recognizable things—and she nibbled at them whilst her father sat frowning and silent over his coffee. He was worried, dreading the scene at Amsterdam.

Jenny was feeling better. She had slept on the hop from Karachi to Baghdad and now in the warm sunshine she felt less afraid. She would explain to Mummy that she could not stay long in England; Mummy would help her to get back; there was nothing to worry about. No one could force her to remain in England; whatever her father might say she was a Burmese citizen; the head man himself had said so. The Burmese did not have to do any more what the British told them—Aung had explained all this. They had their own government now, and she was one of them. There was nothing to be afraid of.

Nothing to be afraid of at Baghdad or Beirut, but Amsterdam was different. Amsterdam was a new world, quite unrecognizable. On the 'plane the passengers were told, 'We are approaching Europe. It is winter in Europe; it is very cold. Passengers should have warm clothes.' To Jenny the coldness at Amsterdam was quite unbelievable. The sun shone, but there was no warmth in it; none at all. People looked different now; they had pink faces and wore the ugly European clothes, the women with big fur coats and their legs sticking out naked-looking in the stocking things. They wore things on their heads like turbans, but they were not turbans.

They all went into buildings that seemed made of glass, and inside it was so hot it was hard to breathe, but it was better than the coldness outside.

"You must change into European clothes," her father said, and handed her a small suitcase. "They are all in here. I will ask one of the girls here to help you——"

A young woman in a uniform took her down some stairs into the ladies' cloakroom, where a woman in a white overall took charge of her. She took a kindly interest in the young Burmese girl going to England for the first time, but Jenny did not understand much of what was said to her. She took off her *longyi* and *eingyi* and pulled the red woollen dress on over her hair. It was ugly and clumsy, she thought, but it was warm. She pulled on the stockings but they would not stay up. The woman showed her how to twist them round and knot them above her knees, and helped her fasten the sandals. She handed Jenny a brush and comb and touched her hair. Jenny shook her head. Her hair was all right; she brushed her fringe, then saw a bowl of powder on the dressing-table with some cotton wool and began flouring her face.

"No, no," the attendant protested. "Not like that." She went over to Jenny and with another piece of cotton wool began removing most of the powder.

Jenny moved away from her, angrily, but to say what she felt in English was too difficult. She pushed her Burmese clothes into the suitcase, pulled on the overcoat, and went back up the stairs. At the top she found her father waiting.

"You haven't done your hair!" he exclaimed.

"It is all right," she said.

"It is not all right. You cannot wear your hair in the Burmese style with European clothes. Go back and change it. The cloakroom woman will help you."

"I cannot explain to her," she protested.

He would get the stewardess on the next 'plane to fix it, he thought; she looked quite absurd as she was. He led the way to a settee in a corner of the lounge. As they crossed the room Jenny's stockings fell down. She bent to pull them up but did not understand how the woman had twisted them. She looked apologetically at her father.

"They won't stay up," she explained.

"Haven't you suspenders?" he demanded. Then remembered that of course she wouldn't have; he hadn't bought her a suspender-belt in Rangoon.

"You'd better take them off," he said, grimly. "Roll them round your ankles now and when we sit down you can slip them off."

When they were settled in the corner he had selected and she had attended to the stockings he braced himself for the ordeal. He had already had a number of whiskies to that end.

He spoke in Burmese so that there should be no misunderstanding.

"Jenny, I have something very important to say to you. Very soon now, in not much more than an hour, we shall be in England. You will meet your Aunt Jennifer. She will be a mother to you—much more truly a mother to you than Ma Chit, because she is my sister; she is related to you. She will love you and care for you, just like Mummy used to do. In all these years you got used to being without Mummy, didn't you? You didn't miss her any more?"

"I had Ma Chit and Shwe-Shwe and Mi Nu, and then I had Aung."

"Quite so. Now you will have Aunt Jennifer and me. Not Mummy. You will still not have Mummy."

She looked at him, frightened.

"Not Mummy? You said I was to go to England to visit Mummy. Where is Mummy? I don't understand."

"It was better you should think she was in England. It made it easier for you to come. Isn't that so? But now you are nearly there, and it is Aunt Jennifer who is waiting for you, not Mummy. You did not mind not having Mummy all these years. You must not mind now."

Now there was horror in her eyes; the horror of the trapped thing that knows it is doomed. She shrank back against the upholstery of the settee to get as far away from him as possible, and he was fully aware of the shrinking.

"You told lies," she whispered. "You told lies to us all to get me here."

He said, sharply, "I was lied to in 1946 when I came for you. I was cheated once. I could not afford to lose you again. If I had not been lied to then I would not have needed to lie when I finally found you."

She continued to stare at him as though transfixed with horror.

"I don't belong to you," she whispered.

"You are my child," he cried, suddenly angry. "You are all I've got. You are a little girl in need of protection and education. You have grown up as a Burmese peasant. Now you are going to be rehabilitated as a European."

This was not the line he had intended taking; he had not intended harshness, but pleading; but the situation had got out of hand—in spite of all the mental rehearsals which had occupied him all the way from Karachi.

Emotion, which shock had frozen in her, was melted then.

"No," she cried, passionately. "No! You are cruel and wicked! You got me here by a trick! Let me go home! I will never be what you want! I hate you! Let me go home!"

She had sprung to her feet and looked wildly about her, as though seeking escape. She was sobbing hysterically at the end of her outburst, and people turned their heads in her direction. My God, Finching thought, people will think I'm abducting her. . . .

He seized her hands, gripping them, compelling her attention.

"Jenny, listen to me. We haven't seen each other for eight years. Can't you stay with me for three months out of a life time?"

He forced her back on to the settee and when he released her hands she covered her face with them and sobbed quietly, despairingly.

She looked so small and helpless and hopeless sitting there that his anger and exasperation suddenly collapsed in pity.

"Don't hate me," he pleaded. "Try to understand."

Jenny did not answer; the river closed over her again, sweeping her away, drowning her, and now no strong hands reached out to save her. Perhaps this time she would really die. Then she would be born again, be a child again, and for a little while at least there would be no memory of all this pain. Perhaps, even, there would never be any memory. Then as in that other river the dark flood fell back upon itself and she came to the surface, but now it was her spirit which struggled for existence. I must not die, she thought, Aung needs me; I promised to go back. I must believe I will go back. I will make a strong wish. I did not drown the first time; I will not drown now. . . .

When the London 'plane was announced and she rose to cross the lounge with her father she was quite calm. When he took her hand she did not withdraw it; she was unaware of it.

PART III. THE LOTUS

I. MĀLĀ INTO JENNY

T H E 'plane from Amsterdam reached London airport at four-thirty in the afternoon. For Jenny it was the beginning of maladjustment, for the time by which she had been living it was ten-thirty at night, but she was required to stay awake for another six hours. Lack of sleep was beginning to tell on her and she yawned continuously. Her father explained about the difference in time; it was the snag about East-West air-travel, he admitted, that the transition both as regards time and climate was too sudden.

Jenny was too nervously exhausted to take in much of the 'bus ride into London or of the taxi ride from the terminus to the place her father referred to as 'home'—which seemed odd, for home was now six thousand miles away, and when it was midnight here in the West it would be to-morrow in the East, the new day already six hours old. The moon will always arrive here six hours late, she thought, sadly, Aung and I can never look at it at the same time.

She was vaguely aware of grey streets and people in dark clothes. There was a terrifying amount of traffic and an amazing number of people; it was altogether more bewildering than Rangoon. She closed her eyes to shut out London and shut in the picture of Rangoon—sunlight, bright colours, the golden pagoda, Aung. . . .

'Home' was at the top of some dark stairs. There was a grey-haired old woman called Aunt Jennifer who kissed her and said "Welcome home, Jenny." There was a room where, astonishingly, the whole of one wall was covered with books, from floor to ceiling. There was a fire burning in the room, and in front of the fire a big golden cat.

The old woman took her to another room, a small room with white walls and a high bed with a white cover with a design of pink flowers on it. Strips of the same material hung in folds at a deep window. There were no bars or shutters to the window; it was made of glass, like the windows in Rangoon.

"This is your room," Aunt Jennifer said.

Then she showed her a European-style bathroom and demonstrated pulling a chain to make water spurt out.

"I don't think you have such arrangements in your—in Burma," she said, kindly.

"Not in the villages. In Rangoon," Jenny said, struggling with her yawns.

"You poor child! You must be dropping with tiredness. If you would like to go straight to bed I will bring you some hot milk."

"I don't drink milk," Jenny told her. It was Miss Finching's first setback.

"Oh, but you should. It's so good for you!"

"Milk is only for babies."

"Nonsense! But I'll fad you as it's your first day and make you a nice cup of Milko instead—that's half milk half cocoa. Now you would like to wash, I expect."

"No," Jenny said, wearily.

"You can't go to bed without washing." Her aunt's tone was severe.

"I can. But I don't want to go to bed yet—it's too soon."

She looked fearfully at the bed.

"Who is going to sleep with me?" she inquired.

Miss Finching was startled.

"Why—no one. You don't have to have someone sleep with you, do you?"

"Yes," said Jenny.

"Whatever for? You're not afraid of the dark, are you?"

"I'm afraid of ghosts——"

"Ghosts! Nobody in England believes in ghosts."

"In Burma we believe in them. People see them."

Miss Finching gave a small impatient laugh.

"Imagination. Imagination and superstition. You must try to get out of all that. In England we just say our prayers and go *straight* to bye-byes."

"Who do you say your prayers to?"

"To God, of course. Who else?"

"I thought perhaps there was a good *nat* you could pray to."

"There are no *nats*, as you call them, in England, or for that matter anywhere else. You will have to get used to sleeping alone. You may have a candle burning all night if that helps—until you get used to being alone."

"Two candles," Jenny insisted. "One by the window and one by the door. Ghosts won't come where there are lights."

"Very well, then—just until you are acclimatized."

Jenny did not know what the long word meant, and she was too tired to care. So long as she did not have to stay alone in the haunted dark.

With the reassurance of the two candles she decided to go to bed although it was not yet very dark. She even drank the peculiar hot drink her aunt brought, neither liking nor disliking it.

"Tomorrow," her Aunt Jennifer said, as she stood by, waiting to take the cup, "we must get properly organized. We can't have you going to bed wrapped up in one of those sarong things—it's unhygienic, like going bye-byes without washing and without cleaning our teeth. But tonight as you're so tired we'll excuse you."

Jenny was too exhausted to argue with such a foolish old woman. Her aunt bent and kissed her forehead.

"Night-night," she said.

"Good night, auntie," Jenny responded, carefully correct.

It came easy to Jenny to call Miss Finching 'auntie', because in Burma Auntie and Uncle are terms of respect used by the young for old people— that is to say for people over forty. Although Jenny considered her father's sister very old, and also ugly, with her short grey hair and her clothes like a man's Miss Finching was in fact fifty and looked rather younger. She was tall and thin, like her brother, with the same shrewd grey-blue eyes and straight nose. Her face was remarkably free of lines and she had the same clear pink and white complexion as in her youth. People said of her that she was 'not bad-looking'. Young people added 'for her age'. It was her tragedy that no one had ever positively found her attractive; the compliment had always been negative. Her grey hair waved naturally and was cropped close to her head; she wore well-tailored suits and neat blouses. She prided herself on a quiet elegance, avoiding an old-maidish primness on the one hand and masculinity on the other. The general effect was nevertheless masculine.

She disapproved of mannish women. She would like to have been married and had never quite known how it happened that she got left. In her twenties and early thirties there had been friendships with men, two or three of which had seemed quite promising, only somehow or other they had come to nothing. Her mother always said it was because she made her intentions too obvious and the men took fright. Her father declared that it was because she was always too 'jolly' in her attempts to appear at ease in male society, and that there was nothing more deadly in a woman than jollity. Her two sisters, younger than herself, and both of whom had married young, were of the opinion, simply, that she was not feminine enough. Christopher always gallantly assumed that she had not married because she had never met anyone who sufficiently appealed to her. That he alone believed this endeared him to her.

Only one man had ever made advances to her and he had been married; she had been thirty-five then. He had been an M.P.—Labour—and she had been his secretary. She had been a little in love with him, but her moral code was strictly conventional, and that he was separated from his wife did not weigh with her; the fact remained that he was a married man. She resisted his advances, distressed that these had been made, and asked him to accept her resignation. He had told her not to be a prude; she had left him all the same. She had found it all very upsetting, for she had been attracted more strongly to him than to anyone, and if he had been single it might all have been so different—or so she liked to think. In time the episode developed in her imagination as a great romantic passion sacrificed on the altar of principle. He was the only man she ever cried over, and she cried over him, on and off, for years. It was her one little emotional luxury.

She had another secretarial job after that, this time with the Fabian Society—she enjoyed the intellectual Leftish atmosphere and got a little kick out of the fact that her darling Christopher, that dyed-in-the-wool-old-Tory-imperialist, as she affectionately called him, found this predilection of hers mildly shocking. She felt that this little deviation made her more interesting in his eyes, more of a person in her own right. It was out of this self-conscious Liberalism that she stood by him so loyally over his second marriage, which had so dismayed their sisters.

After the war she became interested in social welfare and was appointed to the committee of an East End club for delinquent girls. Eventually she became the club's paid secretary. The work was interesting and she believed in it. She began to think of herself as a bachelor woman rather than as an old maid, and given another name, and linked to a purpose in life, the condition ceased to be distressing. She ceased to weep for her lost love. Through a friend who was leaving England she acquired the lease of a pleasant flat overlooking a Bloomsbury Square, and her bachelor-hood was established.

The war had liberated her, as it had many others. She had gone into Civil Defence and become a Commandant. She had lived then in a college from which the pupils had been evacuated and which was being used as a Civil Defence H.Q. She had enjoyed living 'in college' in this fashion, and wearing a smart uniform and having a position of authority, and all allied to serving her country. She was conventionally patriotic as she was conventionally religious, and it added up to a conventional morality.

She was efficient and kind; sensible and unimaginative; superficially intelligent and fundamentally stupid. She believed herself to be modern, intellectual, liberal-minded. She read the literary reviews, saw all the most 'worth-while' plays, listened to the Third Programme, and voted Labour. She adhered strictly to the Right Wing of the Labour Party and never went so far as to become a member. She persuaded herself that she lived an intellectually full and satisfying life, and that her devotion to her brother and her social welfare work—her 'girls'—provided adequate emotional outlet.

Her manner was brisk and practical, as though life were one long committee meeting. She faced the latest item on the agenda, the advent of her niece from Burma, in a spirit of resolute determination to rehabilitate this 'unfortunate child' to the very best of her ability. She must be restored, as her brother rightly wished, to her English and Christian heritage. It would not be easy, she recognized, particularly as the girl had gone through a form of marriage. If she should prove to be pregnant the problem would be even greater, though no doubt some arrangement could be made for getting the baby adopted.

At the end of the first week, however, Jenny had a period and scandalized her aunt by her careless unselfconsciousness in connection with it. Hygiene, clearly, Miss Finching decided, must be the first lesson. Hygiene and a European conception of modesty. Alas, the poor child had so many lessons to learn, from how to hold her knife and fork to saying her Christian prayers. She had forgotten all her father had taught her in the Bokoko days.

Jenny was docile enough as a pupil, though many of the things her aunt taught her she thought silly, and some disgusting. Her aunt explained that in Europe people did not take baths by pouring jugs of water over themselves; that they filled the bath with hot water and sat in it. This seemed to Jenny a horrible idea and she could never bring herself to wash her face in the water in which she sat. She was shocked, too, by the fact that no one, not even her fastidious aunt, washed hands before taking food; true they did not eat with their fingers, except at the meal called 'tea', but they broke their bread and put it into their mouths with their unwashed fingers. She found eating with cutlery unpleasant; by washing your hands you knew that your fingers were clean, but how could you know that all the spoons and forks and knives laid out on the table were clean? For one thing they were handled by other people—whose hands might or might not be clean. And coming in from the street and walking about in the house in your shoes, even in the bedrooms, that seemed to her as dirty as sitting in your bath water. Her aunt's and her father's ideas of hygiene were not hers.

Other things she was required to do struck her as merely silly—such as sitting perched up on chairs instead of squatting comfortably on the floor; putting on a hat—she knew now what the peculiar turban things were called—when you went out; wrapping yourself up warm at the top and leaving your legs all bare and cold in the flimsy things called nylons.

The coldness did not greatly trouble her, after all, she found; there were years of sun stored in her blood—reserves of it that would last her long enough for the short time she was staying.

On the second day, when she was still feeling stunned and bewildered, her father suggested she should write to Aung and tell him of her safe arrival. "Write and tell him you are safe and well," he said, adding, "I have some letters to write myself and yours can go off with mine. I will address the envelope for you in English." So she had written to Aung telling him she had reached London the previous day, that she missed him, especially at night, and to tell *Mé-Mé* not to be sad. And that she loved them all.

Later her father came in with some letters in his hand and she watched him address the letter to Aung in English, after which he suggested that she should go with him to the post-office. It was a nice sunny day and they would take a 'bus ride and she would see something of London. They went to the post-office and she saw that he dropped some of the letters into one hole in the wall and some into another. She saw the blue airmail form upon which she had written to Aung—that is to say she saw one like it. That particular airmail letter was written to Derek Vernon at Bokoko. The one she had written had been consumed in the domestic boiler in the kitchen of the flat.

When she had written the letter she felt less unhappy. Now in a few days Aung and *Mé-Mé* and all of them would know where she was, and then in a few more days she would receive a letter from him, and then they would not seem so far apart.

Her aunt took her shopping and one of the things they bought was a thing called a suspender-belt, the dangling straps of which had to be attached to the stocking things to keep them up. It fastened tightly round the body and felt stiff and uncomfortable and as soon as she got back to the flat she took it off and her stockings with it. They bought dresses to wear in bed at night, and dresses for daytime, and underclothes and shoes. Nothing that they bought was of the slightest interest to her.

"What will you do with all these things when I go home?" she inquired.

"My girls will be glad of them," Miss Finching replied, and she thought, Poor child, she still thinks of Burma as home.

She took turns with Christopher in taking Jenny about, showing her London. With the object of demonstrating some aspects of the Welfare State she took her on a 'bus ride to the East End, pointing out L.C.C. schools and blocks of modern flats. Jenny was depressed by the greyness of everything. Even the people looked grey, like corpses walking.

"Dockland," her aunt informed her, brightly. She added, in her brisk instructive way, "The district is drab, but really the people are quite comfortably off. Most of the mothers go out to work, you see."

"Who looks after the children?" Jenny inquired.

"Oh, we have any number of nurseries where the children are left and cared for." She added, proudly, "We are a welfare state, you know."

"In Burma, too," Jenny informed her. "*Pyidawtha*, we call it."

Miss Finching was startled.

"You don't mean to say that the natives—the people have social services such as we have in this country? In the villages, I mean?"

"Every village has a community centre and a clinic for mothers and children."

"You surprise me," said Miss Finching.

"Did you think we were savages?" Jenny inquired.

"Not exactly savages, no, but backward, surely?"

"We had the Lord Buddha six hundred years before you had your Jesus-God."

Miss Finching's irritation increased.

"Our Lord was the Way, the Truth, and the Life," she said, sharply. "The Buddha was just a man. A good man, but only a man."

"Not just a man. The Enlightened One. He gave us the Eightfold Path. He was the Blessed One."

"My dear child!" Miss Finching protested.

"It is quite true," Jenny assured her.

"You really have been indoctrinated, haven't you? It is really very wicked of them—a Christian child——"

Jenny did not know the long word her aunt used, but she understood enough to make her angry.

She said, hotly, "My Burmese family are not wicked! They are very good religious people, and they were very kind to me. I think of them all the time and wish I was back with them."

Her eyes filled with tears. She pulled a handkerchief out of the silly handbag she was required to carry around with her everywhere and blew her nose.

"I want to go home," she said. "I don't like it here. Everything is grey and ugly and stupid. There are no flowers, no sun, no pagodas."

"There are some beautiful churches. Tomorrow I will take you to Westminster Abbey. Now stop crying, there's a good girl. People are looking at you. Look over there—that's the Tower of London. Isn't that beautiful? Like something in a fairy-tale——"

Jenny did not think so. It was grey like everything else. Like the sky, and the streets, and silly old auntie's hair, and her ugly clothes. Grey like the people's faces that had never had the sun on them. There was only one thing not grey and ugly in London and that was old auntie's cat, whom they called Royal—Roy for short. They said he was ginger, but ginger was not that colour; he was all gold, dark gold and light gold, and his eyes were jade. When he sat straight up he looked like a little golden Buddha image. Jenny loved him, and often talked to him, softly, secretly, in Burmese. He listened and understood, purring and smiling—she was sure he smiled. When no one was looking she fed him scraps from her own plate, not because he needed them, for she knew he was well-fed, but as an act of merit . . .

"And of *course* there are no flowers just now," she heard her aunt continuing in her precise grey voice. "It's winter. In the spring our parks are full of the most beautiful flowers. And at Kew Gardens—I must take you to Kew Gardens. There is a pagoda there."

Jenny was immediately interested. "A pagoda? With a real Buddha shrine?"

"Of course not. I think it's a tea place."

"Then it's not a real pagoda?"

"It's not used. It's a replica." She made another guess and added, "It's there for ornament."

Jenny relapsed into silence. Grey waters closed over her and she drowned in them.

The visit to the East End was not a success; Miss Finching admitted the fact. Of course on a grey day dockland *was* very grey. One had to make allowances for this child brought up in the tropical sun—in the flamboyant East. The visit to Kew Gardens was more successful. Jenny had never seen a pagoda like the pseudo-Chinese one pointed out to her.

"It's Siamese style," her aunt told her. "Or Japanese—I'm not sure which. In the spring this avenue is a mass of Japanese cherry blossom—so the pagoda is quite in keeping. Of course Kew Gardens are *world* famous . . ."

An icy wind blew along the river, and Miss Finching was glad to take refuge in the Palm House. Why was it invariably a cold day when one visited Kew Gardens—whatever time of the year it was, she thought irritably.

It was lovely in the Palm House, Jenny thought, so beautifully warm—the damp warmth just before the monsoon broke—and it was exciting to see palms again, and plantains, and clumps of bamboo, and the great treeferns. In the distance there was a woman dressed all in red and if you screwed your eyes up a little you could believe she was wearing a *longyi*. Then suddenly there was an Indian family. The man wore the ugly European clothes, but the woman and a little girl wore *saris*—not plain cotton ones such as Ganesh's wife used to wear, but lovely silk ones with gold borders to them and threads of silk woven into the design. The lady and the little girl both wore fur coats, but in the warmth of the glass-house they had let them fall open, revealing the splendour of blue and red and gold silks underneath. Jenny gazed, hungrily, and with a kind of love. To see a face that was not white or grey or pink, but golden brown; to see clothes that were not drab but bright as flowers—oh in England, 'this the greatest blessing!'

"Auntie," she cried, "look! Asians!"

Miss Finching had already observed the Indians. "There are a number of coloured people in London," she replied, in what Jenny thought of as her information-voice. "Indians, Chinese, Negroes. There are in London a number of Indian and Chinese restaurants. I believe there is even a Burmese restaurant——"

Jenny was not listening. The Indians had gone and she was gazing at a plant with an orange flower like the long head of a bird and feeling compassion flow out to it because like herself and the Indians it did not belong in this cold grey land yet stood there so bravely in its splendid glowing indifference. She was glad that it had the palms for company and that once in a way someone from the East came and looked at it, sending their thoughts out to it, and their memories, so that it could live in its English prison.

Miss Finching transferred her attention to the flower. She said, "It's called *Strelitzia Regina*. It comes from Africa, I believe."

Three mornings a week a servant came to clean the rooms. She was referred to, Jenny noticed, as 'the domestic help', or more frequently, by her aunt, as 'my woman'; but that she was a servant was indisputable.

"Servant," Miss Finching explained, "is not a term commonly used in England since the war. Except in government offices, when we speak of civil servants. I think my woman—that is to say Mrs. Sellers—would very much object to being referred to as a servant."

Miss Finching was usually busy with her girls the days Mrs. Sellers came, and her brother usually went to his club because he disliked what he called being Hoovered from pillar to post. Jenny enjoyed being left alone with Mrs. Sellers. For one thing she was not old—or if she was she did not look old, for she had hair the same colour as Royal's coat, and she had bright red lips and bright blue eyes and she wore brightly coloured clothes. She was small and slight and energetic, and wilfully flippant. Quite early on Jenny asked her, "Are you the servant?" and Mrs. Sellers replied, cheerfully, "No, Love, the char."

"In Burma you would be a servant," Jenny stated.

"I dare say, Love, but this is Bloomsbury."

"Have you got a husband?"

"I'd better have, dear, with three kids and two misses."

"I have a husband too," Jenny told her.

"That a fact? You didn't lose much time, did you? Not that I was a fat lot older, but case of have to with me, worse luck. Where's your old man out there?"

Jenny looked puzzled.

"Excuse my French. Yer husband, ducks."

"Yes. He is there. But he is not old. He is only eighteen."

"Aren't you afraid he'll go off with another girl, with you so far away?"

"Oh no. But I want to go back. I don't like it here."

"They can't keep you if you want to go."

"I promised my father I would stay for a little while. He is lonely. I am all he has."

"I dare say. But you got your own life to live. Lonely my foot! He's got his sister, and if he was all that lonely he'd have married again. You take the gipsy's warning, my girl, and get back home to hubby—before it's too late!"

Jenny did not understand about the gipsy but she did gather that Mrs. Sellers was on her side, hers and Aung's, and she was the only one who was. If only a letter would come from Aung, but the weeks went by and there was nothing. Perhaps he had never had her letters. Perhaps the one he had written to her was lost in the post—letters often did get lost in Burma since the war, so people said.

At the end of a month, encouraged by Mrs. Sellers, she told her father, "I want to go home."

He was startled. He had hoped she was settling down. He had gathered that she had enjoyed the Kew outing, and by all accounts she got on with Mrs. Sellers; she was thawing out gradually, he had thought. And now this disappointing attack of homesickness.

"But you've only been here a few weeks," he pointed out. "Must I lose you for eight years only to find you for a few weeks? Listen, Jenny. When I was a prisoner with the Japs all that kept me alive was the thought that one day I would find you. I had lost everything—my wife, my son, my freedom, but one day, I thought, I might have my daughter. There was always the possibility you were still alive. When I was told you had been drowned with the others there seemed nothing left to live for."

"But you did live!"

He smiled, wrily.

"Living becomes a habit!" He reached out and took one of her hands as she stood beside him. "Jenny don't you remember anything of our old life together at Bokoko, when we were all together and happy—with Mummy and little Peter and Ganesh?"

"I remember, but I was a little girl then—a child, only."

"And now you think you're grown-up. If you go back to Tatkon what is your life going to be in ten years' time—twenty years' time—have you thought of that? Do you really want to live all your life in the house of a paddy farmer in a Burmese village? Your mother married me to get away from that life. Don't you think if she was here that she would say the same to you as I do? I am quite sure she would. Both she and her sister married Englishmen to get away from that wretched life. They neither of them regretted their marriages."

"How do you know? They did what their parents wanted, that was all."

"Your mother was happy. She was always singing and smiling. Don't you remember? Can't you feel your mother's spirit guiding you as to what is right to do?"

"If my mother was drowned in 1942 she must be eight years old in another life by now," Jenny said, doggedly.

Christopher gave up.

"You haven't given yourself a chance to get used to the life here yet," he insisted. "In a few months' time you will probably feel quite differently."

Jenny was silent. I am a prisoner here, she thought. Unless someone rescues me I shall never escape. She was thinking not of material rescue but of breaking out of the bondage slowly walling her round, enclosing her in an alien will.

II. DISTANCE AND SILENCE

AFTER that conversation with his daughter Christopher felt deeply depressed. It forced him to face the fact that the Kew visit about which he had been so pleased had been a success simply because Jenny had seen an exotic flower and some Eastern people. And that she got on with Mrs. Sellers because she was outside the family orbit—was not one of the enemy, as he and his sister were, despite all their efforts to create an atmosphere of affection and interest. He found it impossible not to speculate as to how it might have been had Ma Hla been alive—whether Jenny would still have longed to get back to her Burmese family. He had the feeling that the only difference it would have made would have been that Jenny would have had someone on her side in the matter, and he would have had the two of them against him.

The trouble, he thought, is that I was never close to her even when she was a little kid. It was always her mother who played games with her and told her stories—her mother and Ganesh. I was just the background. It was me she screamed for when she was in the river, but not because she loved me best but because I represented strength, protection, the power to save. Then she trusted her father implicitly. But I destroyed her trust. What else could I have done? She would never have agreed to come to England just for my sake. I was a stranger to her—as her mother wouldn't have been. There's supposed to be this special feeling between mothers and sons and fathers and daughters, but it doesn't always work out. Or it works out one-sidedly. Ma Hla kept Jenny close to her because she was lonely in her life with me. She thought I never knew all the Burmese tricks they got up to together as soon as my back was turned, like a couple of naughty children behind daddy's back! I told Ma Hla I'd beat her if she ever took Jenny to a pagoda or put a *longyi* on her. I probably would have too. Poor little Ma Hla. Poor little Jenny. But what am I to *do*, for God's sake? I might as well never have found her if this is the closest we're ever going to get. But how can I expect her to love me and trust me when I got her here on false pretences? If only I could make her see it's for her good. She isn't all Burmese; the English in her must come out. How can I possibly give her back to the life of being a Burmese peasant? Nothing wrong with being a Burmese peasant if you're born to it, but she wasn't. London isn't her world, but Tatkon isn't either. Tatkon can do nothing for her; London can do everything. It can educate her, develop her; then, if she wants to go back to Burma in a few years' time she'll go as an educated young woman—but she won't want to go back to Tatkon and settle down to a life of working in the paddy fields in the intervals of bearing children. I've *got* to keep her here! And I've got to find a way of coming close to her. . . .

His sister, he knew, had completely failed. It wasn't her fault. She had had plenty of experience with girls—tough girls some of them, girls with sexual experience, hard cases; but her own niece had proved the toughest of the lot, because she was tough in a different way, not hostile—it would have been easier if she had been, for hostility was something you could grapple with—but armoured in indifference. Our trouble, I suppose, he acknowledged, is that we can neither of us accept the fact that even though she is only fourteen she is no longer a little girl but a woman, preposterous as that seems. If that damned scoundrel of a boatman hadn't lied to me in 1946 and I'd been allowed to find her then, when she was only a child . . . but they didn't mean I should find her. It wasn't only Po Than, or whatever his blasted name is; he didn't lie to me on his own account; he'd been asked to; they didn't want to give her up, they never intended I should find her. . . .

He reminded himself of this each time he opened, read, and destroyed, one of Aung's letters to Jenny. The first arrived at the end of the first fortnight; he wrote in it of his loneliness, of his disappointment at not getting a letter from India, as she had half promised; he spoke of how long ago it seemed since they had parted on the airfield, and still further away their time together in Rangoon. The next letter, about a fortnight later, showed some anxiety at the continued absence of news, and through the head man he had made some inquiries as to whether the 'plane had reached Europe safely, and it seemed it had; he wondered, therefore, if her letter had gone astray. The third letter a few weeks later showed signs of mistrust; was life in London, with her English family, so fascinating that already she had forgotten those who had been mother and father, brothers and sisters, and husband to her in the little village of Tatkon? By now surely some of her letters, if she had written any, must have arrived.

That was better, Christopher thought; soon now, perhaps, the young man might begin to rebel against his neglectful runaway bride. With any luck he would soon write the kind of letter that could be handed to Jenny. In the meantime Jenny fretted and he sought continually for means to distract her.

He took advantage of some sunny days to introduce her to the London parks. She assumed that the Peter Pan statue in Kensington Gardens was some sort of *nat* shrine and examined it with interest; the winged figures round the base were certainly beings from the spirit world. But when her father explained the story to her, and that the winged creatures were fairies, inventions in whom no one believed, she lost interest; the whole

thing, evidently, had no meaning; it was not a myth, or a legend, and as
no one believed in it it seemed pointless to have made the image. In the
Palace she was interested in the costumes; English people, it would seem,
had always worn a lot of clothes. She liked watching the ducks in Hyde
Park, and was even more fascinated by the pelicans in St. James's Park.
The greenness of the lawns reminded her of the paddy fields when the
paddy was just springing.

She was puzzled by the trees being leafless in the cold weather; when
there was no hot sun to dry and wither them why should the leaves fall?
You would think they would stay green on the trees all the year round as
there was never any hot weather but only, her father said, weather that
was less cold. He explained about the seasons, adding that it was liable to
be cold and to rain at any season. Jenny found it all very confusing—and
unsatisfactory. Her father, however, said that variety and uncertainty had
a certain charm; months of continuous sun, followed by months of continuous rain, as in the tropics, he added, could be very monotonous. Jenny,
nevertheless, thought with nostalgia of the hot sunshine that could be
relied on for weeks and months on end; and the rainy season had its
compensations, for then it was a happy time in the house, with music
and singing to pass the time, and telling stories and playing games. Then
when the fine weather came again it was cool and beautiful, with the
bright sunshine and the wind coming along the river, and it did not begin
to be really hot until the New Year came, with the *thingyan-pwè*, the
beautiful water-festival. . . . She walked beside the Serpentine, and along
by the lake in St. James's Park, and thought of the river at Tatkon, with
the creeks so thickly covered with lotus leaves that you could not see the
water; and she thought of the lake outside Rangoon, with the thin woods
going down to the water and the golden pagoda on its hill in the distance,
the lights on it quivering like something seen through tears, and it was
all like something remembered from a previous life.

At the Tower of London she was fascinated by the Crown jewels. Jewellery was something she understood. "Mummy had some nice jewellery,"
her father told her. "I remember," she said. "It's probably all still there,"
her father went on, "stuck in the mud at the bottom of the river—unless,"
he added bitterly, "Po Than had the idea of salvaging it. There was a
necklace of Môgok rubies I gave your mother for a wedding present."
Jenny said again, "I remember. She had ear-rings and *eingyi* buttons all
to match the necklace. And another set that was all pearls. . . ." Father
and daughter gazed broodingly at the jewels in the great glass case, remembering. "I must get you some jewellery," he said, when they finally
turned away.

The historic aspect of the Tower did not interest her, and she was
sorry the great ravens had their wings clipped—her father said—so that

they could not fly away. She wondered what bad *karma* they had made in a previous existence to be so held captive now—like the brave golden flower in the glass-house at Kew Gardens.

On the way home they reached the Tower Bridge just as it was being raised. Jenny was amazed at the sight of the road rising into mid-air, and childishly amused at the spectacle of a deposit of horse-dung rolling down the slope, but when it was all over she returned to the subject of the wonderful jewels.

For the first time her father saw her animated and excited. I can come close to her, he thought, eagerly, it's just a matter of finding out what interests her. I'll get her some jewellery. And she ought to have some prettier clothes—these things Jennifer got her are too plain. Perhaps we could go shopping together . . . He suddenly saw himself in the role of indulgent father, with adoring daughter. A dry old stick like me, he thought, the traditional sun-dried sahib. But I'm not all that old, dammit. Sixty's not old nowadays, and this young thing is my daughter, and why shouldn't I indulge my paternal instincts? And if she really would come close to me there's nothing in the world I wouldn't do for her. Nothing. . . . Except return her to the life of a Burmese peasant. But if she came close to me she wouldn't want that. Just for ten years. Perhaps less. I won't make old bones. Too many years in the East. And that last lap with the Japs didn't help. In ten years' time she'll still be only twenty-five and by then a nice young Englishman may have loomed up and I can fold my paternal hands and depart in peace. . . .

Following up her interest in the Crown jewels at the Tower he took her shortly after to the Indian section of the Victoria and Albert Museum, and to the Oriental department of the British Museum. He realized that he was what his sister called pandering to the Oriental in her by taking her to see images of Indian deities and the Buddha, but told himself—and Jennifer—that it didn't matter, that after all everyone who had ever known the East at all intimately became interested in its art and religions. He urged that if the Oriental in her was allowed expression she would the sooner adjust to the impact of the West, because she would cease to be on the defensive; then might not the Occidental, which was also part of her but which had lain dormant for eight years, gradually come to the surface? Miss Finching, who had never been to the East and was fond of asserting that she had no wish to go—'all those Benares tables and joss-sticks', she would assert, distastefully—was sceptic. She believed in a strict policy of suppression; only so, she was convinced, was re-education along Western and Christian lines to be achieved.

Christopher, however, was innerly convinced of the necessity for wooing his daughter. He had somehow to convince her that he was on her side—*malgré tout*. He watched her eagerly when they entered the Indian section of the Victoria and Albert Museum, and as he had half expected she exclaimed immediately upon the headless Buddha near the door. He realized that she had not been expecting to see Buddha images. She mistook the Jaina shrine at the top of the steps for a Buddha shrine. She listened with interest when he told her about Mahavera who had lived and taught at the same time as the Buddha. He had the feeling as he talked that he was re-establishing himself in her eyes as the source of knowledge he had once been for her. They paused in front of the figure of Hanuman, and he found that she knew from Ganesh about the monkey-god. Then she spotted the little Ganesha figure in a glass case near by and excitedly drew his attention to it. They gazed up together at the ornately carved teak façade of an old Indian house, and the East stirred to life for both of them, for him with the smell of joss-sticks and spices and horse-dung and the bazaars that is the smell of Bombay, for her the smell of dust and flowers and warm bamboo which is the smell of a Burmese village. He led her across to a gilded copper figure of Avalokitesvara, that profoundly mystical being, exquisitely graceful, golden as the sun, and garlanded with jewels, the glorious one who is to be the thousandth and last Buddha. Jenny gazed enraptured and Finching raked about in his rag-bag of knowledge of the Eastern gods and remembered Avalokita in connection with supreme compassion for all things in the living world—there was an association, too, with Siva, but that, he felt, was too difficult for someone who knew nothing of Hinduism; the deity was better kept within the Buddhist context . . . which made it easy to pass to the golden figure of Tara, turquoise-jewelled and lotus-bearing, madonna of mercy.

"The Tibetan Buddhists think very highly of her," Jenny heard her father saying, but she was lost in a lotus dream of beauty. It did not matter who she was, this golden being for whom the lotus reached from her feet to the crown of her gentle head, yet her very name was beautiful—Tara, green Tara, for Jenny the incarnation of all that the lotus symbolized, the tropical day's brightness, the thin music of the pagoda's crown of little bells, and an inner stillness like a flame burning in a windless place. . . .

After that even the sun god, Surya, riding in his seven-horsed chariot with his queen of the morning, gained no more than a glance from her, but a gilt bronzed figure of Shiva astride the sacred bull startled her again with beauty, so that she turned from the glass case with her eyes alight with pleasure and caught at her father's arm, exclaiming, "Oh, Daddy! Look!"

He could almost have wept with joy—and gratitude. It was the first time she had spontaneously addressed him like that. He put an arm round her shoulder and saw the shining figure with her own eager eyes.

"Yes, darling. It's beautiful," he murmured. It was progress, he thought, with a kind of painful happiness. He, too, had to be rehabilitated—he could acknowledge the fact now, freely, and with humility—in the inner world of her affections.

She looked with interest at some puppets in bright gold-bordered silks. Puppets were something she understood from the *pwès*, though she had never seen any so richly dressed. She wished that Aung could see them, and sadness touched her briefly, then her gaze wandered to a shoulder-belt of looped golden chains with jewelled buckles, and again she exclaimed with excited delight. Gold was so beautiful; it belonged to Buddhism; the golden *hti* hung with golden bells that crowned the pagoda, the golden Buddha image gleaming in the golden light of innumerable candles, and the Shwe Dagon Paya that was all of gold . . . but that was a thought that led back to Aung. She turned away from the golden splendour.

"Let us go and look at the funny little monkey-god again," she said. Not Tara, for she too, with the tall lotus at her side, led back to Aung. Hanuman led back to Ganesh and Bokoko and the old life.

"Tell me about him," she commanded, when they stood again beside the little figure.

"You know about him," he said. "Ganesh told you."

"It is a nice story, about Rama and Sita. I like to hear it."

He smiled. "Once upon a time——" he began.

She interrupted him. "That is how all the Jataka stories begin."

"It is how all the best stories begin," he assured her.

As they walked away together he told her the story of how Sita was abducted by the wicked demon in disguise and how after many adventures and hazards Rama found her with the assistance of Hanuman and his monkey hordes. How Hanuman could jump higher than any of the monkeys and leapt a mountain and a sea.

Jenny smiled dreamily, remembering, and when he had finished she gave him the supreme praise: "You tell it better than Ganesh used to."

"You were only a little girl then. Perhaps you understand it better now."

But it was too near the bone, he thought, this story of the abduction of Sita, and he switched to Vishnu, who was the Buddha in his ninth incarnation, "Though," he added, smiling, "we are not obliged to believe that."

He was happy because he had her attention; because she asked him questions and accepted his replies. For the first time, it seemed to him, there was real communication between them. From time to time he looked at her as she walked by his side up the wide Exhibition Road from the Museum and into the wintry park; she was so very much, he thought, a Westernized version of the little Ma Hla—who also had accepted him as the fount of all knowledge.

"We had a good day, didn't we?" he had sufficient confidence to suggest to her when they got home, and had the satisfaction of seeing her smile, happily, and receiving her dreamy answer, "Oh yes—it was lovely——"

Throughout the evening meal she talked animatedly of the things they had seen, and he was glad Jennifer was away at her girls' club for the evening; he had the feeling that what was in the process of being established between himself and his daughter was as yet so tenuous that the intrusion of a third person at that point would have broken the spell. My luck is in at last, he thought, jubilantly.

When they had carried their supper things through to the kitchen, stacking them neatly for the attention of Mrs. Sellers in the morning, he went to the bookshelves and got out volume after volume of works which contained pictures of Eastern art. Then he unlocked a cedar-wood chest and brought out a very precious book with hand-coloured plates of the thirty-seven *nats* of Burma. Whilst they had been looking at the books on Eastern art together he had debated with himself as to whether he should show her this remarkable work, since she had to be weaned from animism, but the impulse to please her, to continue in her favour, was too strong.

"Now I have something very wonderful to show you," he announced. "There are not many copies of this book in existence."

When he opened the huge volume on the table she gave a little gasp of wonder. The *nats*, in all their terror and splendour. Several times as he slowly turned the great pages she shivered. To see pictures of them all like that . . . It suddenly came to her that books were very wonderful things.

Watching her absorbed in this wonder he realized his first real victory. He was glad that she elected to go to bed before his sister came in. The spell must not be broken. O God in Heaven, his spirit besought, in an agony that was prayer, don't let the spell be broken. Let us be close to each other. For the few years that remain.

Jenny lay in bed looking at the candle wavering dimly near the door, and listening to her father's movements in the sitting-room across the passage—the squirt of the soda syphon, the knocking of his pipe against the hearth, the low burr of his voice when he addressed the cat. He was the enemy, yet somehow no longer the enemy. In the presence of Tara and Avalokita they had been friends; and afterwards, telling the story of Rama and Sita, and looking at books—kingdoms of the mind opening to her, filling her with the desire to read, to explore those kingdoms. Only Aung should be sharing it all with her, all the strange new experiences that laid siege to both mind and body. How could they go on living without each other like this? And why did no letters come, day after day, week after week? Daddy was kind; he wanted that they should be friends, he wanted that she should be happy, but he also wanted that she should forget Aung and Burma, and I can't, she thought, wildly, I don't want to;

I want to go home . . . and once again she turned on her face in the ghostly aloneness of the night smothering her weeping in the pillow.

In the morning, as always, hope rose in her again. I must be patient, she thought. One day, soon, all this English life will seem like a dream, and I will be back in Tatkon telling them all about it, and helping Mé-Mé clean the rice, and working in the fields with them, going to the bazaar, going to the creek with Aung to get the lotus flowers for the Kason Full Moon Day, bathing in the river with Mé-Mé, drying our hair in the sun— the strong hot sun that ripens the mangoes and makes the tall flame-of-the-forest trees shed their blossoms. And then the rains, with the happy time in the house, with music and singing and telling stories, and making baskets, and the lovely time when the rain is over and the cool wind comes up the river, and the festival of lights, and when it's all over, when it's daylight and everyone goes home, Aung and I creeping into our corner, so very tired, so very happy. . . . It will all come again. I must be patient. And while I am here I will try to learn. . . .

She went back to the bookshelves, pulling out some of the volumes of the night before. I will learn to read and write English, she determined, but not with Aunt Jennifer; Daddy shall teach me—and when I go back I will teach Aung.

Her father left for his club, and her aunt for the mystery known as 'my girls.' When Mrs. Sellers arrived she found her sitting on the floor surrounded by volumes.

She observed, plugging in the vacuum cleaner, "Good thing yer auntie's not here to catch you squatting on the floor like a blooming 'eathen!"

"What's a blooming 'eathen?" Jenny inquired, interested.

"Oh Lord, aren't you a igger-*a*-mus! Them as don't know nothing about Almighty Gawd! Them as worships idols. *Them's* 'eathens.'"

She began to sing:

> *"The 'eathen in 'is blindness*
> *Bows down to wood and stone——"*

Jenny informed her, "I was in a Christian temple the other day with my aunt and a lot of the people bowed down as they passed the shrine. It was a big temple called Westminster Abbey."

"Aren't you a one? It's not a temple, dear, but a church. Christians have churches, Jews have synagogues, Indians have temples——"

"Only if they're Hindus," Jenny interrupted her. "If they're Moslems they have mosques."

"Who's giving the lesson, me or you? Go on, Miss Knowall, tell the class what they have in Burma."

"Pagodas, of course."

"Like the one at Kew."

"Not at all like the one at Kew."

"Here endeth the first lesson. I'll have to ask you to put all them books back, Love, I got to give this room a turnout. Come on, I'll give you a hand! Oh Lord, look at the dust! Nasty dirty things, books."

"I think they're exciting. I never understood about books before. I always thought they were just for lessons."

She stood up, brushing the dust from her skirt, and went over to the window.

"Why don't you go for a little walk till I've done the room?" Mrs. Sellers suggested. "It's a lovely day—cold, mind you, but it's nice in the sun. Do you good to get out."

"I've never been out by myself," Jenny said. "Never in my life."

"Crikey! Talk about a sheltered life! Treat yourself to a new experience and go for a toddle now, for half an hour. There has to be a first time for everything."

"I wouldn't know where to go——"

"Just walk yourself round the square. Good Lord, I only wish I could get a thrill as easy!"

She switched on the vacuum-cleaner and began roaring round the room. Jenny was glad to escape into her bedroom, where Royal lay curled up in the middle of her bed—which Miss Finching strictly forbade, but which was nevertheless a frequent occurrence and one encouraged by Jenny.

Jenny leaned over the bed and laid a cheek against the cat's warm flank.

"Darling Roy, I love you! I want to go for a walk, but I'm afraid. You always go out alone. Is it as frightening as I think it is?"

Royal stretched his forelegs, luxuriously, expanding his toes, and yawned.

"There has to be a first time for everything," he told Jenny. "The first time you kiss someone, the first time you open a book, the first time you go for a walk alone. Be off with you. You know it's my day for sleeping on your bed."

That's true, Jenny thought, there has to be a first time for everything. She opened the wardrobe and took out her red coat. In her aunt's absence she did not take the hat. She went down the stairs and across the narrow hall and opened the front door and stepped out into the pillared porch.

The square was completely empty of people. She hesitated, shivering apprehensively, like a swimmer about to plunge into cold water, then, suddenly, Royal was beside her, rubbing against her legs.

"Why, Royal——"

She bent down to stroke the golden head and the front door slammed.

"Now we're shut out! Will you sit here and wait for me, beautiful Roy? Then I will feel braver."

She went down the steps. The cat sat down on the top step and began washing, energetically.

Jenny went on past the houses, all identical with their pillared porches. At the end of the row she turned into a side street, with the feeling that to walk round three more sides of the square would be futile. The side street was a great deal more interesting, with shops of different kinds. There was a bookshop, a teashop with cakes in the window, a shop that sold furniture, and then, astonishingly, a Buddha shrine . . .

There was no doubt about it. There was the great gold Buddha image, seated in the lotus position, and at either side of him small gilded figures of *devas*. She gazed enraptured, but puzzled by the absence of any flowers, candles, bowls of water. Her eyes filled with tears. The beautiful Lord Buddha; but in this cold grey country no one cared, so there were no flowers, no offerings of rice and fruits, no water in remembrance of the time when the Blessed One walked the earth with his monks and thirsted in the heat of the day. She clasped her hands together and repeated the Threefold Refuge in English: *I go for refuge to the Lord Buddha; I go for refuge to the Dhamma; I go for refuge to the Sangha . . .*

Then she retraced her steps to the square, walking slowly, troubled because there was a shrine but no way of worshipping at it, and because across the vast distance and through the long silence the old life rose round her like engulfing waters.

She did not speak to anyone about the Buddha image; it was her secret, but three mornings a week, when Mrs. Sellers came, she went for a walk, always with a flower from one of the vases—a daffodil, or a tulip, or a spray of mimosa, once a few violets stolen from a vase on her aunt's dressing-table—which she would conceal inside her coat. She would stand in front of the shop window secretly saying her devotions, and when no one was looking would lay her offering on the window ledge, before the Buddha's impassive gaze.

She felt both happy and sad after these visits, which she made even in the rain. On the wet days she would make the excuse to Mrs. Sellers that she wanted to go out to post a letter. After the third visit she asked her father for an airmail letter so that she could write to Aung; she had thought she would like to tell him about the shrine, and that she was still waiting and longing for a letter from him, but though her father gave her the blue sheet she did not write the letter. She had no heart for it; it seemed somehow useless—like writing a letter and throwing it out of an aeroplane.

Christopher watched her, anxiously, aware of a relapse in her process of adjustment. He took her to Liberty's and bought her an Indian silk scarf, exquisite in its softness and delicacy of colouring. He bought her a turquoise and silver necklace and ear-rings. In Bond Street he bought her a small Buddha image beautifully carved in ivory. His sister, he knew, would disapprove of the image, but more important now than weaning her from Buddhism and converting her to Christianity was the securing of her happiness. He was even ready to sacrifice her conversion to Christianity if he could bring her close to him and keep her close, though this he did not admit to his sister. To her he excused the image on the grounds that by opposing her in the ideas in which she had unfortunately been brought up they would only drive her further into them. To which Jennifer retorted that there was nevertheless no need to encourage those ideas.

"You're spoiling her," she asserted.

He told her, recklessly, like a young man in love, "I don't care, so long as I can make her forget the last eight years!"

Jennifer knew her brother too well to be deceived. She knew that what he meant was that he would sacrifice any principle to gain his daughter's love. She loved him too much to oppose him. Whatever he did she would be on his side—as he had always been on hers. Nevertheless she regretted that in his hunger for his child's love he was prepared to lay aside her rehabilitation as a Christian. His confiscation of the correspondence she regarded as completely justified and was quick to reassure his occasional twinges of conscience where this was concerned.

"If she were still at school, as she ought to be, you wouldn't hesitate to intercept any letters from any undesirable youth—you would quite rightly feel it your duty to protect her. It is just as much your duty to protect her now."

It was the argument Finching used to himself, and when he felt that he was making headway with Jenny he could believe that his conduct was completely justified; at other times he would be assailed by an uneasiness that was closely allied to guilt—except that he did not admit such a word to his consciousness. He had been driven into lying and deceiving because he had been lied to and deceived—tragically. He had always declared that he hated a liar; he still did—he hated Po Than.

It puzzled him that Jenny did not write the letter after asking for the form. Several times he asked her, "Don't you want to write your letter?"

"I don't know," she told him each time; and once, "It feels like writing to someone I knew in a former life," a statement which greatly heartened him.

It heartened him, too, when she expressed a desire to learn to read and write in English, but he did not follow this up. He could not afford to run the risk of her one day addressing a letter to Burma. So long as she had to hand to him for addressing any letters she might write he was safe. As soon as it was safe for her to be able to write English nothing would give him greater pleasure than to teach her. In the meantime he continued to take her about. He took her to see the ballet at Covent Garden, and though the music meant nothing to her the dancing, the costumes, the scenery, fascinated her. He took her to Trafalgar Square, where they fed the pigeons. A street photographer took a picture of her laughing when a pigeon fed from her hand. He sent for the picture and it was as successful as he had thought it might be. He carried it in his wallet and showed it, proudly, to friends at the club. He ordered some more copies and had one sent to his sisters, for in it Jenny looked, he thought, 'very English'.

Jenny looked at it for a long time when he first showed it to her and it seemed to her like looking at the picture of a stranger. At Tatkon, she thought, sadly, they would never recognize it as a picture of Mālā. But then, of course, it wasn't Mālā; it was Jenny Finching.

As it turned out it proved to be a very useful picture, for shortly after it was taken Finching had a letter from Maung Than asking for news of 'our little Mālā'. He had been asked to write by Maung Ba Tu's family, who had been deeply hurt at receiving no news. As head man he felt responsible for a young girl leaving the village to go so far away, even in the company of her father. Maung Aung had written several times but had received no reply. One letter might have gone astray, perhaps, but scarcely all three.

Christopher replied by return. He wrote cordially that he was sorry that the family had been distressed, and he greatly regretted that his daughter had not written, but the truth was that industriously pursuing her English studies as she was, and absorbed in her new life, she had very little time. That she was well and happy they would all see from the enclosed photograph. She was out at the moment, but when she came in he would ask her if she wished to enclose a few lines of her own. . . .

He sent the letter by registered air-mail. He received no direct reply to it, but a fortnight later another letter came from Aung to Jenny; hitherto his letters had been addressed to Ma Mālā, 'care of Mr. Finching'; this one came addressed to Miss Jenny Finching, though in it he addressed her as Mālā. He wrote, briefly, that as she was clearly so absorbed in her English life, and happy in it, he shared his family's sad conclusion that they had all better regard her Burmese life as a story that had come to an end. For his part he was tired of being married yet not married, and with the approval of his family and Maung Than he was shortly taking another wife.

There was reference neither to past happiness nor to present sorrow. It was, Christopher knew, quite simply a divorce. He read it to Jennifer before passing it to Jenny.

His sister asked, anxiously, "Will she be very upset, do you think?"

"I don't know. I don't think I know much about what goes on in her—I wish I did."

He took the letter into the sitting-room where Jenny sat on the rug in front of the fire stroking the cat with one hand and turning the pages of *Hindu Religion, Customs and Manners* with the other; it was a book she never tired of; she liked it for its pictures of the deities of the Hindu pantheon, and for one in particular—the Buddha as the ninth incarnation of Vishnu. She looked up as her father entered and saw the blue airmail letter in his hand.

"This came for you," he said, "but I'm afraid I opened it by mistake. It's as well I did—it's bad news."

"It's from Aung," she said, and he heard the dread in her voice.

"Yes, from Aung." He hesitated a moment, then added "It's all finished, Jenny."

He held the letter out to her. She took it from him and he watched her whilst she read it. She went on staring at the blue sheet of paper a long time after she had taken in the sense of the words; the curly Burmese script stared back at her. *Taking another wife. . . .*

She said, without raising her head, almost in a whisper, "It was not in our *karma* we should be happy. For me nothing is safe, nothing lasts."

She buried her face in her hands and wept, silently.

He went over to her and knelt down beside her and put his arms round her.

"You've got me to love and care for you," he urged. "You've got your old daddy. I'm safe enough. You won't find me fading out on you."

She did not turn to him as he had hoped. Her body remained rigid, her hands pressed to her face in an effort to stem the tears.

"It's always been like this, whenever I've loved anyone they were always taken away—Mummy, Shwe-Shwe, Aung. . . ."

She got up and dropped the letter on to the fire.

"Shall you write to him?" he asked.

"What is the use when he doesn't get my letters? Besides, what is there to say? He never wanted me to go. He does not want to wait. He cannot believe in me any more. He is right—all that life is a story that has come to an end."

"Can you believe it's for the best?"

"It isn't for good or for bad. It just *is*. The Buddha taught us that life is suffering."

She picked up the book and replaced it on the shelf.

"The English story might be a happy one—as it develops," he suggested.

"I can never forget Aung, or Tatkon." Her voice was low and unsteady, but the face she turned to him was curiously expressionless.

"I should like to go to bed," she added. "If you and Auntie would not mind."

"Yes, of course." He opened the door for her. "You won't be unhappy?"

She made no answer because she had none to make. How does one know what one is going to be, when every moment of living is change?

She lay a long time staring at the candles and listening to the sounds in the flat; the murmur of her father's and her aunt's voice—discussing me, she thought, being glad that my Burmese life is finished. No, she thought, with a sudden spurt of anger, not so easily; we make our own *karma*. . . .

She got out of bed and pulled on her dressing-gown and went barefoot out of the room and across the narrow passage into the sitting-room. Her aunt sat at a desk writing letters, her back to the room. Her father sat by the fire, a small table with the whisky decanter and a syphon beside him. He had been reading a paper but he held it discarded between his knees and was gazing into the fire. He looked up as she entered.

"I have decided to fly back to Burma to see my family," she announced.

Miss Finching turned in her seat.

"No shoes on," she observed. "You will catch cold. What is all this about flying to Burma?"

"I am going to the Embassy to ask them to send me home."

"Come and sit by the fire," her father said. "Don't stand there in the draught."

She went across to the fire and sat in the armchair opposite him.

"I have been thinking. I must go back and find out what is happening. If I see Aung everything will be all right—I am sure of it. It is only because he hasn't had my letters."

"I thought you realized the Burma story was finished."

"I have now recovered from the shock," she told him, in her grave child-adult way. "I have decided I must go back. It is the only way."

"I never heard such nonsense," Miss Finching declared.

"Jenny," her father said, carefully patient, "the Burmese Embassy will not help you. I have gone into this matter. You are a Burmese subject only in Burma. Here you are not only British but you are a minor—that is to say you are under twenty-one and therefore subject to me, your father." He put out a hand and laid it on her knee. "Be a sensible girl," he pleaded. "Even if I were willing to let you go back, which I am not, and if I had the fare to give you, which I haven't, what would be the good of it? What sort of life could you have there, with poor people, in a remote Burmese village?"

"I was happy," she insisted. "We were poor but we always had enough to eat, till the Japanese came—and even then we didn't starve. Afterwards things were better and we were all happy again. We didn't have things—books and furniture and all the things you have here, but we were happy. I am not happy here. I am lonely. I don't belong here. I am in prison here. I want to go home."

"What you want, my girl," said her aunt, "is a good spanking. I never heard such ingratitude."

Christopher gave his sister a quick beseeching look.

"I think Jenny and I had better have a talk about all this," he said.

Miss Finching gathered her correspondence together and closed her lettercase with a snap.

"I'll go and get supper. Perhaps Jenny will join us after all?"

Jenny shook her head. "No," she said. "I couldn't eat."

Christopher had the feeling of all the ground he had gained recently slipping away from him. Now he was uncertain whether to adopt a firm line or an appeal to reason and sentiment.

He said, when they were alone, feeling his way, "You see, Jenny, it's out of the question for you to return to Burma."

"I was to have gone back some time."

"I always hoped you wouldn't want to. Now it's impossible—don't you see? Aung is going to marry another girl."

"He won't if I go back. That is why I must go at once—tomorrow—the day after. Quickly."

"I tell you it's quite impossible. Even if I were willing I haven't the money—not even for you to go by boat, let alone fly."

"You got me here knowing you couldn't raise the money to send me back?"

"I got you here in the belief that once you were here you wouldn't want to go back. These Burmese peasants—how can they mean anything to you? They were kind to you and became fond of you, but they are not related to you. Do I have to remind you that I am?"

"Aung is related to me. He is my husband."

"That marriage is only valid in Burma. Here it doesn't exist—legally, religiously, morally, or in any way at all. You must believe me, Jenny. I have been into all this very thoroughly."

"Why should I believe you? You lied to me to get me here."

"I had to get you here—I had to rescue you. But what I am telling you is true. You have what is called dual nationality, and it is the British one which counts here and you are not therefore entitled to any protection from the Burmese. But you have your father's protection—the protection of the one person in the world who really cares about you, who has your interests really at heart. Good God, Jenny, you are part of me—don't you realize it?"

"I realize," Jenny said slowly, getting up, "that I am trapped. I should never have listened to you when you came to Tatkon."

He watched her cross the room to the door. He wanted to say something to stop her, to bring her back, but there was nothing to say. She opened the door and went out and he heard the door of her own room close.

I've lost her, he thought, despairingly. Now we are both alone, in our separate prisons.

Jennifer came back into the room.

"Supper's ready," she announced, brightly; then, glancing round, "Jenny's gone back to bed? Did you make her see sense?"

He said, heavily, "I made her see that she is my prisoner."

"Really, Christopher——"

He rose, folding his paper. "Let's eat," he said, curtly.

III. VERNON

IN the morning Christopher regarded his daughter anxiously. She was shadowy-eyed and pale but, he thought, composed. Something had to be said, something which would bring her close to him, but he did not know what. Finally he said, aware of the clumsiness of his words, "I hope you aren't feeling too badly about everything?"

She answered, calmly, "I lay awake in the night thinking of all the lies that had been told—the lies Shwe-Shwe asked Po Than to tell when you came to Burma after the war, and the lies Po Than did tell, and the lies *you* told. I thought of all the bad *karma* being made. I thought of the bad *karma* I made when I wished a strong bad wish about Maung Than's sister, so that she wouldn't marry Maung Shwe. But she did marry him, and all I did was make her my enemy. I thought of all the lies and bad thoughts hopping about in our lives like devils in their fiery hell. I thought how they would all go on hopping about until all the badness was used up."

He permitted himself a thin smile.

"Don't you think it is all used up now?"

She shook her head in her grave way—the grown-up way that made her seem more little-girl than ever, he thought.

"We are all unhappy, so how can it be?"

"Maung Aung is going to marry again—is that unhappiness?"

"He is angry and hurt and bitter."

"He will be happy again, and so will you. You have youth on your side."

"I think old people are happier. They don't fall in love."

She stood looking out of the window into the grey square. To be calm and quiet in everything was not easy. You could behave calmly, but inside yourself the devils went on hopping—painfully. And it was bad to feel grief, for grief was attachment, and by attachment, the Lord Buddha taught, are we bound to continual rebirth . . . If there were only a pagoda to go to, to sit at the feet of the Great Image, taking refuge in his peace. . . .

She heard her father saying, "What would you like to do today? I think the sun will break through presently. Perhaps you would like to go to the zoo—you haven't been there yet."

"I don't know what it is."

"It's a big park, like Hyde Park, with gardens, and animals of all kinds from all parts of the world—in cages, of course. Houses specially built for them, that is to say, with bars, so that they can't escape."

"Prisons," said Jenny. "I wouldn't like to see animals in prison. They must miss the forests and jungles, and the beautiful hot sun—and being free." She sighed. "I miss it all so much myself. I feel like one of those animals."

"I'm sorry you feel like that. Is there anywhere you would like to go—apart," he added bitterly, "from back to Burma?"

"Perhaps I will go to that big museum you took me to—the one with the steps and the tall pillars, like a temple. It's quite close to here—I saw it the other day when I was out with auntie."

"The British Museum. Yes, you could go there by yourself, I suppose. It's good for you to get used to going about on your own. I'm off to the club—we might walk part of the way together."

He said, as they crossed the square, "I must get you started on English reading and writing lessons. Then you can read books instead of just looking at them."

"I'd like that. I would like to be able to read books. Have you got a book of the Jataka tales?"

"No. But I expect we could get hold of a copy. When you can read I'll try for one."

He left her at the corner of Museum Street.

"You all right now?"

"Yes-thank-you."

"Have a nice time. No need to confine yourself to the Eastern section, you know, plenty of other interesting things——"

He watched her cross the road and pass in through the great gates, then turned back down Museum Street in search of a 'bus for the West End.

Jenny did not go into the Museum. She waited a few moments then retraced her steps out through the gates and across the road. The formula of the Three-fold Refuge was running in her head, as it had been running continuously since the anguish of that moment in which she had realized that Aung had divorced her. She longed for a shrine before which to kneel in contemplation of the Three Jewels, the Buddha, the *Dhamma* and the *Sangha*. The Pali formula repeated itself in her mind: *Buddham saranam gacchami; Dhammam saranam gacchami; Sangham saranam gacchami* . . .

She found her way back to the 'shrine'. But the Buddha image was gone. The place where it had stood was now occupied by a large Chinese bowl embossed with dragons. Jenny stared, incredulous and baffled. How could a whole shrine disappear like that? She went to the door and peered in—and then to her relief saw the Buddha image. She pushed open the door and entered the Oriental Bookshop. There was the familiar smell of joss-sticks. She approached the image, and as she did so a tall figure ad-

vanced from the dimness beyond. The thin figure of a youngish man. They
recognized each other instantly.

"You remember me, Jenny?" Vernon said.

She continued to stare at him for a long moment before answering.

"I remember you. You are Mr. Vernon."

"Did you know this was my shop?"

"I didn't know it was a shop. I saw the Buddha image and thought it was
a shrine."

"It was you, then, who left the flowers on the window-ledge?"

"You found them?"

"I only got back two days ago. My partner told me. It was my idea to
take the image out of the window—I thought then that whoever had
brought the flowers would come in to inquire for it."

"It was a trick. Like telling my father where I was."

"A trick? Wasn't it right and natural to let your father know?"

"It would have been right and natural to come and tell me who you
were and ask me about letting my father know. Then I would have told
you I didn't want him to know. That I was happy as I was."

"I was going to do that, but I was told it would frighten you away. And
I was asked not to say who had told me where you were."

"I know who it was. It was Maung Shwe's wife—my husband's brother's
wife, Ma Hla. Maung Shwe never wanted me to go, but she always wanted
it. I made a bad wish, but the wish turned against me and she became my
enemy. Through her harm came to me. I made bad *karma*."

He saw the unhappiness in her face, and self-reproach made him part
of it. He said, despairingly, "Was it such a bad thing that your father
should find you and bring you to England? Did you want to spend the rest
of your life with peasants in a Burmese village?"

"I had everything I wanted. I had a husband, a mother, brothers and
sisters. We worked in the fields, and sang songs, and there were pagoda
festivals. We were happy. Here there is nothing."

"You have your father. He loves you."

"He got me here by a trick. He told me I was coming here to see my
mother. Then just before we got here he told me she was drowned when
the ferry overturned at the river-crossing. How can I love him after that?"

"People sometimes manage to forgive each other. Look, I have a room
upstairs. If you will come up we can sit and talk properly——"

"There's no more to say."

"There's everything to say. Jenny—please! I have to go and see your
father. It's important I should talk to you first. I don't want to do you any
more harm. I never realized what I was doing to you. I invariably do the
wrong thing . . . Please let us talk. I might be able to help you now—
truly I might——"

He opened a door at the back of the shop and she saw a flight of stairs.

"If you'll go up," he urged, "I'll just tell them in the office in case anyone comes into the shop——"

She went slowly up the stairs. Half way there was a deep window overlooking walled gardens. There was a tall bare tree with down-drooping branches. She stood looking into it absently waiting for him.

He came up and they went on up to the first floor where he opened a white door. She came into a white panelled room with a great many books.

"Let me take your coat," he said. "It's warm in here."

He took her coat and indicated a low chair beside the fire. He carried the coat to a divan at the other end of the room and came back and seated himself in an armchair opposite her. He was both excited and nervous. There seemed suddenly so much to explain.

"I don't know where to begin," he said. "I wanted to do your father a good turn to make up—for not waiting at the river. It all goes back to the river."

That was true, Jenny thought. Everything went back to the river. One life ended there and another began. But not for her mother or the little child Peter, or for old Husain. For them everything of this existence ended at the river. Now they were all eight years old in their new lives.

She said after a long pause, "If you had waited you would have gone on to the ferry with us, and you might not be here now."

"Being here now was nothing much until today—now suddenly it's important I should be here, so that I can help you. Now it all has purpose and meaning."

He was quite extraordinarily excited, and she was aware of it.

He took out a cigarette case and extracted a cigarette with nervously clumsy fingers. I'm all to bits, he thought. It's a strange feeling facing the result of your action, face to face with the life you were responsible for changing so drastically.

She asked, puzzled, "How can you help me?"

"I don't know yet. It has to be revealed. I feel it will be. In the meantime perhaps just being your friend will help you."

"My father tries to be my friend. He takes me everywhere. He is kind. Sometimes I even forget that he is the enemy. But it doesn't help. I am still lonely."

"He isn't really your enemy. He loves you. You mean everything to him. He has no one but you."

"To get me he spoiled my life." She stated it simply, without bitterness.

"Listen, Jenny. You married your first love——"

She interrupted him. "My second love. Maung Shwe was my first love.

He saved me from the river and was everything to me, but I was only a child, then, and he didn't wait for me. He married Ma Hla—the one who betrayed me."

"All right, then, you married your second love, but do you really imagine, at fourteen, that that's the beginning and end of love for you?"

"In Burma young girls marry and they never love anyone else all their lives. They are quite happy. I think I would have been like that, too. Life was very simple, but we were all happy. Here life is complicated, and I don't think people are very happy. Are you happy?"

He was startled by the sudden childish candour of her eyes searching his face.

"Me? No, not particularly. Like you I am lonely. I have no one I particularly care about or who cares about me."

"You have no family?"

"I have parents. They went to Kenya when India became independent."

"Where is that?"

"Kenya? It's in Africa. Have you ever seen a map of the world?"

"Aung showed me one once, but I never knew which was land and which was sea."

"I'll show you."

He got up and pulled an atlas globe out from a bookshelf and stood it on a table in the window.

"Come and look. It's as well to know something about the planet on which you live. You know I suppose that the world is round?"

"Like the sun and moon?"

"And the stars. But we'll deal with them later."

She stood beside him whilst he turned the globe pointing out Burma, India, Europe, England, Africa. The sea was painted blue and this time she was not confused. She began to be interested, moving the globe, discovering places. He produced a large-scale relief map of Burma and traced for her the route by which they had planned to cross into India. She saw the mountains and the valley and the fine thread of the river. He showed her Bokoko and Mynmyo and Tatkon, and, when she asked him, Rangoon. Then she turned back to the globe to see how they had flown across the world to Europe, to Amsterdam and to London. She began to understand about flying away from or into the sun, and the six hours difference in time.

"But if you went the other way round," he said, "Westward, to America——"

He turned the globe and began explaining about the earth moving round the sun. Then he got out a book with maps of the firmament.

"Our world, you see, is really very small."

She regarded the chart, wonderingly.

"Aung used to explain about the stars. Jupiter is my star because I was born on a Thursday, and my symbol is the rat——"

"That is something different—superstition——"

"In Burma," she told him, simply, "we believe in it. Aung is not superstitious. He does not believe in *nats* and ghosts, but he believes in the stars. Perhaps our stars have something to do with our being separated so soon in our marriage."

Derek offered no comment. It was one of the many things upon which he had no settled views. He turned a page and they looked together at a photograph of the moon, showing mountain ranges and craters.

"There are mountains on the moon?" Her eyes were alight with wonder. He found himself wondering what she knew, this child who knew so little of what is called general information. There were things she knew of which he knew nothing—this he recognized; love, she knew, romantic and physical; and the suffering that is an inescapable part of it.

"Yes, there are mountains on the moon. It is even thought that one day human beings will land on the moon."

She sighed. "There is so much I don't know."

"It's not important to know that there are mountains on the moon or that the world is round."

"What is important to know?"

Her eyes searched his face again, gravely. There was a curious Eastern calmness in her face, he thought, a serenity such as he had seen in the faces of the people at the pagodas.

"How to make the best of one's life. I've done nothing with mine. It has no sense of direction. When I worked in the forestry service with your father I was interested in the work—I liked the open-air life, and the East was always home for me. I loved Burma. I thought it the most beautiful country in the world—more beautiful than India, or anywhere in Europe. And I thought the Burmese people the happiest in the world—even the poorest villager seemed contented, and there was none of the tragic poverty of India. It's still true, all that. I got myself back to Burma when the Japs came in because of a romantic idea of fighting for Burma. It seemed right at the time. But afterwards it didn't make sense. We never asked the Burmese if they wanted to be liberated from the Japs—in fact in the beginning, until the Japs started getting uppish, they didn't want to be. They regarded them as liberators. But we weren't concerned with what they wanted. We went into Burma for our own ends, not theirs. We ravaged their beautiful country, from end to end. We destroyed the walled city of imperial Mandalay."

He moved away from the table with the open atlases and books. He had forgotten the grave, listening girl. He was thinking aloud.

"I was one of the destroyers of the country I loved. I helped to bring suffering to the people I loved."

She said, quickly, "At the end the Burmese people were glad the British had come back and driven the Japanese out. We did not like the Japanese any more. We even hated them. Everyone hated them."

"Wars make people hate. It isn't only the fighting—the bombing, the killing, that makes war evil. It's all that is part of it—the hating, the armies of occupation, the horrors of liberation, the refugees. The human tragedy. It wasn't clear to me at the time. I wanted to get out of war-time England —I'd never felt at home in it even in peace time. I wanted to get back into the sun. I tacked a patriotic motive on to my desire, and went back as a soldier. The war didn't look so noble at close quarters. I once saw a high-up British officer turn a dead Japanese soldier over with his foot, and then give the body a kick. "Yellow vermin," he said. But the dead soldier had been a human being, loving and loved, and activated by the same patriotic motives as the British officer—who was an educated man, and I suppose in civilian life normally intelligent and sensitive. In the Indian Service Corps I didn't have to do any killing, or order any, and at the time I was glad of that. Afterwards I thought that there was no difference, morally speaking, between the people who made the guns and the rest of it and those who used them. I neither made munitions nor used them, but I was part of the machine of war, and there's a sense in which the fragment is the whole."

He flung the stub of his cigarette into the fire and immediately proceeded to light another.

"Well, so that was that. I was muddled about the war as about everything else, and I came out of it with neither glory nor personal satisfaction. I got back to Burma as soon as I could. I had no very clear plan. I just wanted to get back and took the first opportunity. I did a tour of the forests with the D.F.O. of the Bokoko division. He took me to a wedding at Mynmyo."

"At Mynmyo?"

"Yes, Mynmyo. I've asked myself so often since why I had to get back just when that wedding was taking place at Mynmyo—why I had to be taken to it, to meet someone who told me Christopher Finching's daughter was still alive—that it was her husband who had saved her from the river, and that she was married to the younger brother."

"I always knew it was Ma Hla. My father didn't know, but I knew."

"You mean you guessed?"

"It was more than that. I knew. Not at first. It came to me in Rangoon when my husband told me how his brother had asked Po Than, the boatman, to lie to my father if he ever came looking for me, because he and Aung and Mé-Mé and Nu didn't want me to be taken away from them. But I knew Ma Hla wanted it—even when I was a child and jealous of her and Maung Shwe she wanted it. My father doesn't know who told you where I was, or how you found out. I knew someone must have told you, and no one else would have. It was *karma*. Bad actions will have bad consequences. There were all the lies that were told. Before that there was the evil wish I had made at a ruined pagoda where there is a bad *nat*."

"But that I had to come back into your life—at that place where I had gone out of it eight years ago—it seems so strange——"

She shook her head. "Not strange. When you accept the law of *karma* everything is explained."

"Even your finding your way to this shop and thinking the Buddha image in the window was a shrine, and coming here day after day until our lives link up once again? Isn't that strange?"

"It all began the day we all set out together for India."

"You think our destinies were all settled that day we left Bokoko in 1942?"

"Not destiny. We began to make then what is happening now." She frowned a little. "In English it is hard to explain. But you know what is *karma*."

"The results of action—what the Christians call reaping according to what is sown, except that for the Buddhists it is not confined to one lifetime. Yes, I know."

"You believe these things?"

"I don't know, Jenny. I am uncertain of everything. Except one thing. That I want to help you in this phase of your life—to be your friend. I've never been certain of anything—not deeply certain. But I am certain about this, and that I can help you."

He threw the remains of the cigarette on the fire and this time he did not light another. He was no longer nervous but confident, eager. His thin sallow face was alight with that eagerness, and a little of that irradiation reached out to her. Somewhere at the centre of her being she was touched; she could not have said whether with compassion or response to his implicit plea. She was aware of him emotionally, as she had been initially of Maung Shwe and later of Aung; aware and a little disturbed, a little troubled, but also interested.

"We must be friends," he insisted, and then, recklessly, "We need each other. We are both alone—and lonely."

She said, broodingly, "If I need you you will be taken away from me. When my mother was drowned I needed Maung Shwe, and Ma Hla took him away from me. I turned to Aung—and you see what happens. I must not need you—no."

"You are safe with me because I need you so much—perhaps more than you will ever need me. I am more than twice your age and it probably sounds strange to you, but it is true."

She asked, suddenly, "Will you teach me to read English?"

"Of course."

"My father would teach me. He would like me to be able to read and write English. But I would sooner that you taught me."

"I will ask your father if I may come to the house every evening for an hour."

"I would sooner come here. If you come to the house Aunt Jennifer will interfere. She will say that she can teach me."

"You don't like your aunt?"

"She is all right. She means to be kind, but she is stupid. She doesn't understand about *nats* and ghosts, and she tries to make me sleep in the dark and say Christian prayers. She doesn't like me to sit on the floor. She thinks that all people who are not white are backward and ignorant." She sighed. "I asked her if her Lord God was white and she was cross and told me not to be blass—I forget the word, but it meant I must not say such a thing."

"Blasphemous. You should have asked her if God was an Englishman and reminded her that Jesus was an Oriental Jew."

"I don't think she likes Jews. I heard her telling Mrs. Sellers one day that you couldn't trust them. Mrs. Sellers doesn't like them either."

"Lots of so-called Christians don't. I don't know how they square it up with their professed beliefs; but then I don't know how they square a lot of things up."

"Perhaps they don't really believe."

He smiled. "Perhaps they don't. Out of the mouths of babes . . . Jenny, I must go back to the shop. I shall telephone your father and let him know I'm back and ask him if I may come round. Shall I say you were here?"

"Yes. There must be no more lies."

"Good. I shall tell him you would like me to teach you to read and write, and I shall ask him if I may take you out. Would you like to go to the ballet?"

"I've been. I liked it very much. I would like to go again—with you. But my father may say no to everything."

"We must make a strong wish that he doesn't."

Downstairs, in the shop, she looked intently at the Buddha image.

"The beautiful Lord Buddha," she murmured. "*Buddham saranam gacchami* . . ."

"Next time you come I will show you all sorts of beautiful things from the East," he told her. "There are some little Tara figures from Tibet."

"I have seen Tara in a museum—beautiful Tara with her tall lotus——"

"The living lotus. Oh, Jenny there is so much to talk about! It is going to be lovely knowing each other. Please say you think so!"

She regarded him, gravely. "It might be," she conceded.

Christopher asked Derek Vernon to come round after dinner, explaining, "My sister will be out and Jenny will have gone to bed, and we can talk freely."

Jenny heard the visitor arrive and the burr of the two men's voices when the sitting-room door closed on them. She lay looking at the small flames of the candles, and feeling curiously safe because Derek Vernon was in the house. In the house and in her life. I have a friend, she thought. Once again I have a friend. It was an exciting thought, but also a little frightening, because life was *anicca*, which is impermanence, and *dukha*, which is suffering, and nothing could change that. I must not love him, she thought, then I will never lose him. There must be no attachment. Where there is attachment sooner or later there comes separation, in life or through death. So the Buddha had taught, and so she had learned by experience.

Christopher asked the young man, after the story of the Buddha 'shrine' and the encounter, "Did she tell you that the boy she married is already marrying again?"

"He didn't lose much time! No, she didn't tell me. Only that whenever she had needed anyone they had always been taken from her. She had a sense of insecurity that is almost a neurosis."

"It's not to be wondered at. But now that the boy is marrying again she'll settle down. There's nothing for her to go back for now."

"I imagine it was a wrench parting with her foster-mother as well as the boy."

"I suppose so—at first. But if she can get over the loss of her real mother she can get over the loss of a foster-mother. Absence doesn't make the heart grow fonder—it helps people to forget, to adjust themselves to another kind of life. Don't you agree?"

"It could be. I've nothing to go on," Derek answered.

"She was unhappy at first, of course," Christopher went on. "She was very upset when she realized her mother wouldn't be here as she'd expected. I felt pretty bad about it; but I had to do it. She wouldn't have left Burma just for my sake, and they wouldn't have let her come. I was worried about possible interference from the Embassy at first, but it seems there's an article of the Hague Convention by which a State may not give diplomatic protection to one of its nationals against a State whose nationality that person also possesses—and Jenny has dual nationality, of course. In England her active nationality is British."

He was aware, but did not add, that in a third State she would be considered to have only one nationality, and that the nationality of the State in which she habitually resided, and would therefore be entitled to the protection of that State.

"She may adjust herself to being British, but I don't think you'll win her over to Christianity," Derek said.

"So long as I win her over to being one of us again I no longer mind that so much. There are, after all, European Buddhists. My sister feels it more than I do. She blames me for taking Jenny to the Oriental sections of the V. and A. and the B.M. I don't mind telling you that I don't regret doing that—it brought us anyhow within measurable distance of each other."

"What do you plan for her now?"

"Just to educate her a bit. She ought to read and write English, for one thing. When the weather's better I thought of taking her on some trips to show her England—you know, Canterbury Cathedral and Oxford and Cambridge and the Shakespeare country. My sister had an idea of interesting her in social work later on. Eventually I suppose she'll marry. I'd like to see her settled in the next few years—I won't make old bones. There are days when I don't feel any too good."

"I'd be very willing to take her around any time you're not feeling up to it. In fact I'd like to. I'm also very willing to give her the English lessons. I did a bit of coaching at one time, before I went East."

"My sister has offered to do it, busy as she is. But Jenny doesn't seem to take to her. I could do it, but an outsider is better, I always think. I'd be very grateful if you'd see what you could do. Teach her a bit of English history whilst you're about it. Take her to Hampton Court. And the Tower of London—when I took her I could only get her interested in the Crown Jewels and the ravens. Perhaps you can do better."

"I got her interested in some atlases today, and a book on astronomy. I think she'd learn quickly. There's a school of thought that maintains that when a child hasn't been cluttered up with a lot of learning in its early years it learns quickly in its teens. Jenny has the desire to learn——"

"See what you can do then. She's good material. She's like her mother, don't you think? To look at, I mean. Or don't you remember Ma Hla?"

"I remember her very well. She was lovely. Jenny takes after her, I agree."

"Give her another couple of years."

"And then?"

"The finished product should be an attractive and cultivated English girl, and all the Burmese life will seem like a dream."

"That she'll be an attractive and cultivated young woman I don't doubt, but that the Burmese past will seem like a dream I wouldn't be so sure. All her formative years were spent there, you know."

"With what effect? They made a peasant and a Buddhist of her. By the time she reached Rangoon she was already shedding the peasant. They couldn't form her in any other way. If you can wean her away from the Buddhism so much the better, but I don't make a point of it."

Just as well, Derek thought. The Old Man was treating him as though he were engaging him as coach instead of accepting a favour. It didn't matter; the old buzzard had at least given him a free hand. The strong wish had taken effect. They were to be allowed to be friends. He and this child upon whose life he had so drastically impinged. Out of confused and not entirely worthy motives, since the sense of power had come into it.

He walked home feeling quite extraordinarily happy. The chaos of living began to assume shape and order. When the spring came, he thought, they would go to Hampton Court all right, but not for the sake of history, but because of the lotus pools.

IV. THE LILY AND THE LOTUS

FOR Jenny the issues were not so clear cut. She had a friend again, but like her father he was also the enemy. Like her father, too, he was anxious for her to be happy in England, yet but for him she would not have known the anguish of uprooting and separation, and the dissolution of her marriage. It was easy for him now that he had been the cause of destroying her old life, the life in which she had been happy, to befriend her in the new life. Like her father and aunt he meant well; they were all three sincerely wanting her to settle down happily in her English life. No doubt the people who looked after those animals in the zoo place her father had told her about did everything possible to make the animals happy, gave them, no doubt, nice comfortable cages and plenty of good food and looked after them if they got ill, even let them mate under proper supervision, and bring up their young. It never occurred to those kind people that a cage was still a cage, however roomy, and not in the least like a forest or jungle, and that the good food was not the natural food the animal hunted and killed for itself, and that being shut up with an animal of the opposite sex at the mating time was not like the natural forest and jungle courtship. She sighed, thinking of it. One day, no doubt, she too would be presented to a suitable partner and expected to marry —to make an English marriage.

Her aunt approved of her learning to read and write English but not of her going every afternoon to Derek Vernon's flat over the shop. She protested to her brother, "Surely you or I could have given her lessons?"

"She will learn more quickly from Vernon because she takes to him—which, unfortunately, she hasn't to either of us."

"I am sure she has become very fond of you, at least."

"I think the most that can be said is that she no longer actively dislikes me—that she tolerates me. Whereas Vernon interests her. No doubt he doesn't seem to her as old-fogyish as we do. The Burmese regard everyone over forty as old. In Burma when you cease to be young you're old, and that's all there is to it. And in a sense they're right. There's a point at which youth stops. Somewhere in the thirties. Suddenly, overnight, you know you're old. Or you suddenly see yourself in a mirror and realize it. Middle-age is merely a Western courtesy-title—a euphemism. Derek Vernon is about thirty-five and looks younger. He's still young, therefore. And his shop with its Buddha images and so forth is like a shrine for her. What is the objection to her going there? Are you afraid he'll seduce her?"

"Of course not." She bridled. "I'm sure he's a very nice young man——"

That *is* what you thought, old girl, all the same, he thought. There were times when Jennifer irritated him.

"What, then?" he demanded.

"It seems unnecessary, that's all. Also it doesn't help with her Christian training. She told me the other day that Mr. Vernon told her he considers himself a Buddhist—'as near as dammit'." Her tone was indignant.

Christopher chuckled. "I've never heard you use such an expression, Jennifer. Where'd you get it from? One of your girls?"

"It's the expression Mr. Vernon used to Jenny, apparently. Of course if you like her to pick up such expressions——"

"If she doesn't hear them from him she'll hear them from other people. In time, no doubt, she'll start going to the pictures and learn to speak American."

Miss Finching considered that her brother was pleased to be facetious, and, determined to keep the conversation serious, she continued, "I was thinking that when she was proficient in English she might take a commercial course and learn shorthand and typing and come and work at the club. We could use a secretary, and it would be good training in social welfare work."

"It might be a good idea," Christopher conceded. "One step at a time, though. In the meantime she seems to be acquiring at least a smattering of general education with my ex-assistant."

That was true; Derek gave her an hour's English lesson every day, and at week-ends he took her to the art galleries and museums. In this way she did begin to acquire an idea of European culture through the ages, and indirectly it was a way of teaching her history and geography. All this was pleasant enough, though it was sometimes bewildering, and she was not always as interested as Derek expected her to be. The Roman Britain section of the British Museum aroused no interest in her; she was always impatient to get to the Asian section just beyond. The Egyptian mummies left her as cold as the Elgin marbles, and in the picture galleries she quickly realized that there is a limit to the number of paintings in which it is possible to be interested. So many Virgin Marys and Infant Jesuses; and the baby was often very ugly, so big and fat and pink, and even when newly-born always, curiously, the size of a child of a year or more old. She liked some of the Italian primitives painted on wood, because they were simple and child-like, with stiff little figures and flowers, and plenty of gold-leaf—which was something she understood.

She enjoyed herself more and found much more to interest her at the Oriental Bookshop, where she could handle Oriental figures and dip into books full of fascinating pictures of Eastern places and the characters

of Eastern religious mythology. She would happily spend whole afternoons at the shop looking at books about the East. Increasingly she longed
to be able to read them. It was this more than anything which stimulated
her desire to learn to read and write English. If she could not be in the
East it would be something at least to be able to read about it. But one
day, she thought, I shall go back. She had no ideas as to the when or how
of it, only the deep conviction.

She adapted herself to European life—to the wearing of shoes and
European clothes, to European food, even to such insanitary habits as
eating with cutlery and sitting in her bath water. She went regularly with
her aunt to the hair-dresser's to have her hair trimmed and set; she even
accompanied her aunt to services in St. Paul's Cathedral occasionally—
this was one of the 'progressive' aspects of Miss Finching, St. Paul's being
a place at which there was often an unconventional sermon—on some
subject such as the church in relation to war, or the church in relation
to the question of colour-bar, and so on. Jenny was sometimes interested
in the talk from the pulpit, but she found all the standing up and kneeling
down confusing and tedious. The altar interested her, but it needed many
more flowers, and candles—what was an altar without flowers and candles?
Her aunt, to whom she made this observation, said that at Easter in all
the churches there were a lot of flowers, but candles only in Roman Catholic churches, or High Anglican. She began to tell her about the Reformation, but at the end of the explanation Jenny could only think that as the
Reformation had done away with the candles and images and incense
she was on the side of these other people, the Papists, her aunt called
them, who were against it.

She asked Derek when they next met, "What do you think about the
Reformation?"

He was startled. "Who's been giving you history lessons?"

"Daddy told me about it when I was a little girl, but my aunt told me
more about it when we were at St. Paul's on Sunday. She says it was a
good thing. Daddy thinks so too. What do you think?"

"I agree with them. Though had I lived in England at the time I'd
probably have been on the other side, detesting puritanism." He smiled.
It was too vast a subject to go into with someone with as little knowledge
of European history as Jenny, he felt. He found himself wondering how
Miss Finching had dealt with it—had she begun with Luther? She had,
in fact, confined herself to England and begun with Henry VIII.

"You mean Oliver Cromwell and all that?"

"All that and much more, before and after. But I also detest corruption
in high places—corruption and hypocrisy—particularly in high spiritual
places. It's no use asking me about it, Jenny. I'd have to give one of those
difficult answers such as the Buddha was always giving—yes and yet not-

yes, agreement and not-agreement. You, I am sure, are against the Reformation because it took the images out of the churches—isn't that it?"

She nodded, and he continued, "Well, you've got a point there. But religions have a way of being smothered by their outward symbols—the doctrines get lost in the ritual. It's my objection to the Roman Catholic church, and to a good deal that passes for Buddhism at the pagodas."

"I like it," she said, simply. "I like masses of flowers and candles and joss-sticks, and hundreds of little gold and silver bells, and great golden images."

"But the Buddha himself just sat under a tree and talked. He didn't tell people to make images of him and lay flowers and burn candles and incense—any more than Christ did."

"There's no harm in it," she persisted. "It makes the Lord Buddha real to us, and it's a way of paying homage. How else can we pay homage?"

"By respecting the moral laws laid down by the Buddha—or the Christ. Look, Jenny, it isn't the lotus flowers you lay at the feet of the Lord Buddha that matter, it's what the lotus stands for, don't you see? So long as you know that, then it doesn't matter if you never offer a single flower or light a single candle. That goes for the Christians, too. Christ said, 'Consider the lilies of the field.' All right, let's consider them, the lilies of the field, the lotus of the waters—lily or lotus it doesn't matter, the symbol's the same—purity springing from impurity, the lily springing from the dark earth, rooted in the dung of cattle, the lotus rooted in the black mud of lake or creek, each rising in its living beauty out of darkness and impurity, like the first life in the world rising out of the primordial chaos." He had again forgotten her and was thinking aloud. "The creative force and immortality—the assertion that all life is one, and death, the return to the earth from which life springs, only a new beginning. It makes sense that in the legend the Buddha should have left the imprint of the lotus at every step."

He came out of his reverie and saw her rapt face, and tenderness flooded him.

"Between the Reformation and the lotus we'd better try and get to Hampton Court next week-end," he said.

I'm a confused and confusing sort of teacher for her, he thought, ruefully, but perhaps some thing gets through that lets in a little light for her. Actually he illuminated for her more than he knew, so that she was educated unawares.

They visited Hampton Court on a mild Saturday afternoon in late May. The fountains and the gardens—sweeps of lawn seen through arches of dark trees and edged with a scarlet flame of tulips—and the high dark walls of the palace charmed her, but it was not of King Henry VIII or Cardinal Wolsey she thought as they wandered through the palace, but, marvelling at the four-poster beds, of Aung and the sleeping-platform in a corner of the living-room of the bamboo house at Tatkon. She was greatly impressed by the great brocaded silk curtains which could be drawn round such beds, more beautiful even than the golden net mosquito curtains that drape a Burmese bridal bed. She tried to imagine herself and Aung snug and secret in such beds as these, and a fierce wave of longing for him swept her, so that when Derek told her about Henry VIII's wives she could only think of Aung taking another wife. She could no more imagine such a thing as imagine herself taking another husband. She and Aung belonged to each other; they had agreed upon that; how, then, could either belong to anyone else? Aung had never looked at another girl; he had waited for her to grow up—unlike Shwe-Shwe. . . .

They came out into the sunlight and crossed a courtyard and there was a clock with a blue face, high up, and an old stone staircase with the steps worn away by the feet of centuries, there were arches which Derek called cloisters, there was an ancient kitchen, and interest reasserted itself and Tatkon receded.

They visited the great and ancient vine in its glasshouse, and admired the Knot garden, a gaudy mosaic of tulips, and walked between trellises of clipped trees down to the river and sat on a seat and watched the boats for a little while. "I must tell Aung," she thought, involuntarily, and "Aung would like this." Then they crossed the broad walk with the herbaceous border at one side and came to the wild part where the water-lily leaves were so thick upon the stream as almost to conceal the water—as on the creek on the Mynmyo river at Tatkon. She exclaimed with delight, and tears filled her eyes, as when she had come suddenly upon the Buddha image in the Bloomsbury shop window. "There's a creek at Tatkon full of them," she told him. "Aung and I used to go there every May to gather them for the pagoda, for the Kason Full Moon festival." She looked up at him.

"I must go back one day—soon. You do see that I must go back, don't you?"

"Yes," he said, slowly, "I do see. It's your country—England isn't." He hesitated, then added, "But you no longer have a husband there." It had to be said.

"Aung is still there. I want to see him again. I *must* see him again!"

She stood up and they walked on beside the stream in silence. Presently he said, "Have patience a little longer, Jenny. Later in the year I will be going to Burma again myself, and I will go and find Aung for you."

The eyes she turned on him blazed with a dark fire of hope.

"I wish you could go at once. Couldn't you go at once?"

"Not at once. But I will try to go sooner than I'd planned. Only you mustn't count on it altering anything for you. You'd better get used to the idea in advance that it probably won't change anything. People change. Life changes. From moment to moment, even." He smiled, ruefully, and added, "That's good Buddhism, anyhow!"

That night Jenny lit the nightlight which was usually beside her bed, and which was all the illumination her aunt had for some time allowed her against the haunted dark, and placed it in front of the small ivory Buddha image. Then she lay in bed looking at it for a long time. It was a very small Buddha image, but it cast a shadow bigger than itself, and when you closed your eyes it became a great golden image whose shadow filled the room.

V. THE EASTERN GATE

DEREK had not intended returning to Burma that year; it was too expensive an undertaking and the business did not warrant it. Purely financially he did not see how it was to be done; he had already put everything he had into the business and his last trip; and even going by sea, and tourist class, he would need at least two hundred pounds, and, he reflected, frowning at the thought, I do not have, as the Americans say, two hundred pounds . . . nor the means of raising it. Two alternatives then remain: to save it, which would take about two years, or borrow it—but from whom? And even if it were possible to borrow the money did one put oneself in debt for so considerable a sum merely in order to carry out some quixotic scheme of expiation?

Because, of course, that was what it amounted to—I have, he thought wrily, what the Freudians call a guilt-complex regarding Jenny Finching. First, I had it about her old man, for deserting him on the trek; and then to expiate that I betray his daughter's whereabouts to him, trying to kid myself I thought it was my duty to do so, but a sense of duty was never my strong point. My need, let's face it, was to assert myself. I got a hell of a kick out of sending that cable to Finching and feeling I was taking a hand in several people's destinies. Now here I go wallowing in guilt all over again! What it is to have been brought up a Christian, with all that absolution-and-remission-of-sins business—it sticks, regardless! To hell with all that—through my infernal interference I've made a mess of this kid's life and I've got to get it straightened out . . . but can I? Supposing I do somehow get to Burma and find Maung Aung, how does that help, with him married to someone else? And isn't it better if Jenny is left to settle down in her English life and forget Burma? The trouble, of course, is that she isn't settling down or doing any forgetting. The old man's plan isn't working out. Having sampled the benefits of Western civilization she would still sooner live as a poor paddy cultivator's wife in a Burmese village. And why not? What's so special about flush sanitation, standing in 'bus queues and going to the cinema? So supposing I do get back and find Maung Aung and tell him, Mālā still loves you and wants only to be back with you—then what? There's still no way of getting his Mālā back to him, and he's no doubt very well pleased with the wife on the spot. Certainly a wife some six thousand miles away and with whom one stands no chance of being reunited for five or six years, until she comes of age, isn't much of a proposition. Going back wouldn't help.

I should never have put the idea into her head. Which means I've run true to form and done the wrong thing again. . . .

He went on giving Jenny English lessons and taking her out, sometimes only for walks in Kensington Gardens, sometimes further afield to Windsor, for another glimpse of English history, to Richmond, where they went on the river, to Box Hill to show her the Surrey landscape. All these outings were conducted with her father's approval. The more she saw of England and English life the better. He himself took her to Brighton for the day during the summer—too many Jews around, to be sure, but it was an aspect of English life. He also took her to Oxford—he felt a personal responsibility there. Jennifer took her to the girls' club one evening in the hope of interesting her in the work. Jenny watched girls of her own age and older playing table-tennis and doing other odd and quite pointless things in what her aunt described as 'the gym', they also danced with each other to radio music; it all seemed to her very singular. Her aunt explained that most of the girls were in trouble with the police and that it was a way of keeping them off the streets and out of further mischief. She explained about juvenile delinquency and something called 'probation'. Miss Finching assumed her explaining manner and Jenny her listening face. So far as Jenny could make out the place was a kind of rehabilitation centre for female dacoits. "In Burma we have rehabilitation centres for repentant insurgents," she volunteered. "Really," said Miss Finching, "how very extraordinary!" in what Jenny thought of as her not-believing voice. "Yes," Jenny insisted, "but not for dacoits." Miss Finching replied that she should think not. After that both Miss Finchings gave up trying to explain to each other.

Christopher had more success with the Oxford outing; Jenny was interested in seeing where he received his education. She gazed respectfully at the various college buildings, and with special attention at the one he indicated as his own. They stood in a grassy square he called the 'quad' and he pointed out the window of his room. She could only think that it was all rather like some of the big buildings in Rangoon, but when she said this, thinking to please him, he frowned and said quite harshly, "Not in the least like Rangoon!" But afterwards he thought that she had nothing else with which to compare it, and she had at least been interested. She thought, privately, that the *pongyi-kyaung* at Tatkon, where Aung and Maung Shwe had received their education, was much more beautiful with its many roofs rising up out of palms and plantains and flowering trees, than anything in Oxford.

On the whole Christopher was satisfied with his daughter's development. Because she no longer spoke about wanting to go back to Burma he believed she was reconciled to English life. It was difficult, he felt, to know what went on inside her—he had never really known with her mother, he reflected, ruefully—but he saw no evidence that she was fretting. At times he could even feel that she was happy—not, negatively, no longer unhappy but positively happy. In this, however, he was mistaken; she was no longer, for the most part, acutely unhappy, but happiness was a series of Burmese memories and had nothing to do with the present. She was a prisoner resigned to the sentence and waiting for it to pass. Only sometimes at night the old wild unhappiness would sweep her, the consuming loneliness and longing, but of this she spoke to no one, not even to Derek. Life was suffering, but it was also change. You can neither drown nor swim in the same river twice; it is always flowing, and the flow is change, eternal change; turning instinctively to the teaching of the Buddha, in that lay her hope—as it had lain for her mother.

Before she could read English Derek introduced her to *The Light of Asia*. It immediately appealed to her and she never wearied of him reading extracts to her, and soon came to know her favourite lines by heart—

> Lo, as the wind is, so is mortal life,
> A moan, a sob, a sigh, a storm, a strife.

And—

> This is its touch upon the burnished rose,
> The fashion of its hand shaped lotus leaves.

As soon as she could read he gave her a copy of the little book for her own and she would read it at all hours of the day and night. Here, distilled into poetry, was the story of the noble Prince Siddartha who became the Buddha, and the essence of his teaching. Here were to be found the Four Noble Truths, the Noble Eightfold Path, the doctrine of *Karma*, the Five Precepts, the Three Gems of the *Tiratana* and at the end the mystical lotus. She liked reading, too, about the beautiful Princess Yasodhara, to whom the Prince Siddartha, the Buddha-to-be, was married, upon whose 'dark breasts' he lay sleeping, and whom he called his lotus-flower, and tears would fill her eyes reading of the hour of his great renunciation, when he kissed the sleeping face of his beloved and went out from her, out from the palace, never to return, casting away the world to save the world, 'since there is hope for man only in man'.

Poetry replaced for her the singing and music of the Tatkon days. It did sing, she would think, and it was a kind of silent music. There was another little book Derek gave her, *Love Songs of Asia*, 'rendered by Powys Mathers', which also she read endlessly. There was a long poem called 'Black Marigolds', rendered from the Sanskrit of the first century, over which she would weep, racked with memory, the heavy heart swelling and bursting for lost love, lotus-eyed, 'a black-haired lover on the breasts of day', recalling Aung's wild weeping the night before they left Tatkon, and the morning 'wearied out with love'. And now for her, too, 'love's great sleeplessness wandering all night'. . . .

When Miss Finching came upon these two books in Jenny's room she was startled and dismayed. That her niece could now read, and liked doing so, she knew and approved; she had tried to introduce her to what she considered suitable literature—*Wuthering Heights, Jane Eyre, Pride and Prejudice,* and, fantastically, the *Intelligent Woman's Guide to Socialism.* None of these works had in the least interested Jenny. There were far more interesting books to be found at the Oriental Bookshop. She had also found a number to interest her on her father's bookshelves—*Hindu Religions, Customs, Manners,* Fielding Hall's *Soul of a People,* which she read avidly and thought a lovely book, especially the piece about the Shwe Dagon Pagoda, and the people flowing up and down the stairs like a coloured stream, and several other standard works on Burma. She did not understand either the character or manners of the people in the novels her aunt selected for her, nor comprehend the background. As for socialism she only understood it in relation to *Pyidawtha* the Welfare State in the new Burma.

Miss Finching had been very disappointed, and had tried again with poetry, presenting her with a copy of the *Oxford Book of English Verse.* Jenny tried, dutifully, beginning at the beginning, but the old English defeated her, and when she had *The Light of Asia* and the *Love Songs of Asia* she felt she needed nothing more. Miss Finching had not read, but knew about, Sir Edwin Arnold's famous poem; she disapproved of it because it presented in poetic terms a godless faith, and as such could only be regarded as a pernicious work to fall into the hands of anyone not strongly rooted in the Christian religion. She frowned when she found it lying on Jenny's bedside-table; there was plenty of good Christian religious poetry available. When she saw underneath it the *Love Songs of Asia* she clicked her tongue against the roof of her mouth. She picked it up and turned the pages and found pencil markings against what she considered a number of unhealthily erotic lines. Black-haired lover on the breasts of day, indeed! Everyone, of course, knew that Orientals were over-sexed. . . . It was true that Jenny had, unfortunately, had some sexual experience, like some of the delinquent girls for which the club catered, but for that very reason alone she should not be reading this sort of thing.

Jenny was out, and she took the books to her brother in the sitting-room. He sat at a writing desk in the window and she placed the two slim volumes beside the blotting-pad.

"I don't know if you consider this suitable literature for Jenny," she remarked, adding, "I see from the inscriptions in both that they were given her by Derek Vernon."

Christopher transferred his attention from the letter he had been writing, to the neat lettering, black on a red background of the Powys Mathers work. He murmured the title aloud, then turned some pages and immediately his eye alighted on the marked lines.

"Awful stuff," his sister suggested.

He continued to turn the pages, frowning, stroking his moustache.

"Certainly not the sort of stuff it'll do a girl like Jenny any good to read," he said at last, and reached for the telephone. He dialled the bookshop number and continued turning the pages whilst the assistant who had answered went to find Mr. Vernon. When Derek came to the telephone, Christopher immediately roared at him.

"Look here, Vernon, old man, d'you think it's helping Jenny now that she can read to give her things like *The Light of Asia* and erotic Oriental poetry? There's plenty of good English stuff—"

"Is it the Orientalism or the eroticism you object to?" Derek inquired.

"Both!" Christopher snapped.

"The printed word is hers now that she can read," Derek pointed out. "We can hardly censor her reading matter."

"There's such a thing as guidance."

"Her virginity's not to be restored by wandering lonely as a cloud with Wordsworth, you know, if you'll pardon my saying so."

"That's a remark in damned bad taste, and you know it!"

"She's a young married woman, not a little girl," the voice at the other end insisted.

"If that's your attitude I must forbid her to visit you and require you not to have anything more to do with her!"

Christopher jammed down the receiver, shaking with anger. His sister, who was accustomed to his outbursts of irritability—which she always attributed to the East, which, she understood, was ruinous to the European liver—had never before seen him upset, as he manifestly was.

"I'll speak to her when she comes in," he said, thrusting the two books into a pigeon-hole in his desk. "Where is she now?"

"Probably at the bookshop," Miss Finching said, grimly. She added, "I don't see how we're going to prevent her going there—short of locking her up!"

"She should never have been allowed out unaccompanied in the first place!"

"I can't always be here, I have to go to the club, and she's never interested to come with me. And you can hardly take her to yours. We can ask her not to go to the shop any more or to see him, but I don't see how we can enforce it."

Christopher rose and began pacing up and down, frowning, chewing at his moustache.

"It's a damned pity he doesn't go back to Burma and stay there. He's always saying he'd like to. If he'd only undertake to keep out of the way for a year, to give Jenny a chance to settle down."

"Perhaps he'd agree to that. Why don't you ask him?"

"After I've blown him up?"

"That's nothing. He worked for you all those years—he must be used to being blown up."

"I'm not his boss any more."

"All the same, he knows how you are. Ring him up later in the day and ask him to come round and have a chat about things. I'll take Jenny to a news-reel—perhaps the pictures will be better for her than reading the sort of thing she is reading."

At that point Jenny arrived back from Lincoln's Inn Fields where she had been sitting on a bench reading from a collection of *Lyrics from the Chinese*, done into English by Helen Waddell, Derek's latest gift to her. It was a book she found enthralling from the first line in the introduction, "It is by candlelight one enters Babylon," though the nostalgia it aroused in her was almost too great to be borne.

VI. MACHIAVELLIAN

THE only effect of her father's strictures on her reading was to make Jenny secretive. He did not return the two volumes to her. "I'll keep them locked up in my desk for a time so that you won't be tempted to read them and can go on to something more worth while," he said. He added, "You've got the *Oxford Book of English Verse* your aunt gave you—persevere with that until you acquire a taste for good English poetry." He demanded to see the *Lyrics from the Chinese*. He kept it until the following day, when, not having found anything voluptuous or erotic in it, he returned it to her. She accepted it back from him sullenly. "I want my other books," she said. "You have no right to keep them. They were given to me as presents." He told her, "I am only minding them for the time being. They are quite safe. You shall have them back later on, when you have read some of the things your aunt and I would like you to read."

"What do you want me to read?"

Poetry was not Christopher Finching's strong point. It meant very little to him.

"Some of our old English poets—Keats, Tennyson, Wordsworth." They should be safe enough, he thought, recalling dull hours at school.

"Then will you give me back my books?"

He smiled. "When I am satisfied that you are cured of the taste for that sort of thing!"

She was silent. She made no attempt to read the poets of her father's choice. The next day she went to the bookshop and Derek replaced the books for her.

"He shan't have these," she declared, passionately. "I shall hide them."

"How can you? You've no desk or drawer to lock them in."

"I shall find a place."

She took them back to the house hidden inside her dress. In her room she tucked them under the mattress, though she knew it would not be safe to leave them there. She kept the Oxford Book beside her bed; she made no attempt to read the other two books in the house, and when she went out they left with her, tucked inside her dress. Finally she hit upon the plan of hiding them in the chimney behind the electric fire.

Derek was extremely indignant at the confiscation of the books. How dared the old bastard! Whilst he was still pondering what ought to be done about it Christopher telephoned him. He came straight to the point.

"I'm afraid I lost my temper yesterday, Vernon. I wondered if you'd lunch with me at the club and we could have a talk about our problem child. You aren't free today by any chance, I suppose?"

Derek was free, and very willing to meet Finching, but he had the feeling that he would 'put up a better show', as he thought of it, in his own territory. He replied that he could never 'lunch' because it meant leaving a young assistant in sole charge of shop and office, which he did not care to do for any length of time; he suggested that Finching should 'come in for a drink after six', when both would be closed. Christopher agreed to come that evening.

He arrived before the shop was closed and had a look round. Derek showed him various things—some Tibetan masks, a Siamese Buddha figure in green bronze, a seated Tara figure in gilded copper, a porcelain statuette of the Chinese goddess, Kwan Inn, lotus flowers on her breast and feet— "Jenny likes that little figure very much," Derek said. "I thought of giving it to her, but thought I'd better find out first if you'd approve!"

He smiled, as he said it, deliberately turning on the charm. He had had no intention of giving Jenny the statuette: it was far too costly. He told the lie involuntarily; there was no conscious motive behind it; Christopher, however, seized upon the opportunity it presented of making his point.

"It's what I want to talk about, old boy. There's no harm in her taking an interest in Oriental art, and it's natural she should, but when it comes to Oriental erotica——"

"Would you call *The Light of Asia* that?" Derek was still smiling.

"No, but undesirable from the point of view of converting anyone to Christianity, you'll agree! The other things, the love songs, I'd call definitely erotic."

"Not more than much of Shakespeare," Derek suggested, leading the way upstairs.

Christopher moved about restlessly among the young man's books and Oriental *objets-d'art*, examining Chinese paintings on silk, a blue porcelain *chinthe*, a brass Buddha.

"You've some nice things," he observed. Derek handed him a large whisky and he sank into an armchair. Derek had a sudden memory of him on the verandah of the house at Bokoko, sunk deep in a cane chair, his long legs sprawling as now. He had aged a lot, he thought, since those days; his hair and moustache were quite grey now, and surely he had not always been so cadaverous, his grey-blue eyes so deeply sunk under the bushy brows? He poured himself a drink and seated himself in the armchair opposite his ex-chief.

Christopher raised his glass. "Cheers," he said, and when he had sipped announced, "I'm worried about Jenny. It's why I wanted to see you. I'm going to be frank with you, Vernon." He hesitated, regarding his drink morosely.

"By all means," Derek murmured.

"My sister and I are grateful to you for all you've done for Jenny—teaching her to read and write in English, and taking her about, and so on, but we feel the time has come now to make a break. If she's ever to get Burma out of her system, that is to say."

"You regard that as important?"

Christopher turned his morose regard on the young man.

"I regard it as absolutely essential if she's ever to settle down happily in this country. At first I took her around to the Indian section of the V. and A., and to the British Museum Oriental Section—partly so that she wouldn't feel so alien here, cut off from everything she was used to, and partly, I don't mind telling you, because I wanted her to feel sympathetic to me. But now that she's been here six months and can read English, and her Burmese marriage is disposed of, I feel—my sister and I both feel—no purpose is served in continuing to encourage her Eastern interests. You've come to represent a link with the East for her, Vernon, and so long as that link exists she'll go on brooding on the past and never become integrated in her English life."

"You're not suggesting I should cease to exist, I hope?"

Derek was irritated now to the edge of anger.

"I'm suggesting you should cease to exist as a link with the East for my daughter," Christopher snapped.

"I can hardly prevent her coming here—a stone's throw from your own house."

"You can prevent it by telling her not to come—that the friendship must end."

"No!" Derek was now angry. "I can't do that. She already has an *idée fixe* that whenever she cares for anyone that person is taken away from her—I can't add to that. Not possibly. If you think about it you can't want me to. It would be too cruel—abominably cruel. She's suffered enough."

"You wouldn't agree it's cruel to prevent her from becoming an integrated person?"

"It was cruel ever to uproot her from Burma."

"That comes strangely from you—who were responsible for it."

"I didn't realize it at the time. Any more than you did."

"I knew it would be painful for her, but I believed she'd get over it—that blood would tell, given a chance. I still think it will—given a chance. We're not giving her a chance by encouraging her thoughts to dwell on the East. It's got to end, Vernon. If you can't tell her not to see you any more then you must go away. Your business takes you to the East—it would be a very good thing if it could take you there now, for as long as possible."

"If I had the money I'd go back to the East this winter like a shot. But I haven't the money. I can't hope to get back till the end of next year at the earliest."

"I could advance you the money. Next year is too late. Now is the crucial time with Jenny. Another eighteen months of living between two worlds and she's lost to this English one. If you could get away now——"

"At the beginning of the rains? Aren't you asking rather a lot? Not merely am I to clear out to oblige you, regardless of whether it's convenient to me or not, but I'm to do it at the outset of the monsoon!"

"I'm asking a lot because I've a lot at stake. Jenny was beginning to come close to me. She'd never been as close, but I lost her again from the day she walked into your bookshop. If that hadn't happened, with Maung Aung out of the picture everything might have worked out as I'd hoped. Your clearing out now is my only chance."

Derek was silent. He realized that he had Finching in his hand now. He had only, after the initial show of reluctance, to agree to allow Finching to advance him the money to return to Burma immediately. I seem to be cast for the Judas role, he thought, wrily. Yet was it that? Even if he found Maung Aung it might well make no difference to Jenny's life. The boy had married again. He was hardly likely to put aside his new wife simply because of the news that his first still loved him; but it would satisfy Jenny to have first-hand news of him, and his clearing out would satisfy the old man. Betrayal, he persuaded himself, was not necessarily implicit in the picture. And it might even be true, as Finching insisted, that it would be good for Jenny if he faded out for a time, so long as she didn't believe it was done with the object of ending the friendship. It was unlikely that his investigations in Burma would affect her life. But if he really believed that why had he ever told her he would go and find Aung and why had it become important to him?

He came out of his reverie to hear Christopher saying, "The matter is all the more important to me because I'm a sick man, Vernon. I can't last. I can't hope to last out long enough to see Jenny happy in an English marriage, but with your co-operation at least I can last long enough to see her liberated from the Burmese past."

"You talk as though you've only a few years to live——"

"I have. It's later than I thought. Much later." He swallowed the rest of his drink and heaved himself up out of the chair.

"You'll co-operate, old boy?"

"Yes," Derek said, slowly. "Tell me exactly what you propose——"

"Let's go and have a meal and talk the thing into shape."

Derek knew that he was now committed to the adventure, but no longer

sure of the purity of his motives. What was to have been the simple act
of expiation was already complicated by a sense of treachery, and an
absurdly Machiavellian sense of power.

He co-operated with Finching to the extent of leaving England almost
immediately, but he sailed not for Rangoon but for Nairobi. His parents
continually urged him to visit them and this seemed to be the opportunity. Finching had made it clear that he didn't care where he went so
long as he went—for a long time. He had undertaken to be away for a
year. He even thought he might keep his word in this matter. By spending
three months in Kenya on the way out, until the monsoon abated in
Burma, and taking in Siam and Ceylon on the way back, he thought he
might manage it. It would have been useless going to Burma during the
rains, he had explained to Jenny, because the fair-weather road out of
Bokoko up to the Mynmyo Valley would be impassable. She must therefore be patient during the long absence, for he would eventually get to
Burma, to Tatkon, and then he would take the message of her unchang-
ing love to Ma Chit and the others and have a talk with Maung Aung
alone and assure him that she had written and kept faith, and that, in
her own words, 'nothing fades or changes'. He would be away a whole
year, and in that time she must be 'calm and quiet in everything', as set
forth in the *Mingala-sutta*, remembering that though life was suffering
it was also change.

Jenny gave grave assent to all this. The river was always there, but
the water was different from moment to moment. You were borne along
by the river; you could not hope to escape it this side of Nirvana; through
life after life it would bear you, and you could only submit to it, go with
that eternal flow, and the less you struggled the less chance you had of
drowning—as Maung Shwe had explained to her when the dark waters
had washed over her in what seemed now another life lived more than a
lifetime ago. She had not felt that she was losing Derek as she had lost
others she had loved; she was confident that he would come back, bringing her news of the people she still thought of as her family. She thought
that Ma Chit and Mi Nu would cry with happiness to know that she had
not forgotten them, and Shwe-Shwe would be happy, too, and old Maung
Ba Tu, and *Pwa-pwa*, and they would nod their heads and say—she was
certain of it—"One day she will come back to us." What Aung would say
she could not imagine because she could not imagine him married to
someone else. When she thought of him everything dimmed into confusion.

Derek left her with the feeling that she would be all right without him,
since she had faith in his mission; and if in his absence she managed
to come closer to her father it would be to the good, since it was indeed,

from what Finching had told him when they had dined at his club, unlikely he would make old bones, and it was already so much later than
anyone suspected. With every intention of double-crossing him Derek
could nevertheless feel compassion for him—the Judas kiss, he thought,
sardonically.

VII. THE FAITHFUL HEART

ONE of the things which puzzled Jenny about English life was the lack of festivals. There were religious feasts—her aunt had explained about Christmas, Easter, Whitsun—and holidays at these times, but nothing special happened; people went to the sea or to the country, it seemed, but there were no lights outside the churches, and though there were special flower decorations inside the churches at Easter there were none at Whitsun, and you would not know it was a religious feast. Her aunt explained that at the feast of the birth of the Lord Jesus there were often special little trees, strung with lights, outside the churches, and a very tall tree was placed in Trafalgar Square, and the fountains were illuminated, and people sang hymns—religious songs—in the Square, but no, they did not dance, and there was no open-air theatre, nothing at all like the Burmese *pwè*. But there was an open-air theatre in Regent's Park in the summer, and when there was something suitable on they might go to it.

Jenny liked that idea very much, and one warm June night they all three went to see A *Midsummer Night's Dream*. Except that the great crowd of people sat on seats instead of on mats on the ground it was quite like *pwè*, Jenny thought. It was lovely to sit out in the open and see the stars come out and watch people in beautiful costumes singing and dancing in front of the lighted trees and bushes at the back of the stage. She could not follow the Shakespearian English, but she had read the story the day before, in a book containing a number of tales from Shakespeare which her aunt had produced from the shelves for her, and it pleased her that it was a fairy tale, full of magical happenings. She watched it all completely engrossed, and when the interval came turned excitedly both to her father and her aunt, her face alight with pleasure, exclaiming, "Oh, it's so beautiful! Just like our Burmese *pwè*! I don't want it to end! I want it to go on all night. For hours and hours and hours."

"You would find it very cold, I'm afraid, as the night wore on," her aunt told her. "As it is, you will find you'll need the rug when it begins again."

Jenny was disappointed that when they strolled out among the trees neither her father nor her aunt showed any inclination to buy anything to eat or drink—not that she was either hungry or thirsty, but it would have been in keeping with the atmosphere of *pwè*. Instead her aunt was censorious concerning the scramble for refreshments; she could never understand, she said, why people couldn't go to the theatre for a few hours without feeling obliged to put something into their stomachs.

"There are always food stalls when there is *pwè* in Burma," Jenny told her. "Many more than here. There's a lovely smell of frying, everywhere, and there are people selling balloons and all sorts of things."

"We have that sort of thing at fairs," her father explained, "but no open-air theatre with it."

"You'd better take her to Hampstead Heath on August bank holiday!" Miss Finching said. Her tone was ironic. To her astonishment her brother replied, "I'd thought of doing so."

"Really, Chris!" said Miss Finching.

"It's an aspect of English life—Jenny might as well see it all! Next year I think we might go to the Derby."

At the mention of 'next year' Jenny felt one of the recurrent waves of despair wash over her. Derek had explained that until she was twenty-one she could not go back to Burma without her father's consent and had urged that she should try to be patient and endure these English years and gain something from them, and she had agreed to try. If she interested herself in the life about her the time would soon pass, he had said; she had tried to believe that and sometimes succeeded in doing so; only the river had a way of closing over her so often, dark waves of longing and loneliness and despair, and a kind of panic, as though she would drown in those engulfing waves, and they had a way of closing round her unexpectedly, as now, in the midst of happiness and forgetfulness.

Then they went back to their seats and the actors came on to the stage again, and strange and lovely things happened, and the stars came out, and she could forget again. But Aunt Jennifer was right; it was a little cold now that it was dark; you could not sit there all night until the dawn, as in Burma.

When they left the theatre, flowing with the dark tide of people, out into the park, she thought that in Burma it was already tomorrow. It would just be getting light. The crows would be making a great commotion in the big mango tree and people would be stirring everywhere, lighting the charcoal fires, drawing water, preparing the rice for when the *pongyis* came with their begging-bowls. The air would be cool and sweet. Mé-Mé would be changing the glasses of water in front of the shrine in the corner of the room; Mya would be crossing the compound to gather jasmine and the little mauve and white and pink asters. Perhaps there had been a thunderstorm in the night; perhaps it was raining, and the *pongyis* were making their rounds with big black umbrellas. . . .

She came out of her reverie to hear her aunt saying, "Well, that was your first Shakespeare. You must try to read it. It's not difficult."

Jenny was silent. Her father had not returned her the confiscated copies of the *Light of Asia* and the *Love Songs of Asia*, and the secret copies still lived in the chimney.

She still had her night-light when she went to bed, though her aunt
never ceased to observe that it was 'childish' to be afraid of the dark, and
'ridiculous' to believe in ghosts . . . though it seemed to Jenny a good
deal more sensible than a number of things Christians believed in, or
said they believed in. The Christians did believe in at least one ghost,
anyhow—the Holy Ghost, they called it. When she asked about this, and
why it was wrong to believe in ghosts in general but right to believe in the
Holy Ghost, her aunt replied, severely, that there was all the difference in
the world, and explained about the Holy Trinity. But, thought Jenny, a
ghost was a ghost, even if it was part of a trinity of gods—which in some
mysterious fashion were all one—and whether it was holy or evil. And holy
or unholy a ghost was better not encountered.

So every lonely haunted night Jenny lay in the soft English bed gazing
at the night-light set before the little ivory Buddha image, and whatever
had happened during the day, even when it was something beautiful like
the visit to the open-air theatre, her thoughts flowed out to the bamboo
house beside the Mynmyo river, to Mé-Mé and Pé-Pé, to Shwe-Shwe
at the other end of the village, to Aung wherever he might be, even
though his head rested on the breast of another wife in the place where
they had lain together, listening to the rain, listening to the rush of the
swollen river, listening to the stillness when the rains were over.

Sometimes she circled the pillow with her arms, burying her face in
it, weeping, recalling the despairing passion she and Aung had shared that
last night together in the Chinese hotel in Rangoon; then it would seem
impossible to continue with this English life, easier to die. Only you did
not die, and when the day came the torment lessened and made it possible
to go on. Craving was suffering—but how to put the craving away from
one and be calm and quiet in everything, as the Buddha counselled? It
was not easy; indeed it was very difficult. Once Derek had sailed she held
close to the thought that when the rains were over he would go to Tatkon
and tell them all that nothing had faded in her heart, nothing changed,
and that she had courage to face the days and weeks and months and
years of this English imprisonment only in the thought that one day she
would be with them all again, even though Aung no longer wanted her
for a wife. Only that was something beyond her imagining. Only her
mind acknowledged it; her heart refuted it utterly.

On the whole Finching was satisfied with his daughter's progress. In
six months she had learned to read English well; she had not learned to
write it well, but this was not important: it was probable, he told himself,
that even had she learned to write English as a child her handwriting
would have been bad. I should have taken her to England as soon as she
was a few years old, or had Jennifer come out for her, he thought; at six

she would have gone to a boarding-school, and none of the 1942 business would have happened . . . He switched his thoughts from that bitterness and continued his review of Jenny's rehabilitation as an English girl. She had adapted herself well to English customs, and though she still preferred sitting on the floor to sitting on a chair he did not often catch her squatting on her haunches—a habit which irritated him, as it had irritated him in Ma Hla. She no longer demanded to be sent back to Burma. And since Derek Vernon's departure she seemed to be altogether more settled down. She did not permit him to feel close to her, but she seemed to have an affection for him. He was 'Daddy' for her again, and on their various excursions she always seemed happy and interested. She was inclined to be argumentative with her aunt, but then it had to be admitted that Jennifer was not always as tactful as was desirable—she was the born reformer, he thought—and her attitude to her niece was very much that of a probation officer to a delinquent. It was a difficult position, of course, the middle-aged virgin and the young girl, little more than a child, who had disposed of her virginity at an age when most English girls are still at school.

It was a fact that Miss Finching regarded her niece's marriage as a sexual escapade only a few degrees from downright delinquency. Jenny's lack of response to the Christian church was part of the delinquency—and here again she was not far removed from the girls at the club. True she had her own brand of religion, whereas they had none, but it was a religion without God, and as such hardly to be regarded as a religion. Miss Finching did not share her brother's satisfaction concerning the transformation of Mālā into Jenny. It was quite absurd that after six months in England a girl of her age should have to have a night-light when she went to bed in a London flat in which were two other people. Absurd that she should still retain primitive superstitions concerning evil spirits. Absurd that she should continue to regard English life and customs so persistently through Burmese eyes. Absurd that now that she could read and write English she should be mooning about doing nothing useful with her days. In that, of course, Christopher was to blame. He should have insisted that she went to a commercial college and took a six months course of business training; then she could have done useful secretarial work at the club, which might have led to some responsible social welfare work later on. Christopher should have backed her up in trying to develop this interest in the girl; but all he seemed able to think of was developing her affection for himself. Poor old Chris! It was natural he should attach so much importance to his daughter's love, but surely her intellectual and moral development were also extremely important? The trouble, of course, was that Christopher himself had no social conscience—he had lived too long in the East, removed from social problems; and then with the war his own personal tragedy had intervened.

Miss Finching, also, would have liked to have felt close to Jenny; but for that it would have been necessary for Jenny to have looked up to her, to have needed her love, to have gone out to her as a mother-substitute; and Jenny did not go out in any way; she remained shut up inside herself, so that it was impossible to know what she was thinking and feeling. The inscrutable East, thought Miss Finching, who took it for granted that 'Asiatics' were a quite different order of human beings, whose hearts and minds worked quite differently from those of Western peoples. Only when she caressed and talked to the cat was this strange girl's face expressive, she thought, and then it would be suffused with tenderness. That, too, was absurd. "He's so beautiful!" Jenny would cry. "So warm and silky and golden, and such lovely stripes. Like a very little tiger. But then he is a tiger, isn't he, auntie?" Miss Finching disliked so much effusiveness over a cat, even so beautiful a cat as Royal, and even more she disliked being called 'auntie'. It made her feel old. And spinsterish. It might be a term of respect in Burma, but in England it was merely—dowdy. She had a horror of dowdiness, mental or physical, which is why her suits and shirts were always immaculately tailored, and why she kept up with the progressive weekly reviews—though Christopher, with conservative iconoclasm, dubbed them *Bad Writing* and *Rotten Reading*.

When August Bank Holiday came she was shocked to discover that her brother was serious about taking Jenny to Hampstead Heath. She was even more shocked when they got back latish that night in obviously high spirits having had a wonderful time.

"We went on the roundabouts five times!" Jenny announced triumphantly. "Then I went up in a wheel thing with little carriages and you get turned upside down high up in the air. It was lovely! I was looking at the moon upside down. But Daddy wouldn't go on that! It was better than any *pwè* I ever went to! We don't have lovely things that turn you upside down, and no roundabouts."

Her aunt said, caustically, "I'm glad there's at least one way in which England beats Burma! Even if it is only with 'appy 'ampstead!"

But the child in Jenny which responded to the magic of the open-air theatre at night, and to the fun-of-the-fair on Hampstead Heath, was a much smaller part of her mental and emotional make-up than either her father or her aunt realized. Childhood had ended for her that full-moon day of May at the creek when Aung had put his arms round her and kissed her in that strange new disturbing way. All that remained was the occasional flash common to most adults. She no longer thought as a child or felt as a child. She had a childlike capacity for falling under the spell of anything which excited or interested her, a child's simplicity and candour, a Burmese capacity for readily entering into any gaiety that was going; but always below the façade of childish enjoyment was the deep-rooted loneliness and longing, and everything that interested her or gave her pleasure was involuntarily related to Aung, whether it was the gilded beauty of the Avalokita and Tara figures in the Oriental section of the Victoria and Albert Museum, or the excitement of the roundabouts and swings on Hampstead Heath. He was unfailingly her last thought on falling to sleep, her first thought on waking, and bound up with most of her thoughts and reactions in between.

When Mrs. Sellers asked her, "What news of hubby?" she could not bring herself to tell her, "He has taken another wife." It was not only pride which prohibited her; it was as though saying the words aloud would make a fact of something which unsaid remained only an evil dream. She would reply, "He is all right, but he wants me back," which was a way of giving substance to the impassioned wish; bodied forth in words it took on the semblance of reality. Mrs. Sellers's vigorous, "So I should think," heartened her, and when the woman inquired, solicitously, "And when will you be going home, dear?" she would reply, resolutely, "Soon now, I think." Merely to say the words gave her courage. Derek would go and see them all at Tatkon, in a few months, in a few weeks, and they would know that she still thought of them and loved them, and then somehow everything would be all right. Derek had said she should not build too much on his visit to Tatkon, that beyond reaffirming her love for her Burmese family nothing might come of it. Intellectually she accepted that, bravely. Inwardly she was possessed by the irrational faith that when they all knew that she had not changed, in spite of what Aung had written everything must be all right. She could not conceive of a future in which she would not return to Burma—which for her meant return to Aung as his wife. That Aung no longer wanted her did not make sense; the intellectual knowledge had no reality; only what her heart insisted, that Aung still waited for her, longing for her as she longed for him, made sense.

Once in a burst of uncontrollable homesickness she told her aunt, "I don't believe Aung has married again! He wouldn't do it!"

"Then why do you suppose he wrote you that he had?" Miss Finching demanded.

"Perhaps to make me hurry home—to frighten me. Perhaps to punish me for going away. I don't know. Only I don't believe it!"

Miss Finching said, dryly, "You're like some of the girls we sometimes get at the club—even when the doctor has examined them and found them to be pregnant they insist that they're not, that they couldn't be. Some of them keep it up even when they're in labour. It's a neurosis with them."

"I don't know what that is," said Jenny.

"An obsession—a fixed idea, because they can't bear to face the facts. They have become incapable of facing the facts."

"Am I like that?"

"Apparently."

Jenny sighed. "Sometimes it's hard to know what is real and what isn't."

"What on earth do you mean?"

"Ghosts aren't facts like tables and chairs but they're real. Sometimes people see them and that makes them facts."

"Nonsense," said Miss Finching. She did not want to reopen the subject of ghosts. She knew by experience that it always led back to the Holy Ghost, which she found irritating.

She added, firmly, "It is a fact that your so-called husband has married again and doesn't want you, and you might as well make up your mind to it. Like the girls when the doctor puts the babies in bed beside them—the indisputable facts."

I would have to see another wife in bed with Aung before his new marriage became a fact for me, Jenny thought, but she did not say it, because auntie, after all, was what the English called a single lady, who did not understand about these things, and even mentioning about the girls and their babies had made her go rather red in the face, which in English people with their pink faces was a sign that they felt uncomfortable.

Derek sent her air-mailed postcards from Mombasa and Nairobi, and later, in the autumn, from Bombay. They had agreed that he would not write letters, because her father would wish to see them. The postcards were merely to indicate how far he had got with the journey and that he was thinking of her. There was a postcard of the Shwe Dagon Pagoda from Rangoon and then silence. The picture of the pagoda delighted her. It showed the great bell-shaped *stupa* between tall palms, with three satellite pagodas at its base. Gazing at it she saw again the glittering golden mass tapering to the 'umbrella' hung with hundreds of gold and silver bells, and the small multiple-roofed pagodas at its base, red-lacquered, old and dark.

She stood the postcard on the mantelpiece in her room beside the little Buddha image. Her father suggested they should buy a frame for it— "Encouraging her," snorted Miss Finching.

"She's all right now," Christopher assured her; "quite settled down since Vernon cleared out."

"What are we going to do with her?" Jennifer demanded.

"What do you mean, 'do' with her? What does one usually do with a young girl except let her grow up?"

"An English girl of that age is usually either at school or in a job."

"This young girl's circumstances are different." He was a little irritated.

"Then you propose to let her just go on mooning about uselessly until you can see a chance of marrying her off?"

"Unless she shows some inclination to do something different—yes, why not?"

"It's a very reactionary attitude, that's all."

"I am a reactionary—you've always known that!"

She went off on another tack.

"Do you think you're being fair to Jenny? You might as well have left her in Burma if you're going to let her waste her time here."

"You don't really mean that." He was now angry. "You know perfectly well that there could have been no question of leaving her in Burma. You talked of trying to interest her in social welfare work. You might still succeed in that. Give her time—she hasn't been here a year yet!"

He was, nevertheless, a little disturbed by his sister's remarks. Perhaps something more should be done about the girl. If it were possible to coach her up to matriculation standard perhaps she would like to go to London University, where she would meet young people of her own age and perhaps make friendships? Then arose the problem of how to find a coach—it would have to be a woman, he thought—and he shelved the matter, telling himself that it would be time enough to give it serious thought when she had been a year in the country. Would it in any case be possible to bring her up to matriculation standard, starting from scratch? She had learned to read quickly because she was interested, but would she as readily learn mathematics, history, another language? He shrank from tackling her himself about the idea from dread of hearing her say once again that she wanted to return to Burma. On the surface she had settled down, but who knew what went on in the brain behind those long almond-shaped eyes? It seemed safest, so long as she seemed happy, to let well alone.

Although he was not able to feel himself as close to her as he would have liked, nevertheless he could now feel she had affection for him, and he found her companionable. On bright autumn mornings they took walks together through Hyde Park and Kensington Gardens, when one minute she would be scuffling through the leaves like a child, and the next be silent and withdrawn, her face grave, her eyes brooding. They admired the dahlias together, fed the ducks, watched the riders in the Row. He asked her if she would like to learn to ride and she shook her head; she would not at all like to do that—and her thoughts went back immediately to riding the bullocks across the paddy fields at threshing time, and across the river to the swamped fields at the other side when the rains had come and ploughing could begin. The ducks reminded her of the paddy birds at Tatkon, and the wild ducks who came down on to the flooded lands at Bokoko when the monsoon broke, all the hollows between the sand dunes becoming lakes. The scarlet flame of dahlias instantly recalled the flame-of-the-forest trees with their scarlet lily-like flowers, just as in the spring the mauve lilac had reminded her of the jacaranda trees that grew round the *pongyi-kyaung* at Tatkon. But she no longer drew the comparisons audibly. Daddy was kind, and short of sending her back to Burma wanted her to be happy, and there was no point in disappointing him and hurting him. When the periodic bouts of home-sickness swept her she concealed them from him; they anyhow came upon her most overwhelmingly in the nights.

As Christmas drew near she became aware of what she recognized as a feeling of festival in the air. It seemed to her a much more interesting festival than Easter or Whitsun, at which nothing much appeared to happen, except that people had days free from work. At this festival, it seemed, they decorated their houses, and there were even street decorations. Christmas, the celebration of the birthday of the Lord Christ, was evidently quite as important to the Christians as Kason, the celebration of the birth, enlightenment and death, of the Lord Buddha, was to Buddhists. Jenny thought it a pity that it could not be celebrated in the summer, so that the churches could be filled with flowers. Why, she inquired of her aunt, could not the Lord Christ's birthday be celebrated at Easter at the same time as his passing into Nirvana?

"Our Lord did not pass into Nirvana," her aunt informed her. "He ascended into Heaven."

"Isn't it the same?"

"You know perfectly well it's not the same. I've already explained to you. Heaven is the life everlasting. Nirvana is extinction."

"Not extinction," said Jenny, in her Burmese way.

"Then what is it, pray?"

"It is an end of rebirth in this world, but the Lord Buddha would not describe this blessed condition to us."

"I should think not indeed!"

These discussions always irritated Miss Finching. It exasperated her that with every aspect of Christianity presented to her Jenny reverted to Buddhism. The Easter flowers in the churches reminded her of the flowers offered at the pagodas at Kason; the lights on the Christmas trees reminded her of the lights of the *Thadingyut* festival at the end of Lent. She even found a similarity between the Buddhist Lent and the Christian one, in that both ended with a festival and the beginning of better weather. She found no difficulty in accepting that the Lord Christ was immaculately conceived because the Lord Buddha was reputedly conceived by his mother, Maya (the name of Mary inevitably reminded her of Maya; Queen Maya, and Mary, Queen of Heaven) in a dream of a white elephant bearing a white lotus in its trunk. The Christ child was born in a stable; the Bodhisatta under a great tree, his mother standing to give birth, and the Bodhisatta was born without stain, and to him as to the Christ child came great kings to pay him homage.

The similarity between the Christian and the Buddhist birth story ended there, for Queen Maya died seven days after giving birth to the Bodhisatta, as the mothers of Bodhisattas must, but Jenny liked the Christ-child story, and when her father took her to the crypt of St. Martin-in-the-Fields to see the crib, with images of Mary, Queen of Heaven, and the Infant Jesus, and the kings kneeling in the straw, she was very happy. Images were something she understood, and flower-decorated altars, and lighted candles, and incense, and worship; and decorating houses for a religious festival. On Christmas Eve she went with her father to a crowded street he called Berwick Market, with stalls at each side, like a bazaar—her father agreed that it was like a bazaar—and bought an armful of holly and a great bunch of mistletoe. She did not care for the dark prickly holly, but she thought the mistletoe most beautiful, with its little stiff wings of leaves and its white berries at the base of each like pearls.

She enjoyed helping her aunt put the holly behind the picture frames and hanging the mistletoe from the lamp in the hall. She enjoyed decorating the Christmas tree, and was delighted when her father turned on the coloured lights, though it was even more beautiful she thought when the candles were lit. She was astonished, however, that with all this there was no Christ image in the house, not even a Christ picture. And not even, she found at church on Christmas morning, in the church; only a cross, to remind you of his torture and death.

"Only Roman Catholics go in for images and pictures," her aunt explained, so that all over again Jenny thought, secretly, that if she were going to be Christian she would be a Roman Catholic Christian.

When she said that she would like to go into a Roman Catholic church her aunt said certainly not, and to her surprise her father was equally firm about it. She resolved to ask Derek to take her to one when he returned to England. The Roman Catholic Christians, it occurred to her, were like the Theraveda Buddhists, because they kept to the old original doctrines and customs; the Mahayana Buddhists had broken away like the Protestant Christians. It was all very interesting.

Giving presents at Christmas was a nice idea, too, only it was surprising that none were given to the monks. Her aunt explained that there were no monks in the Protestant church, only when it became what was called High Anglican and came close to Roman Catholicism—"everything bar the Pope," her father added, helpfully.

"You could give presents to the priests, then," Jenny suggested.

"In a sense we do, with what we give in the collection at church."

It was not the same, Jenny thought, not like giving rice and fruit and cheroots and umbrellas and new robes.

Her father gave her five pounds, so that she could buy some Christmas presents. He explained that the presents had to be surprises, so that she could buy her aunt's when she was out with him and his when she was out with her aunt. Unless, of course, he added, she felt capable of going shopping on her own.

Jenny elected to go on her own. She did not give much thought to the selection of her gifts. Her father liked Burmese cigars, so that it was a simple matter to go and buy him a box. She was surprised at the big hole it made in her money—more than three whole pounds, just for a hundred. Her aunt liked a certain perfume—a musky perfume, Jenny thought, and disliked it; her aunt said that it was 'masculine'. Jenny bought her a small bottle, and was again astonished at how much money it used up. She was left with only ten shillings to spend on Mrs. Sellers. She was sorry about that, for she would have preferred to have spent more on Mrs. Sellers and less on her aunt. She wished she had bought for Mrs. Sellers first; there were so many things that Mrs. Sellers liked, long ear-rings, bead necklaces, glittering brooches—things it would have been fun to buy. But what could you buy for ten shillings? In England the most ordinary things, such as cigars and perfume, cost such an astonishing amount of money.

She consulted her father. "What can I get Mrs. Sellers for ten shillings —which is all I have left?"

"You could just give her the money," he suggested.

"Oh no. That wouldn't be at all a nice idea. You only give money to beggars."

"Not in England, you don't. You'd better consult your aunt."

Miss Finching was unhelpful.

"She would probably be as glad of the money as anything," she said.

"I think that's a sordid idea!" Jenny declared.

"Sordid? What's sordid about it?"

"I don't know, really. It's a new word I've found. I thought I'd try it out. Am I using it wrong?"

"Wrongly. No, you can say sordid if you like, though I don't see what's sordid about giving money as a present. You could give her handkerchiefs, perhaps."

"I think that's really sordid—things you blow on. *Squalid!* Like giving toilet paper!"

"Really, Jenny!"

"Well, it is. I'd like to give her some booze, only I don't know what kind."

"Booze is an extremely vulgar word. I suppose you got it from Mrs. Sellers."

"I didn't know it was vulgar. I once told her that Buddhists didn't drink alcohol and she said that she was partial to a drop of booze. I thought it was just another name for alcohol."

"It is. But it's not used in polite society. And, anyhow, is it right for a Buddhist to give anyone alcohol?"

"Perhaps not. I shall give her some nylons."

"Do you consider that a suitable gift?"

"Oh yes, she likes them, and she laddered her last pair the other day. Do they cost more than ten shillings?"

"It depends on the quality. You should be able to get some for that. But it's not a very sensible gift, do you think, for a woman in her position?"

Jenny looked puzzled.

"Presents are sensible if they're what the other person likes and uses, aren't they?"

"People often like and use foolish things."

"But if they like them it's nice for them to have them, isn't it?"

Miss Finching gave up. She had bought Jenny a dark red woollen cardigan, though, no doubt, she would have preferred it pillar-box red. Christopher, she knew, had spent thirty pounds on a gold necklace for her—a quite ridiculous waste of money, but then poor Christopher was altogether ridiculous about this unsatisfactory daughter of his.

Jenny was initiated into the business of wrapping the Christmas gifts in fancy paper with a holly design all over it, and attaching to each package a similarly fancy label. Then the gifts were placed at the foot of the Christmas tree, for distribution Christmas morning. Only Mrs. Sellers had to be given hers on the morning of Christmas Eve. She made a great show of surprise and puzzlement when Jenny handed her the package, holding it up and shaking it, then unwrapping it with slow deliberation, inquiring as she did so, "Whatever can it be?" She had suspected that it was a handkerchief and when she saw the stockings she was genuinely surprised and delighted.

"Bless your heart, Love! Just what I was wanting! Thank you ever so, dear! I must give you a kiss!"

She went over to the girl and hugged and kissed her with genuine affection. Then announced, "As a matter of fact I got something for you!"

She produced from her shabby black handbag a tiny package wrapped in gold paper.

Jenny unwrapped it wonderingly and lifted the lid of the little cardboard box. Mrs. Sellers' present was a pair of ornate pendant ear-rings.

Jenny had no idea whether the pearls and diamonds were real or not; she only knew that they were pretty, and she exclaimed excitedly, "Oh they're lovely!" Then she removed the turquoise ear-rings her father had given her and hooked in the new ones.

"They look lovely on you!" Mrs. Sellers cried. "I knew they would! I saw them in a shop window weeks ago, and I said to myself, They're just the thing for our Jenny, so I left ten bob on 'em and then took a bit in each week!"

Jenny skipped about the room, the long ear-rings swinging against her face.

"They're lovely!" she repeated. "I always wanted this kind."

Mrs. Sellers gazed at her with loving admiration.

"They do suit you, I must say," she declared, happily.

"Thank you, thank you, thank you!" Jenny cried, and swung Mrs. Sellers round with her in her caperings.

She felt a sudden rush of affection for Mrs. Sellers, the kind of affection she felt for Ma Chit—which was something quite different from the affection she felt for her father, and for Derek. Just as Ma Chit had been her Burmese mother; Mrs. Sellers seemed suddenly her English one . . . as Miss Finching, with her persistent disapproval, could never be. Mrs. Sellers was on her side, as Ma Chit had been, and her real mother in those lovely secret times together, when Mummy had become Mé-Mé, and Jenny had become Mālā the little flower.

Most of the excitement of the Christmas festival seemed to Jenny to take place beforehand. People made a great deal of preparation, choosing gifts and sending cards and decorating their houses and what they called 'dressing' their little trees, and they got in a lot of special food, but when the great day actually arrived the excitement was all over once the gifts had been distributed. You felt uncomfortable and sleepy after the huge mid-day meal which was called the Christmas dinner, and there was nothing whatsoever to do—at least there was nothing to do in the Finching household.

In Mrs. Sellers's house, it seemed, there were going to be a great many people gathered and what she called a high old time was expected to be had by all. When Jenny, interested, asked what that meant Mrs. Sellers explained that games would be played—"Kids' games, but the grown-ups enjoy them just as much, once they get going—all the old-fashioned games, postman's knock and hunt-the-slipper and musical-chairs. It does you good to make a fool of yourself once a year, and there'll be plenty of kids anyhow, and you got to keep them amused. There's my three to start off with. We got a bit of booze in, too—port and ginger-wine for the ladies and beer for the men. I always make a big iced cake, with plenty of jellies for the kids. We enjoy ourselves, I can tell you!"

Jenny had asked her about the games and she had explained them. 'Postman's knock' she thought sounded silly—she would not at all like to have to kiss strangers like that—but 'musical chairs' and 'hunt-the-slipper' sounded fun.

"And my hubby does card tricks," Mrs. Sellers went on, "and my sister's a dab hand at telling fortunes in teacups, and of course the young people clear a bit of space and dance to the wireless."

It sounded fun, Jenny thought, but then it turned out that all that took place the day after Christmas, because on Christmas Day itself the trains and 'buses stopped running early, so people couldn't stay late. "On Christmas Day itself," said Mrs. Sellers, "we usually go to my mother's or she and Dad come to us, because we all live close. The kids are happy enough with their new toys, and we light up the tree both days. But the real fun-and-games is Boxing Day, of course."

Jenny thought of all this happy activity at Mrs. Sellers's house as she mooned about the flat in what seemed a series of Sundays—three Sundays in a row. Her father did not go to his club because, he said, there would be no one there, and her aunt did not go to her girls for the same reason. With the emptiness of the Christmas days in mind her father had bought some games—ludo and draughts. He had hoped that from draughts she might progress to chess, but she found ludo much more fun than draughts, and it had the advantage that they could all three play it, adding to the excitement. So that they sat round in the book-lined room in the grey afternoons playing ludo—and Jenny thought what a pity it was she hadn't had a set in Tatkon so that she and Aung and Mya and Ma Chit could have played on some of the rainy days. She liked the coloured buttons with which it was played, and the excitement of racing up the coloured paths.

On Boxing Night she went with her father to the circus at Olympia; her aunt, who had a number of objections to the circus in all its manifestations, stayed at home and wrote letters of thanks for gifts and Christmas cards. Jenny was interested in the acrobats and liked the pretty little horses trotting to music, but she felt sorry for the lions who must live all their lives in cages and jump at the crack of a whip. She liked the clowns better than anything; they were something she understood, from the *pwès*. She would have liked them to have been there all the time, as at a *pwè*; but they seemed only to fill in between more important numbers.

Christopher did not greatly care for circuses, though he had no objection to them in principle, as his sister had. He liked to see horses jump, not trot round a ring with plumes in their manes and made to waltz and bow and other tomfoolery, and he admired good horsemanship, but not acrobatics on horseback; performing animals, whether wild or domestic, bored him, and he had no taste for people who ascended to dizzy heights and hung on by their teeth or rode bicycles along tight ropes whilst the multitude gazed upward and waited for them to fall. He was inclined to agree with Jenny that the clowns were the best part of the show.

As much as anything he enjoyed watching Jenny. She looked lovely, he thought, when she was laughing and happy—so like her mother at the same age that she could have been her reincarnation. His Christmas gift, a snake necklace of gold with ruby eyes, looked well round her young throat, and her pleasure in it had been a source of great satisfaction to him. Nothing made him happier than to hear her exclaim—whether of a gift or something he had taken her to see—"Oh, Daddy, it's lovely!" He felt then that she was close to him, and he liked to believe that with every occasion of such delight Burma receded yet a little further from her.

The English winter was not suiting him; it never did, but that year he seemed to be feeling it more acutely. He continually toyed with the idea of taking up his roots from England and going to live in some warmer part of the world—in the West Indies, perhaps, or South Africa. With the deterioration of his health he had decreasing inclination to make the effort, and the upheaval seemed less and less worth while. I should never have stayed in England when I got back after the war, he thought. I should have done what old man Vernon did and cleared out to Africa. I might have done a bit of farming, or got myself some sort of administrative job. Instead of rotting in England where no one has any use for retired sahibs.

Only it was too late now. He had been for some time now painfully—both physically and mentally—aware of how late it was. There was no question of the best being yet to be; the best was already the day he set out with his family from Bokoko on the flight to India. He had not even been allowed to find his remaining child when he had gone back for her. Had he found her then, in 1946, the whole story would have been different, not only for her but for himself. Then, only ten years old, and after only four years of Burmese life, she would not have been so estranged from him and her lost world. The process of rehabilitation would have been quicker and easier; and he might have cleared out from England and made a proper home for them both somewhere in the sun. By the time he found her it was too late, both for her and for him. Too late for her because of all that had happened to her, the long saturation in Burmese custom and religion; her marriage, her Burmese-Buddhist habit of thought; too late for him because by then he was too far gone in his liver disease which was his heritage from the East in general and his Japanese internment in particular.

He faced the fact that there would have to be an operation fairly soon if he was to last out a few more years. He had resisted the idea when it had first been presented to him, from a profound mistrust of what he called 'the medicos'. They were too fond of pumping the latest novelty drug into the human body and of having it carved up. They tried to make a little information go a long way—so far as he was concerned a damn sight too far! But for Jenny he would have been content to let nature take its course—it led less often to the grave than the medicos liked to make out. Lately, however, he had had the feeling that nature was hustling along that road rather faster than he found convenient—since there was Jenny.

He did not discuss the matter with his sister. She would be all in favour, he knew, of an early operation; she had had her gall-bladder and appendix removed some years ago and in common with many people who have successfully survived surgery had become an enthusiast, with a keen eye for any possible candidate for admission to their ranks. He would deal with the matter in his own time—when Vernon was back. He felt confident that after a year's separation from his influence Jenny would not again become subject to it. She could be considered immunized; and Vernon would be company for her when he himself was laid up in hospital for a long spell. It was a pity she and Jennifer didn't get on better together, but there it was. In a few years' time she might even do worse than marry Vernon. He would look after her probably better than a younger man, and as to being some twenty years older than her the difference would diminish as she got older; when she was Vernon's present age he would still only be in his fifties, which in a healthy man was little if any different from being in the forties.

He knew that his sister would be astounded to know that he was now thinking on these lines, but as his disease took a more virulent and pronounced hold on him he felt impelled to plan for the all-too-near future. Derek Vernon could be for Jenny what he had been for the little Ma Hla— father and husband combined. They could spend the rest of their lives reading the Love Songs of Asia together, he thought—so long as he could be sure in advance that Jenny was safe from any possible reversion to the Asian in her blood.

VIII. MESSENGER FROM MĀLĀ

D E R E K reached Bokoko on the full-moon day of October, and arrived in Tatkon when the *pongyis* were passing down the main street between the offerings which flanked the way.

The jeep waited at the side of the road for the procession to pass, and when the last orange-robed figure was lost in the multi-coloured following crowd, the driver inquired for the house of Maung Ba Tu.

"But there will be no one there just now," the young man who directed them explained. "Only the old grandmother. The rest of the family are up at the head man's house."

"Is Maung Aung there?" Derek interposed.

"Maung Aung has been at the Mass Education training centre in Rangoon since the New Year."

"Is his wife with him?"

"His wife's in England with her father."

"I see. Will you tell us how to get to the head man's house."

Perhaps he had changed his mind about marrying again, Derek thought; perhaps it was merely a threat to induce Jenny to return—made in the belief that it lay within her power to do so.

Maung Than's house, at the end of the main street, was festive with red and yellow paper streamers and gaily coloured paper lanterns. Long tables had been arranged under an awning at the front of the house and a great company of men and boys seated on benches were helping themselves from the numerous dishes. Westernized Indian music was relayed from a loud-speaker which raucously amplified its natural harshness. With the shrill chatter of the women hovering in attendance on the men or gossiping in knots on the verandah, and the shrieks of gambolling children and the screeching of the ever-present crows, the din was deafening. Everyone was obviously having a very good time, even the pi-dogs prowling round the tables and wolfing the rice put down for them on plantain leaves.

Everyone stared with interest when the jeep drew up and a dark-haired young man wearing an emerald green silk *longyi* and Burmese slippers got out. He was a good deal darker than many Burmans, and by some he was assumed to be an Indian, until a young woman was heard to exclaim, in shrill surprise, "The Englishman! Mr. Vernon!"

Then Ma Hla detached herself from a group of women and came forward, smiling, to greet the stranger. Her thin delicately shaped lips were very red, her face very white with *thanaka*, and the oleander blossoms in her oiled black hair blended with the reds and pinks of her silk *longyi*. He felt again the shock of her beauty.

"Last time we met at a wedding," she reminded him, "now at our pagoda festival. Do you wish to see my brother?"

"I naturally wish to pay my respects to the head man," he told her, in his not very good Burmese, "but actually I am looking for the family of Maung Ba Tu."

"They are all here. I will find them for you. But here is Ma Mya-Mya whom you met last time—my husband's younger sister."

He recognized the girl at whom she smiled. Mya regarded him unsmilingly, instinctively mistrustful.

"Go and fetch your mother," Ma Hla commanded her.

The girl went into the house and Ma Hla inquired of him, smiling, but shrewd-eyed, "What brings you back to Burma after a year, Mr. Vernon?"

"I have messages from Maung Aung's wife, Mālā."

"It is a very long way to come to bring messages in person."

The gaze he turned on her was as penetrating as her own, though he too smiled, amiably.

"Unfortunately letters to and from this country don't always arrive."

She answered smoothly, "that is true. There have been complaints about it in the newspapers. It is a government department that needs clearing up. Many people say so. Ah, here is Mya back with Ma Chit and Mi Nu. We will leave you—to give your messages."

Derek saw the young girl closely followed by an older girl, manifestly her sister, and a withered little old woman whose greying hair was tightly drawn from a wrinkled monkey-face and screwed into an unsightly knob high at the back of her head. Ma Hla went into the house drawing the young girl after her.

Derek said, "I have a message from Mālā. Is there anywhere quiet where we can talk? It is so noisy here."

Ma Chit stared at him.

"From Mālā—my son Maung Aung's wife?"

"Yes. Where can we go?"

"We cannot get away from the music, but it is not so loud if we go to the other side of the compound, to my son Maung Shwe's house."

"If you will lead the way——"

He followed her through the crowd round the house and across the compound to a small bamboo house set among palms and plantains on the far side. The raucous music receded as they approached it.

Mi Nu asked abruptly, as they crossed the compound, "Are you the English friend who told Mālā's father where she was living?"

"Yes. But don't ask me who told me."

"We believe that it was my older brother's wife, Ma Hla. We heard that there was an Englishman at the wedding at Mynmyo she went to with Mya. We asked her and she says that she spoke to you because she had seen you before when you were in the forest service, but she says she did not tell you where Mālā was, and Mya says she does not know what Ma Hla talked to you about."

"Why do you believe it was Ma Hla?"

"Because she never liked Mālā. Nor did Mya. They always wanted her father to come for her when the war was over."

Derek was silent. There seemed no point in causing trouble in the family by admitting that Ma Hla had been the informer.

They came to Maung Shwe's one-storey house and leaving their slippers on the verandah stepped inside. Mi Nu brought mats rolled up in a corner, and spread them on the floor.

When they were seated Ma Chit said, almost angrily, "What have you to tell us of Mālā?"

"She asked me to tell you that she keeps you all in her heart—that nothing fades or changes."

"Then why doesn't she write to us? Not even to her husband, Maung Aung, did she write. Not one letter. He grew ill, my poor boy, watching and waiting for letters that did not come. If she loved him why didn't she write?"

"She did write, Ma Chit. She wrote first from Karachi, and then again soon after she arrived in England. She also waited for letters that did not come."

"Letters very often get lost in this country," Mi Nu said. "It is a common complaint."

"You are sure she wrote?" Ma Chit asked.

"Quite sure; as sure as I am that she still loves him and all of you and longs to be back with you. She is not at all happy in England with her father."

Mi Nu said quickly, "I think that is not quite true, Mr. Vernon. Her father sent a picture of her to Maung Than showing her looking very happy indeed. He wrote that he would leave a space at the end of his letter for her to add some message, but she did not add anything. We all saw the picture and the letter—Maung Than gave it to Ma Hla to show to us all. It was after that Maung Aung went away from here to Rangoon, to train with the Mass Education people. His heart was broken. Isn't that so, Mé-Mé?"

The old woman nodded, her eyes filling with tears.

"My poor boy," she repeated.

Derek said, "We had a letter from Maung Aung after that saying he was marrying again. It was a great shock to Mālā."

They both stared at him.

"Maung Aung did not write to her," Mi Nu said. "We asked him to write once again, but he had no heart for it. He just went away. He would never divorce Mālā. At first he said he would join the *sangha* and train to be ordained, but Maung Shwe persuaded him against it. He said that Burma had plenty of *pongyis*, but a great need of people to train as Mass Education officers. So he went to Rangoon for that purpose."

"He didn't marry anyone?"

"He didn't marry anyone and he isn't likely to. Maung Aung has a faithful heart." Mi Nu spoke with passion.

"Then who wrote the letter to Mālā's father that was signed with his name?"

Mi Nu answered bitterly, "The same person who told you where Mālā was living. Who else?"

Involuntarily Derek exclaimed, "But why should she? I mean why should she be so anxious that Mālā shouldn't come back? Not liking her doesn't seem sufficient reason. She wasn't living in the same house with her. I don't understand."

"She was jealous of Maung Shwe's love for Mālā. Even when Mālā was a little girl, our new little sister."

"Mālā was jealous, too," the mother put in. "She didn't want Shwe-Shwe to marry Ma Hla. She prayed to an evil *nat* to prevent it, but evil came to rest on Mālā instead. Aung told me this; he was with her when she made the bad wish."

"Mālā is not bad," Mi Nu said, quickly. "You mustn't think that. She was a little girl who had lost everyone who belonged to her, so Maung Shwe had to be mother and father and brother to her, and she thought he would be lost to her when he married. She used to say she would marry him when she grew up, only he didn't wait for her."

"But Aung did," Derek said.

"Aung did—he was younger; and then in the end she lost him too. Do you not think it strange, Mr. Derek Vernon, that the only letter Mālā ever had from Aung was the one he didn't write? That she had none of the letters he did write, and that he had none from her? It is true our postal service is bad at present, but is it not strange that she received the letter which was to end everything?"

"I do think it strange."

The old bastard must have stopped the outgoing ones and pinched the incoming ones, he thought. I wouldn't put it past him.

They sat for a few moments in a brooding silence. Derek was aware of the eyes of the mother and the girl upon him: and of his shirt clinging damply to his sweating skin. He pulled out a handkerchief from the breast pocket of the shirt and wiped round his neck. The day had warmed up.

A lizard chattered noisily somewhere out of sight. The music from the other house came sultrily on the hot scented air.

"What will you do?" Mi Nu inquired at last.

"I must find Aung. That is the first thing."

"You will find him at the Mass Education Training Centre outside Rangoon. If he has gone from there they will tell you where he is." Mi Nu turned to her mother. "I think we should offer Mr. Derek Vernon some refreshment."

"Yes. We will go back to the other house."

They rose to their feet and Mi Nu rolled up the mats and replaced them in the corner.

Derek asked, as they went back across the compound to the head man's house, "What are you going to tell Ma Hla about my visit?"

Again the girl looked inquiringly at her mother.

Ma Chit said, "We cannot cause trouble between her and her husband. I think we should say nothing about the letter, therefore. There is no need to say anything but that you brought us greetings from Mālā." She lifted her wizened monkey-like face to Derek. "Do you think she will come back to us one day?"

"I think one day. But for some years yet she is controlled by her father."

"Maung Than told us that our Embassy in London would help her if her father attempted to keep her against her will."

"Unfortunately that proved to be not the case. She has Burmese nationality, but also British, and so long as she is in England it is the British one which counts. The Embassy would not interfere with a British subject in England. Only if she could get to another country could it help her, for then she could be purely Burmese again. But she cannot get to another country because she cannot get a passport without the written consent of her father. And if her father dies before she is twenty-one her aunt will be her guardian, so the position is not changed. We have to be patient, Ma Chit. The years pass quickly."

"Not when two young people love each other," the girl interposed, vehemently. "When you are young and in love six years can be a life time —six months, even. It would be easier for Mālā and Aung if they did not know that each still loved the other. Then they would make their lives apart from each other, Mālā in London, Aung in the villages he is sent to. But when they know—how is it going to be for them then, Mr. Derek Vernon?"

"It is going to be hard for them," Derek said, "but not as hard as though they were lost to each other forever."

"Mr. Derek Vernon is right," the mother said. "People do wait for each other. Even young people. Aung has the faithful heart—you said so yourself. He is a Sunday child and his name means successful, and he will be successful in his marriage. We will go to the pagoda and make a strong wish for him that all will be well."

"What are you going to tell Maung Shwe?" Derek asked.

"That you have brought love and greetings from Mālā and the promise that she will return to us as soon as she is free to come."

"Shwe-Shwe will be very happy," the girl murmured.

At Maung Than's house he was urged to be seated at a table and Mi Nu brought a beaten brass bowl full of water and a small hand-towel; he went with her on to the verandah and cupped his hands whilst she poured water over them. When he had washed his hands he went back to the table and rice was ladled on to the plate in front of him and a small bowl of thin soup with leaves floating in it placed beside the plate. He was bidden help himself to the numerous dishes spread out before him— several kinds of fish, including prawns, a dish of chicken, some lightly curried vegetables, sweet and sour dishes balancing each other, a dish of salad consisting of a white flower like an orchid, some citron leaves, raw cauliflower, green mangoes.

The head man came and was introduced and apologized for the absence of cutlery.

"We are simple people," he explained, adding, "but you have been in the forest service and know how it is with us in the villages."

Derek assured him that he was well used to eating with his fingers and quite happy to do so.

Maung Than bade him be seated again and continue with his meal. He sat down opposite him and urged him to try this and that dish, then he said, "So you bring us news of Maung Aung's wife."

"I bring her greetings and her love," Derek said, adding, "She wishes to return to Burma and be reunited with her husband. Unfortunately her father will not permit it."

"Our Embassy will assist her," Maung Than stated, importantly.

Once again Derek explained the situation, and when he had finished speaking a tall handsome young man who stood behind the head man, and who had been listening intently, demanded, "Why did she not write to us here—to her foster-mother, Ma Chit, to her husband, Maung Aung, to her sister, Mi Nu, and to me—her brother, Maung Shwe? We had no news of her until Maung Than wrote to her father, and then we had his letter with the photograph showing how happy she was in England, and to that letter she could not trouble to add even a word of greeting. How can she send her love when she treats us like that?"

Derek looked up into the young man's stern face, surrounded by other intent faces, golden-skinned, almond-eyed. But Maung Shwe's was the most beautiful face, Derek thought; it was quite strikingly beautiful, the face of the little Mālā's first love.

"She did write," Derek assured him, "and it is not her fault that the letters did not arrive. Whose fault it is that she did not receive any letters —who shall say?"

An old man edged his way through the knot of people gathered round Maung Shwe and the head man.

"This is my father, Maung Ba Tu," Maung Shwe said.

The old man nodded to Derek and sat down beside Maung Than.

"My wife tells me that Mālā has not forgotten us as we all thought and will one day come back to us, and that you will go and see our poor Aung and tell him this good news."

"I shall go to Rangoon tomorrow," Derek assured him.

"Will she be content to live our poor life again after living in London?" the old man asked, peering at the stranger mistrustfully.

"She does not like London life. The Burmese in her blood has proved to be stronger than the English."

"In Anglo-Burmans it is not usually so," Maung Than said. He had a way of making the simplest statement sound important, Derek thought. "They usually wish to wear European clothes and to be very British indeed, ashamed of their Eastern blood."

"Not all of them," Derek asserted, as dogmatically. "I have met some who are proud of their Eastern blood. Certainly Mālā is proud to be Bur- mese. Her mother was very dear to her."

"She was happy here," Maung Shwe said, sombrely. "Why did you tell her father where she was?"

"It was surely the natural thing to do—to inform a father of his long-lost child's whereabouts? Did you expect me to return to England knowing that she was alive yet allowing him to continue believing her dead?"

"Mr. Vernon is correct," the head man adjudicated. "He could not have acted otherwise."

"Who told you where she was?" Maung Shwe demanded. Meeting his penetrating gaze Derek had the sudden panic-stricken feeling of having been caught at the focal point of a searchlight. It would have been easy, and satisfyingly dramatic, to have said, curtly, "Your wife!" But Ma Hla had taken her place beside him and her gaze was on him equally intently, but whereas his raked like a searchlight hers beseeched him. In a split second of hesitation he made his decision.

He permitted a small smile, faintly apologetic. "Already in Bokoko I had heard a rumour about an Anglo-Burmese girl married to a Burmese boy at Tatkon. It took very few inquiries to convince me that it was Jenny Finching."

Maung Shwe persisted, the searchlight raking again.

"Mr. Finching heard no rumours that she was alive when he went to Bokoko in 1945. Doesn't that seem strange to you?"

"Not in the least." Derek turned on now what a woman had once described as his fully-fashioned smile. "She was a child in 1945, not a newly-married young woman. A wedding attracts attention, particularly when it's an Anglo-Burmese girl marrying a Burman. People who barely noticed her as a child naturally began to speculate about her when she married. What I do find strange is that you should find anything remarkable in people at a wedding at Mynmyo talking about a recent wedding at Tatkon."

"It seems strange that you didn't come to Tatkon to check the story for yourself—that you should be so certain that you could cable Mr. Christopher Finching only on the strength of rumours."

Derek had not been prepared for that one. He suddenly rebelled at the cross-examination. He pushed his plate away from him and reached for the bowl of water at his elbow to wash his right hand. A towel was handed over his shoulder. He dried his hand briskly and got up.

"Maung Shwe, what exactly do you suspect?"

He was confident the young man would not accept the challenge. Maung Shwe made a small helpless gesture and turned away.

"Nothing. I was puzzled, that is all. I am only sorry you went to the wedding at Mynmyo."

"Call it the inevitable working out of the law of *karma*." Derek's tone now was faintly ironic. "I must go," he added. "Will someone please find my driver?"

When he went out to the jeep the head man and Maung Ba Tu and his family, including Ma Hla, accompanied him.

"When do you return to England?" Maung Than inquired.

"Not for some months. Then Mālā shall write some letters to all of you that I will post for her myself, registering them, and you will stand a chance of receiving them. In the meantime, please don't write to her, for I'm afraid she wouldn't get them—any more than she got the others. I will have Aung write her a letter which I will take to her personally."

Ma Chit said, her smile uncertain, "Give her my love, and tell her that I am still her old *Mé-Mé*."

"Tell her we all send our love," Mi Nu said, quickly. She added, "And take our love to Maung Aung in Rangoon."

"I will do all that," Derek promised. He glanced at Ma Hla who stood with her arm round the waist of the unsmiling Mya.

"Give Aung our love too," said Ma Hla, her smile quite as fully-fashioned as Mr. Derek Vernon's.

They all watched the jeep till it disappeared at the end of the street, then they turned back to the house. The Indian music was still blaring away. The dishes were being moved from the tables and the betel box passed round.

Ma Hla and Mya went on towards the house, their arms round each other's waists.

"Do you suppose she really will come back in six years time?" Mya asked.

"Of course not. Long before then she'll have married an Englishman—probably Mr. Derek Vernon."

"Do you think so? But he's very old, isn't he?"

"You have to be a hundred before they consider you old in England," Ma Hla assured her.

Laughing they disappeared into the house.

Maung Shwe followed slowly with his parents and the head man.

"It's a strange business," he said, broodingly. "I had the impression Mr. Vernon was hiding something. I don't trust him."

"He took the trouble to come here," Maung Than pointed out. "He has nothing to gain by not being honest with us."

"I got the feeling he is like a puppeteer who likes to pull strings and make things happen. Tomorrow he will cause the puppet called Maung Aung to dance at the end of the string . . ."

IX. THE 'LAST CHUKKA'

I t was with a shock that in January Jenny realized she had been in England for a year. The three months they had all taken for granted at Tatkon would be the maximum length of the visit had become twelve months, a whole year, which, if it had been proposed at the time, would have seemed an impossibility. In a sense it had passed remarkably quickly. In another sense she seemed to have been in England so long that it was exhausting even to think of it. A whole year; and in such a little time Aung had grown tired of waiting for her, had lost faith in her, because the letters never came, and the unthinkable thing—that was still unthinkable, unimaginable—had happened and he had taken another wife.

In January she thought, Derek has seen Aung by now, talked with him, and with all of them. At least they will know I didn't change, and that I did write. Aung will know it. Even if it can make no difference he must know it.

The months that followed Christmas were more difficult for her than they had been the previous year. Then, although she had been wildly unhappy, she had at least believed she would soon be going back to Burma, going home, with Aung waiting for her. This year she had no such faith, and no hope of returning for years. Also she felt the cold as she had not felt it when she had newly arrived full of sun. The snow no longer excited her; it merely filled her with dread when she went out into it, the cold an enemy that leapt out to devour her out of that glistening whiteness. And day after day of cold greyness seemed to eat into her brain as the cold ate into her flesh. She thought continually of how beautiful it would be in Burma at that time, not yet too hot, and the sun shining every day and all day. The frangipani would be in bloom beside the bamboo house and the river flowing tranquilly between its low sandy banks, past the lotus-filled creeks. The coppersmith bird would knock-knock-knock all day long in the hot stillness, and the you're-ill-bird—only to the Burmese it never said that —calling wildly as it started up suddenly from the big old mango tree. Mi Nu would still go to the river to wash her hair, but now she would take her babies with her. Mya would now have Mé-Mé to herself, though probably by now she had caught the eye of some village boy and have less time both for Mé-Mé and for Ma Hla. She wondered if old Pwa-pwa was still stalking about, so straight and thin, with her death's-head face and her sunken eyes—the dear old woman from whom as a child she had shrunk, as too like one of the pagoda images of the three states to which we all must come, and then come to feel affection for, as for Maung Ba Tu, who had at first seemed so old, and then in time not old at all.

She thought of them all endlessly in the grey English January days, with the snows melting into the February rains and the rains into the March gales. The winter seemed endless—and Derek to have been away much more than a year, although it was then not yet a year. In the summer she had not missed going to the bookshop so much, for there had been all the things she did with her father—Derby Day on Epsom downs, the visit to Oxford, the day trips to the sea, the walks in the parks, the open-air theatre, the day on Hampstead Heath with the roundabouts and swings. All these experiences left her with a good deal to think about, and she had had a sense of growing friendship with her father. With Aung no longer in the background and no Derek in the foreground she had inevitably come closer to him. He was all she had now, she told herself, and the realization that he loved her she found increasingly comforting. He loved her and wanted her close to him; no one else did. What Derek felt for her she knew to be different; he was her friend, he wanted to help her, but away from her for a year she did not think he would miss her greatly; he would be interested in so many other things. Only to her father was she important; he was the living link between her and her mother. Derek was also a link with the past, with the old Bokoko days, but her childhood memories of him as a young man coming and going, her father's assistant, were dim. She remembered him most vividly poring over the maps with her father before starting out on the long difficult trek.

That her father was now often not well she knew, but after Christmas he seemed to be unwell more often, and worse; some days he sat by the hearth all day, staring into the fire, not even reading, with no energy to go to the club, or to do what his sister was continually urging him to do—go out and get some air. She went on at him, too, about the whisky he liked to drink. "You know it's bad for your liver," she would assert. "I dare say," he told her once, in Jenny's hearing, his voice weary, "but it's good for my spirits." Old auntie was too bossy, Jenny thought, resentfully; she tried to order Daddy about as though he were a little boy, or one of the bad girls at her club. Mrs. Sellers was much nicer, in every way, than old auntie, and on the days she came when Daddy wasn't well enough to do more than sit by the fire she would cheerfully go out and buy him a bottle of whisky when he asked her; sometimes she would come with a bottle, which she would never produce until Miss Finching had gone off to her girls. Jenny came to understand that all this was a secret between Daddy and Mrs. Sellers—a secret from old auntie, for he made no attempt to hide it from her, Jenny. He knows I'm on his side, she thought, happily.

"Your Dad's very poorly," Mrs. Sellers remarked to her one day. "I suppose be rights he ought not to be drinking, if it's his liver as he says, but

I'm a firm believer in a little of what yer fancy, meself. It's a depressing thing, anything to do with the liver."

"Auntie wants him to go into hospital and have an operation," Jenny told her, gravely. "She's always saying it and it makes him cross."

"No wonder. Bossy old maid! She treats everyone, me included, like one of the dead-end kids at her club." She mimicked, " 'Now Mrs. Sellers this morning if you will be so good as to scrub the bathroom floor!' As if I don't know what has to be done on a Wednesday, after all these years. But she has to say it. Domineering, that's what. Some people are never happy unless they're ordering someone else around! Your dad's as different again —most pleasant. A proper gentleman!"

Jenny felt bound to say, "In Burma he used to order the servants around. He used to shout at them."

"Out there in all that heat I suppose it's different, and him the liverish type anyway. I always take people as I find them, though, and I find your dad as easy and pleasant as your aunt's domineering, and that's a fact! Don't you go letting on to her about me getting him his booze on the sly!"

"Of course I won't. I'm on his side, the same as you are."

"That's right: Now mind out of the way, there's a good girl, while I give this surround a cat-lick and a promise."

The days her father sat listlessly by the fire, *The Times* fallen to his feet unheeded, Jenny would be troubled. She would crouch beside him on the floor, her head against his knees. He would put out a hand and stroke her sleek dark hair.

"Do you feel very ill?" she would ask, anxiously.

"Not too good," he would reply. "Not any too good."

She pleaded once, "Couldn't a doctor make you well? The doctor we had to Mummy when she was ill on our journey made her better."

"This is different," he told her. "They can't do anything for this except cut me open. I'll let them have their will of me sometime, I suppose, but I haven't your aunt's passion for operations."

Sometimes, when she seemed very despondent and worried, he would assure her that when the better weather came he would be better.

"Then we'll have some good times together again, eh? Perhaps we'll go to Paris together at Whitsun. How would you like to make a jaunt like that with your old daddy, eh? I used to think one day I'd take your mother there."

He had told her before about Paris, the cafés in the streets, and the chestnut trees, and the tall Eiffel tower thrusting up into the sky, a thousand feet high, more than three times the height of the Shwe Dagon Pagoda.

"I would like it," Jenny told him; "but when you said about going there the other day auntie said it was the worst place in the world for anyone with liver trouble! She said it would kill anyone like you off quicker than anything! Don't you remember?"

"A beautiful death!" he said grimly, as he had then, and reached for the whisky decanter.

"It wouldn't kill me," he added, swinging the neat whisky round in his glass. "Doing what makes you happy helps to keep you alive. I was damned ill when the Japs got me, and dam' near kicked the bucket, but I was determined not to die till I'd found out whether my daughter was dead or alive. Now I've got to stay alive to look after her—till she gets herself a husband to take over."

She shook her head. "I don't want another husband. I shall be an old maid, like auntie."

He smiled. "You can't exactly be an old maid now, you know."

"I thought an old maid was someone who wasn't married."

"Yes, but you have been. There are also unmarried ladies who are certainly not old maids."

It was one of those complicated English things, Jenny thought, abandoning the attempt to understand.

He added, boldly, "Wouldn't you like to marry Derek one day?"

She gazed at him in dismay. "Oh no, he's much too old!"

"I was much older when I married your mother."

"All the same," Jenny protested, decisively.

"I might ask him to become your guardian, then. Would you mind that?"

"To guard me? I don't understand."

"Supposing I were to die, and you had no one—no husband. Then there should be someone to look after you."

"I suppose auntie would."

"Auntie is busy with her girls. Besides, you get on better with Derek, don't you?"

"Derek is my friend," she said, simply. She brooded on the thought for a moment, then spoke the question that came into her mind.

"If you want to make Derek my guardian, why did you send him away for a whole year?"

"I wanted you to settle down, and I felt he was unsettling you—that his being here wasn't helping you to forget Burma."

"I think about Burma just as much when he's not here. I won't ever forget it. I can't. One day I want to go back."

"There'd be no harm in going back for a visit later on, but not to live. As a matter of fact I doubt if you could live that village life again in any case. I don't mean physically, but mentally. You would be bored now."

"Not if I had Aung—and children."

"That's out. You know that."

She sighed. "Then I don't know," she said. "Perhaps you're right. I don't know."

That she could concede that he might be right was progress, he thought, a quite considerable progress.

When Derek Vernon sailed from Rangoon at the end of April on the long voyage home he had every intention of getting in touch with Jenny immediately on arrival and handing her, privately, the letter he brought her from Aung. He was even impatient to bring her the good news. It did not occur to him that he might do otherwise until he had been a week at sea, by which time he had chewed the cud of this particular idea so often that he was tired of it, and he began to amuse himself with the idea of telling a quite different story. He lay in a deck chair on the sun deck considering all the possibilities; and as always when he was considering doing something which would gratify his complex desire to have a hand in shaping the destinies of others he began to justify his puppeteering to himself. The Old Man would not welcome the news that Maung Aung had not married again and was willing to wait for Jenny to return to him in a few years time; he would find such news very disturbing, and he would not want Jenny to know. And might it not be better not to tell Jenny? If she had begun to settle down in England what was the point of unsettling her? He had warned her to expect nothing of his on-the-spot investigations; she would not be disappointed if he merely confirmed that Aung had lost heart and married again.

Then we shall come closer, he thought. One day we might even go back to Burma together. I am the person closest to her now; with nothing to hope for in Burma she would come closer still—there would be nothing so very strange about that. When she is eighteen I shall only be thirty-eight —which isn't old, even by Burmese standards.

The thought startled him. Until then he had not consciously thought of himself as in love with her. His mind played round the thought in the long monotonous days at sea. Once she knew that Aung was faithfully waiting for her she would be lost to him forever. And then he would be alone again; a lost person, with people—women particularly—vaguely sorry for him, feeling affection for him, mothering him, wanting to marry him off to someone else, and none coming close to him. No one had ever come so close as this little Mālā; with no one had he felt as at ease and as assured as with her. He had been a fool to butt in again on her affairs, to allow himself to feel the need for atonement for the results of his first intrusion into her life.

By the time the ship berthed at Southampton he had determined not to give Jenny the letter with which Aung had entrusted him. Yet he could not quite bring himself to destroy it. So long as he had it in safe keeping he could pretend to himself that perhaps he would not carry out his plan; he was still not committed to it. He decided to have a talk with the Old Man first.

He telephoned the Finching flat the day after he arrived back in London and Miss Finching answered. When he asked to speak to her brother she told him, "He's in hospital. He was operated on three weeks ago."

"I have some very important news from Burma for him," Derek said. "Is he strong enough to see me, do you think?"

Miss Finching assured him that he was; that he had been having visitors and was glad of them, being a little bored. He was in a private ward and could receive visitors almost any time. She gave him particulars.

Derek said that he would go along that afternoon, and asked her, "Would you mind not letting Jenny know I am back? I want to see her father first."

Miss Finching promised. She was only too glad to promise. She thought it a pity Mr. Vernon had returned. Christopher had not yet broken it to her that he intended to ask Derek to agree to be Jenny's guardian should he himself die before she was twenty-one. Jenny, she thought, had improved a great deal in the year that Derek Vernon had been away; she had been much more affectionate to her father, and altogether more settled. She no longer hoped to gain the girl's affection for herself. All that could be hoped for now was that in a few years' time she would make a suitable marriage, since she was obviously uninterested in any form of career.

Christopher was dozing when the nurse opened the door of the small room to show Derek in. Derek was shocked by his appearance. He had always been thin; now he was cadaverous. The Old Man was more than ill, he thought, involuntarily, he was on the way out. When the nurse spoke to him, softly, telling him he had a visitor he opened his eyes and for a moment or two stared at the young man without recognition. In the old Bokoko days Derek had so often been disconcerted by the directness of those blue-grey eyes—relentless eyes, he had always thought them, eyes that demanded truth and accepted no subterfuges or excuses. Now they disconcerted him by their deadness. Feeling sorry for the Old Man was a new experience. He had always been so unnerved by him in the past; he was unnerved by him now, but in a new way.

"Don't stay too long," the nurse murmured to Derek as she went out, "he's not so well today."

When full consciousness asserted itself Finching's eyes lit with recognition.

"Hullo, Vernon. When did you get back? Sit down, won't you?"

Derek seated himself in the cane chair beside the bed.

"I got back yesterday and 'phoned your sister. She said you would be equal to a visit. How are you feeling?"

Christopher ignored the question. He raised himself a little in the bed and ran a hand over his moustache.

"Have you seen Jenny? She's improved a lot in the last twelve months—quite a young lady now."

"I asked your sister not to let her know I was back. I wanted to see you first." He hesitated a moment, deliberately, to heighten the effect of what he was about to say, then, as he hoped, dramatically, "I've some very interesting news from Burma."

He paused again and Christopher said, in the old impatient way, "Well, out with it, then!"

"It seems that that boy Jenny married out there didn't marry again after all—someone who didn't want Jenny to come back wrote that letter."

Christopher passed his hand over his moustache again.

"How do you know?"

"I had an impulse when I was in Rangoon to go to Tatkon and find out what had happened. Later I saw the boy himself in Rangoon—working with this new Mass Education scheme."

"What does he feel about things?"

"About Jenny? He's prepared to wait years for her if need be."

"Jenny mustn't know—that's clear. It'll only unsettle her all over again."

"That's what I thought. It's why I asked your sister not to let her know I was back. I thought we should first discuss what course to follow."

"Good man. But if you just don't say anything about having been in Burma everything will be the same as before."

"Except that the young man will start writing again."

"Letters from Burma often don't arrive. Look, Vernon, I'm glad you came in. There's something I've been wanting to talk to you about for some time. This is my last *chukka*, you know."

Derek looked at him, uncertain of his meaning.

Finching's eyes rested on him in the old direct disconcerting way.

"I'm not going to get well," he said dryly.

"What makes you think so? I gathered from your sister the operation had been successful."

"From the point of view of keeping me alive a bit longer, yes. I may be around another year or two, but in not much shape and most likely not for long. As they say nowadays I've had it."

"I'm sorry," Derek said, conventionally. He was not sure whether he was or not.

"You needn't be," Christopher said, curtly. "I've mighty little left to live for. I got Jenny out of Burma and she's now as fond of me as she's ever likely to be. All I want now is to see her in good hands. Without beating about the bush, Vernon, I'd like to see her safely married to a decent Englishman."

Derek looked away from that disconcertingly direct gaze.

"She's a bit young—from the English point of view," he suggested.

"She's older than an English girl of her age, and she's been married before. What about it, Vernon?"

"You're not suggesting that I should marry her?"

"Not right away. In about a year's time."

"I'm twenty years her senior."

"I was more than twenty years her mother's senior."

The situation was getting out of hand, Derek thought, it was moving too fast. Finching was trying to force a reality out of a tenuous dream. A fantasy was one thing; its reality, established on the structure of a lie, another.

He said, confusedly, "This is something we'd all three of us have to think about very carefully. There's Jenny's point of view to be considered."

"It's up to you to foster the idea in her. She's fond of you. In the meantime I'd like you to agree to be her guardian—in the event"—he smiled the old wry smile—"of my sudden decease."

Derek was still more confused. "I don't understand. You persuade me to clear out for a year and make it possible for me to go, because you think it important to Jenny's well-being, and now you want me to be her guardian—marry her, even——"

"It was important Jenny should settle down. You were giving her Eastern poetry and generally encouraging her to brood about the East. With you around she'd never have got over her home-sickness for Burma. With you away she immediately took an interest in the life about her."

"Aren't you afraid with me around again she'll revert?"

"No. Not unless you tell her the Burmese boy is still waiting for her. That might very well start up the Eastern fever all over again."

"I still don't see why you want to make me her guardian. When you're gone I should have thought her aunt was the natural person to replace you until she comes of age."

"They don't get on. From the start Jenny didn't take to her. Jennifer means well but she has no tact. If she has legal authority over Jenny when I've kicked the bucket it's easy to see what'll happen—Jenny will be unhappy and rebellious and long to be back in Burma. You could take my place. No one else could."

He closed his eyes, suddenly weary.

"Think about it, Vernon, old man. They'll be sending me home in a week or two now, I suppose, but I've got the feeling I won't be around long. I'd like to feel it was all going to be all right with my poor little girl. It would be a relief to me to know I could rely on you."

Derek got up. "I'll come and see you again," he said.

"In the meantime Jenny needn't know you're back."

"Supposing she runs into me at the shop—or in the street?"

"You can have got back the day before. And nothing about having been in Burma."

"O.K."

Horrible expression, Finching thought, but he said only, "Thanks. And thanks for coming."

Her father's illness frightened Jenny and she knew again the panic of the river closing over her. The day he had been taken to hospital she had asked her aunt, fearfully, "Will he die?"

Miss Finching had replied, briskly, "Of course he won't die! What a morbid idea!" She had added, severely, "Our English hospitals are extremely efficient."

Mrs. Sellers had not been so reassuring. "I don't believe in hospitals meself," she had declared, "particularly since they've been naturalized. Now everything's on the natural health you don't get the attention. My old man went in for an operation for rupture and got double pneumonia. But your dad'll be all right, no doubt. He's in one of them amenity wards, isn't he? They take more interest in the private patients. And your dad being such a gentleman, too. The nurses used to call my old man dad and it made him mad, not being that old. But they'll mister your pappa. It's all class."

None of this had made much sense to Jenny, though she had been glad of the assurance that her father would be all right. She went with her aunt to visit him and thought he looked very far from all right. His face looked so grey, and his eyes seemed sunk deep into his head. In 1945 she had seen a dead Japanese soldier lying at the side of the road whose sunken eyes had stared at her just like that, out of deep sockets, above hollowed grey cheeks. She had thought then, awed, that it was the face of death, the mask slipped at last on to every face. She was more fearful of ghosts than usual that night, after the hospital visit.

She made several visits and though her aunt assured her he was what she called 'on the mend' he looked just the same to her. Mrs. Sellers, to whom she always reported on her visits tried to reassure her. "An operation takes it out of you," she would say, and "Lor-love-a-duck, he's not five minutes over his op! What're you getting into a two-and-eight about? Give the old boy a chanst! He's no chicken, don't forget!"

Jenny found the references to ducks and chickens confusing, but evidently Mrs. Sellers considered there was nothing to worry about. And then at last her father came home, and sat again in the deep armchair beside the fire and stroked the cat and dozed, letting *The Times* slide from his knees, then waking up and asking her to pour him a whisky, and Mrs. Sellers took to bringing him supplies again, produced from the bottom of a shabby plastic shopping bag when Miss Finching was safely away with her girls. He would have Jenny lock the bottle away in the cupboard at the bottom of a tall bookcase with glass doors at the top, and return the key to him. Then she would rinse and dry and put away his glass, so that when her aunt returned there was no sign of what Jenny had learned to call a *chota-peg*. Any smell that might linger on the air was dispersed by the fumes of Christopher's pipe. Jennifer would always, involuntarily, glance at the decanter on the sideboard when she came in, but it always contained as much as when she had seen it last. So far as she was concerned Christopher was only having what he called his sundowner, and what she called his night-cap—a term he detested.

When he became stronger he and Jenny began making excursions to Hyde Park and Kensington Gardens again. They would go as far as Hyde Park Corner or the bridge across the Serpentine by taxi and then walk a little until he tired, when they would sit on a bench or on chairs under the trees.

These walks reminded Jenny of her first visits to the parks with Derek and several times she remarked that surely he must soon be home now. Her father would reply that they could expect him any time, no doubt, though it wouldn't surprise him to learn he had gone to Ceylon before sailing for England. Jenny didn't think so; it would be too hot there now, she pointed out.

It was obvious, Christopher realized, that they could not go on indefinitely like that. Only until I feel a bit more fit, he would tell himself, postponing the more difficult time. Two was company—there was no getting away from it. Vernon wasn't a bad chap, but as dull as ditchwater—no sense of humour and no self-confidence. Never had had. And a bore, too, really. He'd make a dull enough husband, in all conscience, but the duller the safer, and as they were fond of each other it ought to work out all right. Only there was no hurry to get all that going. This is my convalescence, he told himself, I want to enjoy it in peace.

The bright young green of the park trees and the sight of crab-apple and cherry-blossom filled him with a longing to see the Japanese cherry trees at Kew. He hadn't been for years, and it was a sight Jenny hadn't yet seen. On a weekday afternoon there wouldn't be many people there. Jennifer considered that he was not strong enough. "A man's as strong as he feels," he told her. She was hurt that he did not suggest they should all three go, and that he chose a day when she went to the club. If she were with them she could see that he did not over-exert himself. She gave Jenny strict instructions to see that her father walked no farther than the avenue of blossom trees and then sat down. They should go to Richmond and get a taxi from there.

"Perfectly good 'buses," Christopher murmured.

"I can't make Daddy do things," Jenny pointed out. "He's not a little boy."

Christopher gave his daughter a quick look. Jennifer wouldn't like that one, he thought, but it was time someone pointed it out to her.

"All men are little boys," Miss Finching said in her brisk way.

Jenny shook her head. "I don't think Daddy's a little boy. He's old."

Christopher laughed. "You think he's old enough to know when he's had enough—whether it's exercise or drink! And you're quite right!"

Father and daughter smiled at each other. They were very much *en accord* these days, Jennifer thought, bitterly, and they played up to each other. Christopher at least should know better. It was unkind, too, because in this playing up to each other they were allied against her. As though I were the enemy, she thought. She did not know which was stronger in her, anger or pain. And in the old days Christopher was always so considerate of her, so careful not to offend or hurt her in any way. Spoiling Jenny he had spoiled himself. The advent of the long-lost Jenny had certainly spoiled their peaceful brother and sister relationship. It was a very great pity, and it added to the hurtfulness that Christopher himself did not see it.

Jenny was very happy about the visit to Kew because it meant that Daddy was better again. She had not been since the winter visit with her aunt when she first arrived in England. Derek had talked of taking her to see the blossom and the bluebells but there had always seemed other things to do. They would go and see the flower that was like a bird in the lovely humidity of the Palm House. They could pretend they were back in Burma. And when Derek came back she would go there with him too. It was strange that he was so long in getting back. He had said he would be away a year. That meant he should be back in May, and it was nearly half way through May already.

Christopher felt lighter-hearted on that outing than he had felt for a long time—not since the day he and Jenny had visited the Indian section of the Victoria and Albert Museum and he had felt her come close to him for the first time. Happiness had come then, but he had not started out with it as now. The sun shone, the day was soft and warm, and the dragging pain somewhere at the centre of his being which he had known for so long, and which had seemed worse since the operation, had eased up. He was no longer so weak, and altogether felt mentally and physically jaunty. When the underground train from Charing Cross came out into the open and slid between the backs of suburban gardens he eyed them all with interest, marvelling at how well some were kept, and how the lilac was coming out everywhere, and how delicately golden-green the young leaves everywhere looked in the bright sunshine.

He felt quite absurdly daring when he crossed the road from Richmond station to get the 'bus to Kew Gardens. Really Jennifer was extraordinarily domineering at times. She always had been, even when they were children together, and even though she had been so pleased to welcome him after the war, but she had been worse since Jenny had come to live with them.

Jenny was also excited and happy.

"We managed it, didn't we?" she exclaimed, as they passed through the turnstile into the gardens. "We managed it without taking taxis!"

She seized his hand, pressing his fingers tightly in her excitement whenever she exclaimed upon anything. She was as happy as in the times when she had walked hand in hand with Aung to the pagoda or to the creek.

She exclaimed upon a dark pink camellia bush in full bloom, upon a small orchard-like group of flowering trees, upon the little ornamental 'Greek temple' on its grassy hill, shadowed with bluebells. They agreed that the pagoda was not a bit like any pagoda in Burma, "But still," her father told her, "you see them like that in China."

Then they came to the broad avenue lined with Japanese cherry-trees, their branches thickly laden with white or rosy blossom trailing to the grass. There were not enough words, then, to exclaim upon such beauty. Jenny tugged at her father's hand as she turned this way and that, directing his attention to right and left, drawing him in under tents of blossom, gazing up at the blue sky through white and pink and pale yellow lattices of blossom. Darting from tree to tree, from right to left, they walked much farther than they both knew. At the pagoda they wandered away in the direction of a small group of trees that offered fresh delights, and suddenly Christopher spotted a bench and realized that he was very tired.

"We'll sit for a bit," he said.

She was instantly concerned for him.

"You're not tired?" she asked, anxiously. "You haven't over-eggserted yourself, like auntie said?"

"No, no. Not at all. But it would be nice to rest here by these beautiful trees, don't you think?"

They sat down together and she kept a tight hold on his hand, still gazing about her, raptly.

"Isn't this a beautiful tree?" she demanded of the one nearest them. "We haven't seen one like this before—its the colour of cassia blossom, isn't it? Look, it's got a label on it with its name." She got up and went over and read out the Latin name with difficulty.

"Spell it," he commanded.

She spelled it like a child spelling out a lesson.

"Oh—*cercis siliquastrum*. Of course. The Judas tree. Not that Judas could have hanged himself from such a flimsy little tree."

She was puzzled.

"What does it mean, Judas tree?"

"Come and sit down and I'll tell you."

She reseated herself beside him and he told her the story of Judas Iscariot—"the first person to make Christianity pay," he explained, sardonically. "Not that it did him any good," he added, "for he went out and hanged himself on a tree. I don't know why traditionally it should be this little flibberty-gibbet of a tree, but there it is."

Jenny brooded on the tale. "Poor man," she said at last, "he must have been dreadfully unhappy to do such a thing. The Lord Buddha preached against taking one's own life. It makes very bad *karma*. That poor Judas would have been born into great misery the next time."

Christopher smiled his wry smile. "It was two thousand years ago. Perhaps by now he has achieved Nirvana!"

"Sometimes people must be reborn hundreds of times. Perhaps thousands. It depends on their *karma*."

She got up again to smell the purplish-pink blossom of the little tree. "You can eat it," he told her. "Try it!"

She pulled off some petals and put them into her mouth. She had expected them to be sweet, like *paducksa* an orchid-like white flower eaten in Burma as salad and used in soups, but they had an acrid taste and she spat them out, making a face.

Her father laughed. "Not like *paducksa* or *pauk*, eh? People use it all the same!"

She looked so pretty, he thought, happily, in her pale blue spring suit, with her bright red and blue Indian silk scarf gipsy-knotted at her throat, a little hat of pale blue feathers like a Juliet cap on her black hair, her lips lightly touched with lipstick giving an odd touch of sophistication to her childish oval face. She was now really prettier than little Ma Hla had ever been, the Mongolian flatness of her face offset by the straight little European nose. That dull stick Vernon would be lucky to get her.

They rested a little longer then went on again towards the Palm House. Christopher was aware that he was still very tired, and the old deep seated pain was nagging again. The Palm House suddenly seemed an impossible distance away. Jenny's fingers still gripped his own and she was talking, but he no longer knew what she said. Suddenly cutting across her eager prattle he heard his own voice, curiously detached from him.

"Jenny, I'm not feeling well. I must sit down."

She regarded him with dismay. This, then, was what her aunt had warned her against. For once fussy old auntie had been right.

"There's a seat over there," she said, and took his arm.

"I can't get to it, I'm afraid. I must rest here."

He lowered himself to the ground and sat with his head in his hands. That was a near thing, he thought, as the blood flowed back, a dam' near thing to a blackout. . . .

Jenny knelt on the grass beside him, her arms round him, dismayed and frightened.

"It's all right," he assured her, when the faintness passed. "I walked about a bit too much, that's all. Not as strong as I kidded myself, it seems. We won't say anything about it to your aunt. There's no need. It would only worry her. We'd better get along to the 'bus now, I think. We'll get a cup of tea in Richmond before we go back to town. . . ."

"I wanted you to see the bird flower," she mourned.

"It'll keep. We'll come again a bit later on—when your silly old daddy's stronger. I just overdid it a bit, that's all."

He spent a sleepless, feverish night, and all next day sat by the fire, though the day was warm, and but for Mrs. Sellers, who thought that Mr. Finching looked 'seedy', the fire would not have been lit. Christopher made light of his malaise to his sister, insisting that he was no more than a little tired from his first day out. Both he and Jenny strenuously denied her suggestion of over-exertion. ("We didn't walk an inch, did we, Daddy?" and, "Jenny will bear me out we did the merest dander. We didn't even toddle as far as the Palm House.")

When he was no better the following day Jennifer bullied him into staying in bed, and when she came in in the evening and found that he had a temperature she called in the doctor.

The doctor proposed a shot of penicillin and Christopher gathered strength to roar at him.

"All you fellers can think of nowadays is shooting the latest fancy drug into the human body! You can take your blasted drug and stuff it up——" he caught Jennifer's eye and finished lamely, "the chimney."

He equally violently opposed the idea of return to hospital for observation.

"I suppose you think you're going to carve me up again? Well, you've got another think coming to you, that's all! You've had all the fun you're going to have at my expense, so you can put that in your pipe and smoke it!"

"There's no need to be rude, Christopher," Miss Finching said. She added, to the doctor, "My brother is inclined to be irascible, I'm afraid."

"Liverish, in fact," the doctor suggested, smiling. He didn't blame the patient. His private opinion was that since he stubbornly refused another operation nothing further could be done for him. Until, near the end, he needed morphia.

It came to Christopher during the next few days that he was nearing the end of the road. The end of all roads. The final road which was darkness and silence, and down which you went alone. He finally consented to go back into hospital to save his sister trouble. He asked her to send Vernon to him there. The time had come to tell her that he had appointed Vernon as Jenny's guardian. "It'll make things easier for you," he told her, adding, "It would simplify things if in a couple of years time he married her."

She took it better than he had expected. If anything was to happen to Christopher—the euphemism somehow softened that final fact-of-life which is death—she would certainly prefer not to be solely responsible for so difficult and unusual a young person as Jenny. Such young people were much easier handled when one was not related to them. And of course if Derek Vernon did marry Jenny in a year or two it certainly would solve the problem of what was to become of her. Then she would be on her own again, the lone bachelor woman; only it was somehow impossible to think of anything happening to Christopher. He had never been well since he had come home from that horrible camp, but he was tough, and not really old—for sixty odd was nothing nowadays.

Jenny, on the other hand, could all too easily imagine her father dead. That he should be taken from her now that she had grown to love him seemed most natural to her. He had again the grey look of the dead Japanese soldier at the roadside. She recognized it as the mask of death. Death she was quite certain had already touched her father, as surely as it had touched the lilac browning in a vase by his bedside.

He wakened from a light doze one afternoon when she was visiting him to tell her, "Derek is back in England. He's coming here this afternoon, so you will see him."

The announcement pierced the misery that enveloped her with light. "Oh, at last!" she cried, "I thought he was never coming back, he was so long away."

"He will be able to look after you when—I am not able to," her father added, and the light was immediately extinguished. The euphemism was wasted on her. She understood that her father expected to die. She herself believed him to be dying, but his words made his death seem frighteningly imminent. He dozed again, and she sat with her head resting against his pillow. This was the end to which we all must come, and for him the time had come. One should not be sad; we have all existed before; we must all exist again. Aung had explained all this to her. Only it seemed that what you knew in your head and what you felt in your heart were two different things. And so though you knew it was foolish to cry nevertheless the tears squeezed out even when your eyes were tightly closed; squeezed out and rolled down until you tasted them salt on your lips.

She started up when the door opened, and then in a few strides Derek had crossed the room and gathered her in his arms. She did not know how it had happened, only that she had somehow gone towards him and his arms had closed round her and her head was against his heart and she had a feeling of unutterable gladness.

"I thought you would never come," she sighed.

He did not speak but pressed her close to him and without releasing her regarded the grey figure on the bed. The eyes did not open. He turned back to Jenny.

"Perhaps we should go—let him sleep?"

She shook her head, her eyes brimming with tears.

"I should like to wait till he opens his eyes again."

"All right." Derek pulled a stool out from under the bed and they sat side by side. He kept one of the girl's hands in his and they talked in low voices.

"Did you go to Burma?"

He nodded. "But don't ask me now. I'll tell you all about everything later."

Christopher stirred and opened his eyes. He stared a moment then said, feebly, "Hullo, Vernon. Nice to see you."

"How are you?" Derek inquired.

"On the way out. Not sorry, either. Should like to have seen Jenny settled, that's all."

"I'll look after her," Derek murmured.

"Good chap. Take her for a walk in the park and explain things to her."

Jenny turned her face into the pillow.

"I don't want you to die," she sobbed. "You're all I've got."

"Derek will look after you. You don't want to cry. Your mother never cried, whatever happened."

That isn't true, she thought; she cried in the bullock-cart on our trek, after you hit me in the face.

She remembered it without resentment. It had all become distant and impersonal.

She felt Derek's hand on her shoulder and heard him say, "Come, my dear, let's go out into the sun. I've a lot to tell you. Daddy's right—crying doesn't help anyone."

She stood up, controlled but stricken. She touched her father's heavily veined hand on the turned back sheet. It had always been so hard for her to make a gesture of affection towards him; even now she could touch him only diffidently.

"Try to stay alive," she pleaded. "Please don't leave me."

He closed his eyes, wearily.

"I think I could sleep now," he said.

"We'll go," Derek said, and took Jenny's arm.

"We should let your father sleep. We'll come back tomorrow."

Christopher opened his eyes and smiled.

"I'll probably still be here," he said, "but if I'm not—be happy!" He looked at Jenny. "Kiss your old daddy, and no more tears. What's the good of being a Buddhist if you cry because an old crock like your daddy gets to the end of one incarnation that hasn't been much good to him?"

Jenny bent over him and kissed his cheek.

"Take Derek to Kew," he murmured. "Show him the Bird-of-Paradise flower. And the little tree . . ."

His voice trailed away and his eyes closed.

They moved away from the bed but when Derek opened the door the sunken blue-grey eyes opened again, the veined hand moved again over the grey moustache, and very faintly he smiled.

He used the Burmese farewell. "*Thwa daw mai*," he said (I will go now).

Only when their backs were turned to him at the door, did he add, in a whisper inaudible to them both, "*M'pyan bu*" (I will not return).

In the taxi they took to the park Jenny pleaded, "He's going to die, isn't he?"

"I'm afraid so."

"I try to be sensible about it, but he's the last person really close to me. When he's gone—then there's no one."

"Don't I count for anything? Aren't we close?"

"You are my friend, but a parent or a husband is different. You know it's different. It's being related that is closeness."

"You can be related and not be close. If you married me you'd be related to me—and closer than you ever were to your father. Why don't you marry me? Your father wants it."

"I am married to Aung. I told my father."

"Supposing you never see Aung again?"

"Then I must stay as I am. A kind of widow."

"I could look after you and make you happy," he urged. "We might even go back to Burma together in a year or two."

"I can't imagine it. I can't imagine being in Burma except with Aung. Don't ask me any more. My head feels like bursting."

They rode the rest of the way in silence. Jenny sat with one hand screening her eyes. Derek stared unseeingly out of the window. He was aware of the old excited sense of power stirring in him. Her whole future was now in his hands. He could release her from her present mystery, give her back to Aung and Burma—to happiness; or he could finally shut down on all that for her, and in that lay his only hope. If he told her the truth now he would be betraying Finching; though Finching would die happily anyhow now, believing that between them they had finally ruled out the Burmese marriage and that all was set for an eventual English one. Believing that Aung was married, Jenny might in a few years think differently about lifelong singleness; she was very young, and with aloneness closing in round her again with her father's death the sentimental desire to cherish the memory of her Burmese marriage to the exclusion of remarriage with someone else might very well die a natural death. That being so it would be most natural she should turn to her friend who was also now her legal guardian. But once tell her the truth and she was irrevocably lost to him.

He had still reached no decision when the taxi halted at Hyde Park Corner. Jenny stood on the pavement in the bright sunshine whilst he paid the taxi-driver. She felt lost and wretched with the indifferent crowds swirling about her like the eddies and currents of a river in spate. It was a relief when they had turned into the park and were walking with grass under their feet and trees filtering the May sunshine through their young green.

They walked in silence for a while, Derek still thinking what he would say, and Jenny too wretched for the effort of words. She asked at last, "Did you see Aung?"

"Supposing I said I saw him and that he made it quite clear he was not prepared to leave his new wife for you—to wait for you?"

She answered in a low voice, "I could do nothing but try to find the courage to endure it."

"You could make a new life with me. You know that I love you."

"I love you, but not as my love. Not as I loved Aung. Not in that special way."

"You might come to it in time. At first you didn't love Aung in that way."

"How could I, when I was a little girl? Tell me what he looked like and what he said. Did you go to Tatkon? Did you see Ma Chit and all of them?"

"Let's sit on those chairs over there under that tree."

They moved across the grass to two chairs set against the massive trunk of a flowering chestnut tree. Usually Jenny liked the chestnut trees because the flowers were like candles, but now she was unaware of anything except the unhappiness which pressed upon head and heart and blinded her to all else.

The sense of power was beginning to ebb in Derek. He thought despairingly, I can open the East up for her again, make her happy with the thought of Aung waiting for her, or I can close the East to her and destroy all hope of being reunited with Aung, but I have no power to bring her close to me. She has this fanatic dedication to the idea of one love, one marriage.

"Yes, I went to Tatkon," he said. "I saw them all. I told them you hadn't forgotten them and sent them your love. Ma Chit and Mi Nu were pleased. Aung was away in Rangoon."

"Did you see his new wife?"

"No."

"What is Aung doing in Rangoon—did they tell you?"

"He is training as a Mass Education officer."

"Oh, but that is good! I am so glad! He will make a good officer to send to the villages because he knows village life so well and all the difficulties of the lives of poor paddy-farmers. Mé-Mé must be very proud of him! Did you see him?"

The face she lifted to him was all eagerness. He was suddenly filled with pity; it was such a small childish face, tear-stained, deep shadows under the eyes, but now lit with such a childish eagerness. Yet in the midst of his compassion the instinct for self-preservation intervened. With a few words he could destroy finally and forever his own chance of happiness.

"Yes, I saw him," he said, hesitated a moment, deliberately, then added, "Jenny, need we discuss all this now? Haven't you enough with Daddy's illness?"

I have taken the fish from the water, he thought, sardonically, but I have not killed it. Is it my fault if it dies? I have not told the truth; but also I have not lied. Except by implication. Is it my fault if the other person reads into my words the meaning I intend to convey but which is not the truth?

"I can't be made any more unhappy than I am," she said. "If Aung is happy I can be glad for him. He has made a good new life for himself."

She turned to him suddenly. "I am so tired. Please take me home. I have such a headache. I can't think any more now."

When they got back to the flat Miss Finching was out. She had left a note: 'The hospital 'phoned. Your father has taken a turn for the worse. You had better get a taxi and come at once.'

Christopher Finching died late that night. His daughter and his sister were at his bedside, but he had been in a coma for several hours when the end came and he did not regain consciousness.

X. THE JUDAS TREE

MISS FINCHING combined a progressive outlook with Christian ortho-
doxy by having her brother cremated with a Church of England religious
service. It was a typical English May day, with the lilacs tossing in a high
wind and the cherry-blossom lacerated by heavy showers that were sometimes icy with hailstones. It was a busy day at the crematorium and the
hearses moved up slowly in a long procession. You had to queue up nowadays even when you were dead, Derek thought.

He and Jenny sat on the tip-up seats in the car provided by the under-
takers, facing Christopher's two sisters who had left their families and
come up to town for the day for the funeral. It was the first time they had
seen their niece from Burma and they were relieved to find that she was
much less Oriental in appearance than they had expected. Indeed, but for
the long almond eyes she could have been European—Spanish, perhaps,
with her black hair and sallow skin. They studied her with frank interest
and asked her the stock questions about how she liked England and if she
had any plans for a career, and Aunt Julia, the younger and prettier of the
two said something about she must come and spend a week-end with them
in Kent—'and meet your cousins', one at least of whom, it seemed, was
married and had 'two sweet children'.

For Jenny her father's sisters had barely the appearance of reality. They
were merely versions of her aunt, tallish, with the Finching deep-set grey-
blue eyes and straight noses; they wore what she now knew to be smart
clothes, not as mannish as Aunt Jennifer's. Aunt Julia wore a hat with a
veil and flowers, and her hair was not grey but blue, and she had long red
fingernails like a bird's claws. Aunt Sophy was grey and bony and wore an
eyeglass dangling on a black cord down the front of her blouse. Jenny was
aware of these details yet the women themselves were as unreal to her as
the people in the streets and the solemn looking men in dark clothes at
the place where they burnt the corpses. Only Derek was real, and her
father hidden from sight in the long box covered with purple velvet and
gay wreaths of red and yellow tulips. Even Aunt Jennifer had ceased to be
real. They were just people who asked her questions and instructed her to
do this and that, no more to do with her than the black-clothed men with
the solemn faces.

Nobody wept, nobody wore black clothes, and Jenny herself did not
weep any more; Daddy had been gone some days now; it was just something you had to get used to, one more person taken away. Perhaps it
would be better for Daddy in his new life, as it had been so bad for him

in this one, with the war, and the Japanese camp, and losing Mummy and baby-brother, and all the loneliness and disappointment.

There was white lilac in the chapel, and a confusion of loud organ music, though no organ visible. People wearing black clothes and a woman with a black veil covering her face came out as they went in, and another hearse waited at the door. The priest man read from a large book and the velvet-covered coffin with the gay flowers slid along and disappeared between two small doors; then they were all trooping out again and some more people came in. They came out into sunshine and the aunts, resolutely cheerful, discussed where to lunch. Aunt Julia thought perhaps she wouldn't stop for lunch if Jennifer didn't mind, as if she went at once she could just get the twelve-thirty from Victoria and be home in time for lunch with Robert, who never got in before two o'clock, and it would enable her woman to get away. Aunt Sophy agreed to a cafeteria lunch with Jennifer and a run out to see the girls' club before rushing off up Oxford Street for some shopping before getting the evening train back. "Might as well use the day," she said energetically, and the look she turned on Jennifer challenged her to be other than bright and sensible. Christopher had not meant much to his married sisters; only Jennifer mourned him, but for her as for Jenny there were no more tears to shed; the first wild grief had spent itself and the process of mental and emotional readjustment already begun, so that she answered her sister with bleak rationality, "I quite agree," adding with a watery smile, "I'm sure it's what poor Chris would have wished."

She turned to Jenny.

"Would you like to come along with Aunt Sophy and me?"

Jenny shook her head—that irritating habit, Jennifer thought.

"I'd sooner stay with Derek."

"Candour before courtesy," observed Aunt Sophy, dryly, and looked inquiringly at Jennifer.

Derek put in, quickly, "The modern young are always outspoken. I think Jenny feels she'd rather not be with people strange to her today, and as her guardian I feel we have things to talk over——"

There was something to be said for having the legal status.

"I don't want to eat lunch," Jenny stated. "I'm not hungry."

"That's all right," Derek said. "We'll go to my place and I'll boil myself an egg and you can make a cup of plain tea."

"I'd like to go to Kew." Jenny regarded her aunts challengingly. She added to Derek, "Daddy said I should take you there."

"It's not very good weather for Kew," he suggested.

"We can go in the Palm House and look at the Bird-of-Paradise flower when the showers come."

"Extraordinary idea," Aunt Sophy murmured.

"It's no more esstrawnery than going to a girls' club or rushing back home on the first train," Jenny asserted.

"There's no need to be rude," Aunt Jennifer said, sharply, and turned to Derek.

"All right. See that she's back by six o'clock, won't you?"

Good-byes were said; the aunt from Kent hailed a taxi, the other two got back into the undertaker's car, Derek and Jenny walked a little and then boarded a 'bus for the West End.

"In Burma you were brought up to show respect to your elders," Derek reminded her with a thin smile, as they seated themselves on the top.

She sighed. "Burma doesn't seem real any more. Since Daddy died all that seems like a dream I had long ago, when I was a little girl."

"I was in Burma too, you know, and I'm still here."

"I didn't know you very well. You weren't with us on our trek and at the river."

"If I had been I might not be here now!"

"It's no use saying that. It wasn't in your *karma* to be at the river with us."

"You're incorrigibly Buddhist, aren't you?"

"I don't know what that means. I believe in the law of *karma*—don't you?"

"I don't know. Sometimes I think so, and sometimes not. Sometimes I think, we determine our own destinies; at other times I think other people determine them for us."

She persisted, with the familiar shake of her head, "We make everything that happens to us."

"Even if this 'bus skids on these wet slippery roads and we're both killed?"

"Yes. We chose to get on to this 'bus at this time."

"Every action is a cause that must have a consequence—yes, I know, and we can't always see ahead the consequences of our actions, which is sometimes a pity and sometimes a jolly good thing. Have you any idea what will be the consequences of going to Kew on this wet day of your father's funeral?"

She looked at him and saw that he smiled a little and realized that he was teasing her.

"No, but it's the right thing to do. I know it. I do sometimes know things without knowing why. Like my mother knew we wouldn't cross the river, and I knew when I was in the river and drowning that she had known it, though she hadn't told me. Now I know that this is something we must do, and that something important will come out of it. It's in my mind, but dark. I can't see it."

"You're a strange girl, Jenny."

"Not strange. It's only that things that are real to other people aren't always real to me, and things not real to other people, like ghosts and spirits, are real to me—much more real than the old aunties with their funny hats. It's only over here that it seems strange; in the East no one would think it strange. In the East we know that ghosts and spirits are real—much more real than people, who are changing every minute, like the rivers and the sea."

"I know that one—about not being able to swim in the same river twice."

"You're laughing at me, but it's true all the same."

"I'm not altogether laughing at you, Jenny. Only I'm not as clear about it all as you are."

They were silent for a little while, then suddenly she said, "I've been thinking since Daddy died that you and he were right, and I should marry you. Then I would really finish with Burma. Inside myself, I mean. I'd be Mrs. then, wouldn't I? Mrs. Vernon. Not Mālā, not even Jenny Finching. Jenny Vernon. Mrs. Derek Vernon. That's right, isn't it?"

He stared straight ahead of him through the glass screen of the 'bus. So it was after all as easy as all that. She had accepted unquestioningly all that he had led her to believe, all his implicit lies.

"Yes," he said, "that's right. But would it be right for you—since you don't love me as you loved Aung?"

"I would sooner live with you than with old auntie. Also if I marry you I won't have to sleep alone, and I don't like sleeping alone. In Burma no one does—it's too lonely, because of ghosts. Before I had Aung to sleep with I slept with Mi Nu and Mya."

"Jenny, you can't marry me or anyone else just because you don't like sleeping alone for fear of ghosts! If you married me and slept with me I should make love to you in the nights—you wouldn't be able to share a bed with me as you did with your Burmese sisters."

"I know that. I've thought about all that. I wouldn't like it at first—being with you in that way. I didn't with Aung at first, but then I got used to it, and in the end I liked what we did together and hoped it would make a baby." She added after a moment, "I came to the inclusion I couldn't live all my life with old auntie."

"Conclusion," he corrected her, and went on. "It's not a reason for marrying someone you're not in love with. I refuse to be a lesser evil! That's what it amounts to."

He looked at her and saw that she was puzzled.

"I thought you wanted us to be married," she said.

"I did—I do. Look, Jenny, we can't discuss it all on the top of the bus. Wait till we get to Kew and then we'll go into it all, my little funny. We get down here, anyhow."

"It's you who're funny," Jenny said, a little petulantly, getting up and staggering off down the length of the 'bus. "I don't understand you. I thought you'd be pleased."

"I'm sorry you don't understand me. I don't blame you. I don't understand myself, so why should anyone else?"

They scrambled down the stairs and stepped off into the Strand, choked with lunch hour crowds. It was still raining.

When they reached Kew the sun had come out, and after the long 'bus ride, and the stuffiness of the long drag out through the suburbs on the District Railway, the air seemed wonderful in its freshness of wet leaves and grass and blossoms.

For Jenny the whole thing was in the nature of a pilgrimage made to the memory of her father, and whatever the aunties might say it had to be made on that day and no other. Therefore she noted with satisfaction that the rain had not washed away all the magnolias, in spite of all the petals spilled on the grass, and that there were still bluebells on the hillock on which the little temple stood. In the avenue of Japanese cherry trees leading up to the pagoda the wind and rain had scattered the pink and white petals of the blossom like confetti. Jenny walked fast, not looking at the flowering trees, and Derek who would willingly have lingered over a loveliness he had not seen in years demanded, "Where are we off to in such a hurry?"

"I'm taking you to the place where Daddy and I sat. He said I was to show you the little tree."

"What tree? Something special?"

"Oh yes. The man who betrayed the Lord Jesus is supposed to have hanged himself from such a tree two thousand years ago."

He stared at her.

"Truly," she assured him. "It's called the Judas tree. It's in full bloom just now."

"Yes," he said. "It would be!"

"Why do you say it like that?"

"How do you mean?"

"As though it made you angry."

"Of course not. I meant this is the month for it."

The little tree was still in bloom, though beginning to shed its petals.

"There!" Jenny exclaimed, triumphantly. "Isn't it lovely? Have you ever seen one before?"

"I don't think so. Not consciously. The flowering Judas."

"I'm sorry it's called that. It's so beautiful, and betraying anyone, especially a friend, is so ugly. It's no wonder he was so miserable afterwards, that poor Judas."

"You feel sorry for him?"

"Oh yes. He must have felt terrible when he went up to the Jesus-God like that and kissed him, and all the time the soldiers were waiting. Then when he got the money, the reward for what he'd done, he couldn't bear it any more. It must be terrible to harm someone who thinks you're a friend and trusts you. I think all Judas people must be very unhappy afterwards."

"Yes." He moved away from the tree and taking off his raincoat folded it inside out and spread it on the bench. "Let's sit for a little."

She seated herself, and said, "You said we could talk here about us being married."

"Yes. Jenny, supposing you knew for certain that Aung hadn't married again but was in Rangoon longing for you? You wouldn't want to marry me then, would you?"

"Of course not. I'd want to go back to Rangoon by the next 'plane. But as we know he's married to someone else what's the use of talking like that? I've got to forget him—like Daddy always said."

"Listen, Jenny. I couldn't tell you the day we were at the hospital together. You'd had shock enough for one day. But Aung isn't married, and he is waiting for you."

She stared at him, bewildered.

"I don't understand. I asked you if you'd seen his new wife and you said no. You didn't say he hadn't got one."

"I couldn't tell you that without explaining the whole thing. I said let's not discuss it, because with your father dying I didn't see how you could stand another shock—even a happy one. It wasn't the time to tell you—to add to your confusion."

She said again, helplessly, "I don't understand. It would have helped me to know. The night Daddy died I nearly died too. I wanted to die—I felt so alone. If I could have known Aung was there . . . But how can he be? That letter he wrote——"

"He didn't write it."

"Then who did?"

"We can't know, but the family think Maung Shwe's wife did. It seems likely."

He put a hand in his jacket pocket and pulled out the letter with which he had been entrusted.

"He gave me this for you. It really is from him. I sat beside him whilst he wrote it."

"And you didn't give it to me till now? How could you be so cruel? You were my friend. How could you have done it? I had a right to have it at once—the day you got back."

"I've told you why I didn't give it to you. I met you the day your father was dying."

"We didn't know then he was dying."

"You didn't know. But I did. I"—one more lie wouldn't hurt at this stage—"I had a talk with the ward-sister as I came in. She said there was no hope."

"When we were in the park you suggested I make a new life with you. Those were the words you used. And all the time you had this letter from Aung to give me. You knew that he was waiting for me. Why did you do that? Perhaps you are a Judas person, too, like Ma Hla."

"I wanted to find out what you felt about me, and I was determined not to give you the emotional upset of knowing about Aung whilst you had all this other worry. I need never have told you the truth, but I told you as soon as I felt it would help you to know. How can you call me a Judas person? Is that fair?"

She buried her face in her hands a moment.

"I don't know. I don't know anything any more."

"I would like you to have married me, and I'm glad to know that if it had been true about Aung you'd have done so. As it is I can be glad for you—that the Burma story has a happy ending. Now read your letter whilst I smoke a cigarette."

She tore open the envelope and took out the thin sheets covered with Burmese script. She stared at them, but the writing swam through the tears that filled her eyes. She turned the pages and took in a sentence here and there. And the last sentence. 'Come back soon, little Mālā, I am waiting. Nothing fades or changes. Your faithful Aung.'

She folded the sheets and put them back into the envelope, and the envelope into her handbag. She took out a handkerchief and wiped her eyes and blew her nose.

"Well?" Derek inquired, and reached out a hand to her.

She took his hand and pressed her lips to it and smoothed it against her face.

"Thank you for bringing the letter," she said. "You were right not to give it to me the day we were at the hospital. It would have been too much. And I'd have felt bad about Daddy. He liked to think I was going to marry you, and if I'd known I was going back to Burma as soon as I could after he was dead I'd have felt I was deceiving him. I would have been deceiving him, for I couldn't have told him, and I'd be sitting here now feeling guilty, instead of so happy."

"We've got to think now what to do. When your father's estate is cleared up you'll have some money—not much, a few hundred pounds. Your air fare back to Rangoon, anyhow. But it'll take a little time."

THE LOTUS 249

"How long?"

"I don't know. I'm not a lawyer. We'll go and see the lawyers tomorrow. They might even advance you some money. You'll be back for the end-of-the-rains festival, anyhow."

"The beautiful *Thadingyut!* Aung and I will celebrate it at the Shwe Dagon Pagoda. It must be most beautiful there for the full-moon festival. Oh, it seems too good to be true! It seems like a dream. Are you sure it isn't just a dream?"

"It's not a dream. Tomorrow we will go to the post-office and send Aung a cable."

"What will we say in it?"

"Whatever you like. It's your cable. Then you must write him a letter, which we will send by registered post. No more letters must miscarry."

"What does that mean?"

"Sorry. Not get there."

"Oh, yes, everything must go right now. It will, won't it?"

"I thought the law of *karma* decided that!"

"Of course. But Aung and I haven't made bad *karma*, and we're going to meet again. I will ask them in Rangoon to let me train to be a Mass Education officer. Do you think they will?"

"I am sure of it. They need people, women especially. Now you'd better take me and show me the Bird-of-Paradise flower. And I seem to remember there's a lotus pool in there, isn't there?"

He added, as they headed across the wet grass for the Palm House, "When you're back in Burma you'll think of me when you gather lotus flowers, won't you? Promise to think of me very tenderly and sentimentally."

"Of course. At Kason when we lay the lotus flowers before the Lord Buddha I will make a strong wish for your happiness."

"Yes, do that. It may help."

"It will help," she assured him. "The strong good thought will go out to you over all the thousands of miles."

She was all love and happiness and faith, he thought, herself like a lotus flower that has struggled up out of darkness into the light; out of more darkness than she knew, a chaos of lies and betrayal, power-lust and deceptions. Can it be, he thought, wrily, that in my own devious way I've done the right thing at last? The far-far-better-thing-than-I-have-ever-done-before? And oughtn't I to feel now all aglow with virtue, the disintegrated person made whole at last? But I don't, he thought; I know quite well how it's going to be, tonight and all the other nights, for a very long time; like the Chinese poem it will be, night after night seeing in the darkness, waking and in dreams——

Her fair face lifted up
Shines in the darkness like a lotus cup.

But now her face was lifted up to him in the bright daylight, lifted up with eager happiness as she led him triumphantly to a flower that glowed against its jungly background like a brilliant bird.

"When I was first over here, and so unhappy," she told him, "it meant so much to me. I loved it and felt sorry for it because it didn't belong here any more than I did. I didn't know it was called the Bird-of-Paradise flower till Daddy said it—last time we saw him. When I'm back in Burma you must bring greetings to it sometimes. Auntie said it was African, but I still think it likes to see people who belong to the East."

"Do you think I belong?"

Her words quite unaccountably excited him.

"Oh yes. You will go back. Don't you feel it? People belong to the places they love—don't you think so? In the other places they're always not-belonging, like this flower. They can't be happy; they're foreign, always, like I've been all this time."

"You must make a strong wish for me, that I get back."

"I will. You know I will. But we make our own *karma*—you must wish too."

He smiled. "A wish so strong that it makes action. A wish as valiant as a dragon banner floating in the sun."

"You're laughing at me!"

"No, my little Mālā, only quoting from the Chinese—who have courage as well as wisdom."

XI. FLIGHT INTO THE DAWN

THERE was a cold bright morning in October when Jenny, wearing over a red floral *longyi* and white nylon *eingyi* the light fur coat her father had bought her for her second European Winter, stood beside Derek at London airport waiting for the 'plane that would take her to Amsterdam, where she would board a Dutch airliner for the Far East flight. Derek had suggested that she might like to go back by another line and route, but she had a curious feeling about returning the way she had come; particularly she wanted, she told him, to be at Amsterdam again, where she had known such panic-stricken unhappiness—to be there again with the feeling of beginning a journey into happiness.

Mrs. Sellers, who had taken a day off work for the occasion, waved frantically from a roof-top. Jenny made out her red hat bobbing behind the fluttering white handkerchief. "I'll miss you, ducks," she had told her, "but when I win the Irish Sweep I'll come out for a holiday, so you'd better keep the kettle boiling." She had laughed when she had said it, but there had been a tremor in her voice. It wasn't much of a lark getting as fond of someone as she had become of this kid and then to say good-bye knowing you didn't stand a celluloid cat's chance in hell of meeting again —'in this incarnation', as Jenny would say. Only she had been glad for Jenny that her stay in England had come to an end at last and that she was going back to her young husband and the country that was home for her. When they had said good-bye at the flat, and Jenny had hugged her and declared that she would never forget her 'English *Mé-Mé*', Mrs. Sellers had, as she described it to her husband, 'dam' near broke down and cried'. There had been nothing for it but to make a joke about watching out she didn't click for twins in the enthusiasm of the reunion. Jenny had also had tears in her eyes, and had been glad of the little joke to laugh at so that she could disguise the fact that she was nearly crying.

She felt a pang now, watching the red hat bobbing and the white handkerchief fluttering. She wished she could get near enough for Mrs. Sellers to see that she was wearing her ear-rings.

She had said good-bye to Miss Finching at the London terminus. She had been glad that her aunt had decided not to come out to the airport with her, making the excuse that she had an important engagement in town which could not be broken. She had been extremely indignant that Derek had not merely raised no objections to his ward returning to Burma but had actually helped her in every way to that end. She regarded it as a crass betrayal of her brother's trust in him, and had said so to Derek—

who acknowledged to himself the truth of her remark and had not attempted to justify his conduct to her. The alternative to betraying Finching would have been to betray Jenny. It was clearly in his *karma*, he had told himself, ironically, that he should play the Judas role one way or another.

To Jenny, Miss Finching had declared that it was a disgrace that she should go against her father's deepest wishes in this way, and within a few months of his death. She had appealed to her conscience, demanding of her if she was not ashamed of herself—a purely Christian appeal which Jenny had simply not understood. She had been sorry old-auntie should be so upset about it all, but nothing could undermine her deep happiness.

They had parted with constraint. Jenny had felt that something should be said—some expression of gratitude for all her aunt had done for her, or tried to do, but she had not been able to find the right words; good intention had wilted under her aunt's disapproval. Miss Finching had kissed her niece without warmth, wished her *bon voyage*, and expressed the hope that she would 'write sometimes'. Jenny had promised that she would. There had seemed nothing else to say. Miss Finching had stood on the pavement outside the terminus building, with all the other people waving friends and relatives off to the Far East.

The last Jenny had seen of her was her tall thin figure, trim in the mannish well-cut clothes, her gloved hand raised in a small elegant gesture of farewell, her long face, with its tight-drawn greyish skin, unsmiling. But when the 'bus had turned the corner and come out into the stream of traffic of the main road she had thought no more of that gaunt disapproving figure. She would have been astonished to know that cross old-auntie had gone back to the flat and sat down and wept from sheer loneliness, and that behind her disapproval was an overwhelming sense of personal failure, of having failed not only her beloved brother but also the unhappy lonely little niece.

With her aunt out of sight and mind Jenny had been able to give herself up to the joy of departure. Now it did not matter how ugly was the English scene, the people in their dark clothes, the long straight road with the ugly little houses, all alike, at each side, and then the great factories, like huge machines that swallowed up live human beings—none of it mattered now, for it had no more to do with her; there was no longer the difficult necessity to accept and adjust; she was leaving it all; going home. . . .

Then she was on the great airport with Derek suddenly silent and sad-looking at her side.

"Don't be sad," she pleaded. "We'll meet again."

"Somewhere, somehow, sometime, I don't doubt. But I'll miss you, Jenny."

"Only at first. You'll get used to my not being there."

If it were only that, he thought, just missing her in the familiar places, missing her in the physical sense. It sounded so foolish to say 'It's in all the non physical ways I'll miss you most,' and yet it was true. He would miss the emotional outlet she had come to represent for him, the light and warmth she had let into the dark wintriness of his life. He was losing the only human being who had ever come close to him, the only human being to whom he had ever come close; the only female with whom he had not felt himself a poor thing, from whom he had not fled with a sense of his own inadequacy.

And we won't meet again, he thought, in spite of the brave dragon banner of somewhere, sometime, hung out to float as best it can in the pallid Western sun. We won't meet because I'd want to carry you off in my arms to live with me and be my love to the end of this incarnation, and you'd belong to someone else. Since I may not be your lover I can't any more be your friend. Once you've gone from me in the flesh you've gone from me in the spirit, too, and I'd better get used to the idea—come to terms with it and make a friend of it, since I've got to live with it.

"Don't worry about me," he said. "I'll be all right."

"What will you do?"

"Carry on at the bookshop for a bit. Wait for a sign. For the traffic lights along the road to turn from red to amber and finally to green."

"Passengers for Amsterdam and the Far East——" announced the impersonal voice of the Public Address System.

They looked at each other.

"Come," he said.

Once again Jenny felt that there should be something to say, but there were no words. At the barrier beyond which only those travelling might go, he turned to her.

"We must say good-bye. Bless you, darling Jenny. Salute the Shwe Dagon Paya for me."

He tilted her face up to him and kissed her, on the lips, for the first time. He was grateful for her gentle response.

She found words, then. "Thank you for everything," she said, her voice unsteady. "I can never thank you enough." Then with sudden passion, the passion of finality and despair, the sense of having reached the point of no-return, "I will remember you always."

He smiled the charming smile which had always concealed his inner desolation.

"I ask no more!" Poignancy had somehow to be turned aside with mockery; yet it was true—he did ask no more, since more was anyhow impossible.

There was the final pressure of their fingers, and then she was gone from

him, lost in the crowd of people of various nationalities moving towards
the exit and the waiting Dutch 'plane.

He watched her moving across to it, a small bright figure that turned
at the steps up to the cabin to wave. Then she disappeared inside and he
went back through the building and out on to the road where people
waited at 'bus stops.

On the 'plane from Amsterdam Jenny wrote Mrs. Sellers a postcard—
provided by the company—to be posted at Beirut, and at Karachi she
wrote Derek an air-mail letter.

There had been a shower at Karachi, and there was the smell of rain on
hot dust and stone, and the scent of jasmine and frangipani. For Jenny it
was the first breath of home and she had the strange sensation of all her
blood changing in some mysterious way, charged with something that
kindled and quickened it, so that she felt newly alive in all her senses. Yet
outwardly she was poised and calm, quite unlike the frightened girl who
had passed through that port twenty-two months ago.

It was exciting when they were airborne again to realize that they were
now six hours ahead of European time and that when tomorrow would be
six hours old in the East it would still be the same old day in the West.
She slept through the short night and wakened to see the tremendous dawn
over India.

From seventeen thousand feet up there was the feeling of the earth's
curve, of the arc of the sky. The whole of the Eastern hemisphere seemed
curved against an immeasurable crimson arras. The great Constellation
headed out across India into a new day, whilst the West still lay in the
darkness of yesterday. The sun moved straight up over the horizon and the
crimson was dissolved into the blue-grey of heat. For hours the 'plane
flew over the burning plain of India and headed out over the Bay of
Bengal. Soon there was red earth broken by a wide river, by lesser rivers,
and lakes, and by stretches of dense green. The land was split up by fingers of water, the mouths of the Irrawaddy, the rivers of the Delta. Jenny's
heart quickened with the recognition of Burma. Soon I shall see him, she
thought, Aung my darling, my love. He will be there, waiting. He said he
would be there. If he is not there I shall die. But it was unthinkable, unimaginable, that he should not be there.

So long it seemed that last lap, longer than the seven hours from
Baghdad to Karachi, longer than the six-hour wait at Karachi, longer than
the night in the air. Then at last the warning light went on, the loudspeaker in the cabin announced the imminent arrival at Mingaladon, airport for Rangoon; passengers buckled their safety-belts. The great engines
shut off, the 'plane circled and circled, and flattened out, and fled along
over red earth, and bumped, and taxied in to a huddle of buildings quite
unlike the chromium and plate-glass splendours of the airports of the

West. A crowd of white figures waited in front of the buildings, and when the 'plane came to rest a few detached themselves and came forward.

The 'plane door opened and the passengers moved out slowly on to the steps. There was the sudden impact of heat. Jenny felt it on her face gratefully. She went down the steps and on to the hot dry earth. Her eyes searched the figures grouped outside the low buildings. Searched until they came to rest on one small slim figure who stood apart. The momentary question in her mind became certainty as the figure raised an arm in salute then came running to meet her.

Nov. 1954–June 1955,
Connemara-London.